EQS for Windows User's Guide

Peter M. Bentler
Eric J. C. Wu

Multivariate Software, Inc.
15720 Ventura Blvd., Suite 306
Encino, CA 91436-2989
Voice: (818) 906-0740 • FAX: (818) 906-8205
E-mail: sales@mvsoft.com

The correct bibliographic citation for this document is as follows:

Bentler, P. M., & Wu, E. J. C. (1995). **EQS for Windows User's Guide**.
Encino, CA: Multivariate Software, Inc.

ISBN 1-885898-01-0

Version 5 June, 1995
Printed in the United States of America

Windows is a trademark of the Microsoft Corporation.
BMDP is a trademark of BMDP Statistical Software, Inc.
SPSS is a trademark of SPSS, Inc.
SAS is a trademark of SAS Institute, Inc.
LISREL is a trademark of Karl Jöreskog and Dag Sörbom.

TABLE OF CONTENTS

PREFACE

By its very nature, structural equation modeling requires computer implementation. The methodology involves optimization of complex nonlinear functions of a very large number of parameters. This process simply cannot be done by hand except in very special circumstances. In a way, the computer must serve as an intimate and supportive friend with whom one can have an easy, helpful, and informative discourse. The earlier releases of EQS improved not only on the extant technical methodologies available in their day, but also were aimed at substantially simplifying the human-computer interaction involved in the modeling process. Judging by the increasing acceptance of EQS in the field, these aims have been achieved substantially.

EQS for Windows now provides another major leap forward in the human-computer interaction known as the structural modeling process. Considering the great user-friendliness of the Windows environment, it will not surprise you to see that this release of EQS for Windows has made creative use of many of the wonderful features of the Windows environment. For example, using Diagrammer, our new model drawing tool, models are now easier to set up and run than ever before. Even a quickly-drawn path diagram will serve as model input as well as model output. You can run models without the use of command language! In addition to functionality, we also provide simple drawing tools that will allow your theory to be shown in state-of-the-art publication-quality form. On-screen, color is used meaningfully to accentuate the presentation; however, color printing is not yet supported.

With the proliferation of computers at work and home, many researchers now use several different computing environments. For example, Windows users sometimes encounter Macintosh, UNIX, or mainframe environments, and, more and more, users from these alternate environments have access to Windows. It was our goal in creating EQS for Windows to be faithful to Windows conventions to the maximum extent possible, and yet achieve substantial cross-system generality in both computer program and documentation so that the Windows user also will feel comfortable when encountering EQS on other computers.

This goal was accomplished in two main ways. First, the model specification input file that has been used to specify EQS models for over a decade has been maintained. This file serves as an intermediary between Diagrammer, Build EQS, and the technical estimation machinery in EQS. Since this file is identical in DOS, Macintosh, UNIX, and mainframe computer systems, users moving to new computers will find an old friend. Second, the graphical user interface was designed to be highly similar to the parallel interface in EQS for Macintosh. As a result, moving between Windows and the Macintosh will be especially easy. Nonetheless, we recognize that this generality has been achieved with a certain amount of awkwardness for the Mac user. For example, we have adhered in both Windows and Macintosh environments to DOS file naming conventions, which are readily accepted in the Windows world but are awkard in the Macintosh world. Nonetheless, this gives maximum compatibility across DOS, Windows, and the Macintosh. There is, thus, also a substantial amount of similarity between this *EQS for Windows User's Guide* and the comparable *EQS for Macintosh User's Guide*. This guide, however, is a bit more recent and, hence, reflective of the newest features.

EQS for Windows is a thoroughly revised and improved version of the authors' EQS/Windows, the first modeling program in the Windows environment. Although Microsoft's Windows 95 environment was not yet released at the time this user's guide was completed, we have been able to verify that this program also will run in this new environment. Chapter 11 describes a few of the environment differences between Windows and Windows 95 that are relevant.

You should find that this release of EQS for Windows provides the smoothest possible transition between the many time-consuming preparatory activities that are an inevitable part of thoughtful data analysis and the formal modeling activity itself. Thus, you have access to a wide variety of graphical and basic statistical analyses, as well as simple ways to move between analyses and modeling. For example, you can move the results of an exploratory factor analysis directly into a modeling setup. You also have access to some of the most up-to-date technical developments in the structural modeling field. Those developments include the Yuan-Bentler corrected asymptotically distribution-free statistics which provide substantially improved small sample performance.

Every gain in ease and functionality of modeling programs has been accompanied by an occasional criticism that the methodology is becoming so easy that untrained investigators now will be able to model thoughtlessly, mechanically, and in violation of scientific and/or statistical principles. The ease and functionality with which any particular action *can* be taken with EQS for Windows is not meant to encourage sloppy research by implying that the action *should* be taken in any given analysis. For example, with EQS for Windows, it is now very easy to see outliers in plots, to mark them, and to eliminate them from an analysis. However, eliminating such outliers sometimes makes sense, and at other times does not. It probably always helps to know about them. Similarly, as noted above, you can now run models directly from Diagrammer without paying any attention to the intermediate EQS input file. Nonetheless, you certainly should know how to interpret the contents (or potential contents) of this input file since it provides the precise specification of the model to be run and allows you to make further specifications beyond those available in Diagrammer. This user's guide cannot be a text or technical treatise on the appropriate use of all methods that are provided. You should let statistical and scientific theory and practice guide all applications.

The technical statistical, algorithmic, and data analytic work that forms a conceptual and experimental basis for EQS was developed in part with support by research grants DA00017 and DA01070 from the U.S. Public Health Service. The results of this research have been, and are being, published in refereed scientific journals, based on major contributions by Mary M. Li, Shinn -T. Wu, Doris Y. -P. Leung, Maia Berkane, Mortaza Jamshidian, Judith Stein, Wai Chan, Man-Lai Tang, Jodie Ullman, Ke-Hai Yuan, and Yiu-Fai Yung. This user's guide was updated and edited by Virginia Lawrence. Elizabeth Houck tested and improved the correspondence between the program and its documentation. Brain Lorber of Multivariate Software provided generous support in the development of EQS for Windows. Phil Cabanday designed the cover for this user's guide, the *EQS for Macintosh User's Guide*, and the *EQS Structural Equations Program Manual*. We also thank Jennifer Row and Kathryn Lewis of BMDP Statistical Software, as well as William Sanders and Keith Roberts. The use of some BMDP datasets in examples is gratefully acknowledged.

A substantial amount of quality-control testing on EQS for Windows was done before its release, and we believe that serious bugs have been virtually eliminated. We owe a great debt of gratitude to many members of the user community who provided excellent guidance for program modification and improvement. The feedback from kind as well as critical beta-testers is gratefully acknowledged. Unfortunately, not all recommended changes could be incorporated into this release of the program. Nonetheless, we look forward to its continued improvement, and welcome your criticisms and suggestions for future versions of the program and its documentation. We especially need your help to locate those problems that have escaped our attention in spite of our best intentions.

1. INTRODUCTION

EQS is a leading structural equations modeling program that has served the scientific and professional community for years. Through its comprehensive yet simple approach to the specification, estimation, and testing of models for mean and covariance structures, it has been applied in many fields ranging from social and behavioral sciences to management, medicine, and market research. It has earned its favorable reputation not only for the many scientific innovations it has made available, but also for its user-friendly, practical features. The EQS program is available on a wide range of computer hardware such as IBM mainframes running OS/MVS, high performance UNIX workstations, IBM PCs, and IBM PC/386/486s running MS-DOS on protected mode.

Now EQS is available for one of the most advanced operating environments — Microsoft Windows. The Windows environment is visually outstanding because of its graphical user interface (GUI). Using that interface, you can accomplish most program actions through visual specifications that make even advanced features of a program easy to use. EQS for Windows was especially designed for the GUI environment.

This version of EQS is substantially improved and expanded from previous versions. There are new data management and analysis features within the GUI interface, as well as improvements to the modeling procedures. EQS now allows you to perform many statistical procedures and data handling functions which previously were awkwardly performed outside of the EQS environment.

The new interface allows you to prepare your raw dataset, impute missing values, visually inspect the data, plot and print graphs, draw a path diagram, and almost automatically construct the set of specifications and equations necessary to run the EQS structural equations program. Regarding the modeling procedures, this version of EQS has improvements in the LM test, the W test, more fit indices, and automatic model modification. Most importantly, EQS for Windows handles categorical as well as continuous variables.

EQS for Windows has two main program elements. The first is the GUI environment with its interactive mode for data visualization and analysis, and its ability to set up regular "batch"-type EQS runs. This *EQS for Windows User's Guide* explains how to use these various features with your data. The second program element is the standard EQS program, which is an integral part of EQS for Windows, but conforms to conventions and procedures that are described in the following reference: Bentler, P. M. (1995). *EQS Structural Equations Program Manual*. Encino, CA: Multivariate Software, Inc.

The actual structural modeling computations are done within the framework of the EQS program as described in the EQS manual. Consequently, the structural modeling input and output remain consistent with the EQS manual, which you should consult for detailed descriptions of various technical features of the program. Of course, this user's guide describes those new features of the EQS program which are not documented in the EQS manual. Also, this user's guide provides, in chapter 7, a review of basic concepts necessary for understanding the EQS approach to structural models. This approach will become familiar to you even if you work primarily with **Diagrammer**, our visual model specification GUI, since standard EQS model files will be automatically generated.

Features of the GUI Interface

Data Entry and Manipulation

EQS for Windows is oriented to the convenient handling of data. As a first priority, the program asks you to provide it with data.

1. If your data are not yet in a data file, it provides a convenient way for you to enter data into the cells of a spreadsheet, resulting in an organized data matrix.

2. If you already have a data file, it gives you access to the data manager which can import ASCII or text data in free or fixed format.

The program allows you to join, merge, and sort data so that several datasets can be put together into a more appropriate format without leaving EQS. It also has the capability to select cases using arithmetic types of criteria. If your data contain dependencies among observations, it can smooth the data by using the moving average method, and it can remove the trend of a data set by estimating the autocorrelations.

Data Imputation

Very often a researcher has missing data in his/her data set. There are two popular ways of handling missing data without estimating the values of missing observations:

1. Delete all cases that have any incomplete observations. This method may be acceptable if you have a large number of cases. Typically, however, one cannot afford to lose valuable data from a subject that is only missing values for one or two variables.

2. Compute means and correlations based on single and pairwise present data.

In addition to these procedures, EQS for Windows provides a choice of several statistically sound methods for imputing values for the missing cells. This may be useful in its own right in the context of a variety of statistical analyses, but when proceeding to structural modeling with EQS, it is essential. The computations within EQS require that there be no missing data entries, and you must be sure that the data matrix you select for analysis is complete.

The pattern of missing data may be of interest itself. EQS allows you to see the pattern of missing data through a graphic display of variables and subjects. You can see if one variable in particular has a great deal of missing data, or if one or more individuals have many empty cells.

Data Exploration

Most researchers who use structural equations programs such as EQS or LISREL go through several steps to explore their datasets before analyzing a structural model. These steps usually include using one of the leading statistical packages such as BMDP, SPSS, or SAS to do frequency tables, cross-tabulations, *t*-tests, ANOVAs, or factor analyses. It is now unnecessary to turn to other statistical packages to perform such analyses, because most of the relevant data description and reduction, as well as the group and mean comparison capabilities, have been built into EQS for Windows.

One frequently omitted step in data exploration is the visual analysis of key univariate and bivariate features of the data. EQS for Windows makes it easy to visualize data for regularities as well as anomalies. For example, you can use EQS to mark cases that do not conform to a regression line, and you can study their effect. By simply clicking on the mouse, you can do an analysis with or without certain cases, or you can remove the cases from the data file or place them into their own dataset for further analysis.

Data Presentation

Another important aspect of data analysis is the presentation of data. One of the most effective ways to communicate information about your data to others is to display features of your data visually. This version of EQS includes a number of useful plotting functions, such as histograms and bivariate plots. You can also use EQS to customize your figure with labels and other features generally available in this graphical environment. More good news is that you can print all of these plots on a laser printer to produce a publication-quality hard copy.

Draw a Diagram and Automatic EQS Model Construction

EQS for Windows has a **Diagrammer** feature that builds an EQS model for you from the path diagram which you provide. Figure 1.1 displays a path diagram created with the Diagrammer.

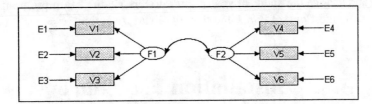

Figure 1.1 Illustrative Two Factors CFA Model

It is our belief that you should not spend much of your valuable time learning and implementing the syntax of a program. Rather, you will be better served by spending your time analyzing your data, and designing and refining your models.

In order to facilitate your thinking, EQS for Windows will ask you to provide a few visual specifications that the program will use to create the EQS command language for you. Of course, you still need to know about the conceptual approach used by EQS, as well as the meaning of various statistics or other program specifications. You should know the basic ideas of modeling, as presented in the *EQS Structural Equations Program Manual*, since you will want to assure yourself that the options you select are appropriate for the model which you want to evaluate.

Your model and data specifications are based on the options that you select from a series of well-defined dialog boxes, rather than your implementation of the specific EQS model syntax. You can leave the details of model construction to the program. An advantage of doing model building with **Diagrammer** is that you will not find it necessary to look in the EQS manual to remind yourself about the correct syntax. Of course, use of this feature is optional, since you can also specify models the old-fashioned way, using the standard EQS model specification language. And you can easily edit any model file created with **Build EQS** if you use the standard full-screen editing features.

Hardware and Software Requirements

EQS for Windows requires certain computer hardware and software for smooth operation. Please make sure that your computer has all of the following characteristics.

1. IBM PC or compatible, with Intel 80386 or higher processor, with a math coprocessor installed.
2. At least 4 megabytes of RAM as suggested by Microsoft for all Windows applications.
3. A mouse.
4. An EGA or VGA graphics adapter and a compatible monitor.
5. A hard disk with at least 3 megabytes of space.
6. Microsoft Windows 3.1 or higher.
7. A valid, installed printer driver. The computer must be configured so that it can print from any Windows application. This is required <u>even if you do not have a printer attached to the computer.</u>

If your computer meets all conditions except #7, please use your Windows diskettes to install a printer driver before you proceed with the installation. You need a Windows printer driver because EQS for Windows formats all plots and diagrams based on the installed printer driver. If you have no installed printer driver, the program will give an error message:
Printing failed. Check control panel for print driver.

You can view and change the status of your printer drivers via the **Main** program group in Microsoft Windows. Click on the **Control Panel** and then the **Printers** option.

Installation Procedure

Your EQS for Windows program is distributed on two diskettes. This program is self-installing, provided that you have the appropriate hardware and Windows operating system. Follow these steps to perform the installation. If you have Windows 95, see the installation instructions in Chapter 11.

1. Insert the EQS for Windows Disk#1 into drive A or drive B of your computer. In Step 4 below, we will assume this is the **A** drive. (If your drive is B, substitute **B** for **A** in Step 4.)

2. Go to the **Program Manager** in Windows. The name **Program Manager** will appear in the title bar. You should see the **File**, **Options**, **Window**, and **Help** menu options in the window.

3. Move the pointer to **File**, and select it by clicking on it. Then, click on **Run...** (Or, click on **File**, drag down to **Run**, and release the mouse button.)

4. The **Run** dialog box will appear, containing the **Command Line** text box. The cursor will be blinking on the left, inside the text box. There, you should type
    A:\SETUP
    inside the text box.

5. Move the pointer to the **OK** button, and click on it. An information box titled **EQS for Windows Setup** will appear, containing the statement **Initializing Setup....**

6. The **EQS for Windows Setup** dialog box will appear.

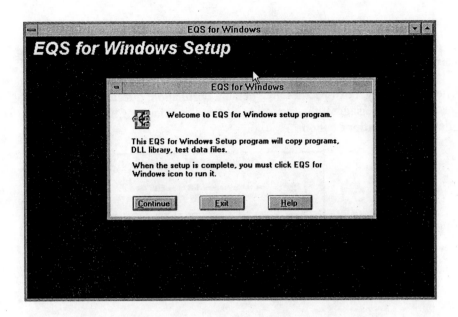

Figure 1.2 EQS for Windows Setup Dialog Box

7. Click on the **Continue** button to bring up the next dialog box. That box instructs you to provide your name and the license number of the EQS for Windows program.

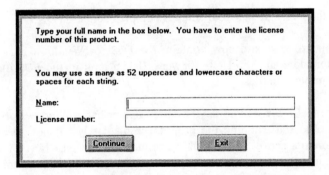

Figure 1.3 Name and License Dialog Box

8. Enter your name and press the <Tab> button on your keyboard.

9. With the cursor in the **License number** field, enter the license number from your EQS for Windows program disk or from this user's guide.

10. Click **Continue**, and you will see the **Name and License Correction Check** dialog box. Your name and license number will appear on your screen. Figure 1.4 shows a name but no number.

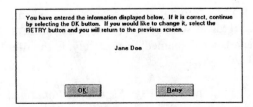

Figure 1.4 Name and License Correction Check

11. If your name and license number are incorrect, click on **Retry** to return to Figure 1.3. When your name and license number are correct, click on **OK**.

12. The next dialog box specifies the default destination directory for your EQS for Windows installation. We suggest that you use C:\EQS, the default. Change the path as necessary, then click on the **Continue** button.

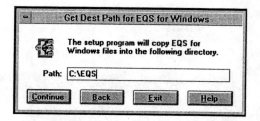

Figure 1.5 EQS Path Dialog Box

13. The EQS for Windows Setup program will install the files from Disk#1.

14. The EQS for Windows Setup program will prompt you for Disk#2. Insert Disk#2 and click on **OK**.

15. When you see the message that your setup is complete, click on **OK**.

Your EQS program group should now contain: the EQS for Windows program icon, the EQS for Windows Convertor icon, and the Help Viewer. If you look in the EQS directory, you will see a directory of the example data files.

You are ready to run EQS for Windows. If your computer has a Windows print driver installed, you can go to Chapter 2 to start running the program immediately. If not, please see **Hardware and Software Requirements** above, and install the printer driver first. If you are unsure whether your computer is configured for printing, you can find out easily. Just click on the EQS icon, and choose **File** and **Print**. If you can print the screen, your setup is fine.

Contents of EQS for Windows Files

In this section we provide some information about important files that EQS for Windows has installed. You should understand the purpose of the EQS and EQS.INI files.

DMAS.EXE and EQS.EXE Files

Previously we stated that EQS for Windows could be considered to have two main parts, the basic Windows interface and background statistical routines, and the EQS structural equations modeling program. These two main parts are contained, respectively, in the files DMAS.EXE and EQS.EXE that are now installed on your hard disk.

The EQS program as described in the 1995 EQS *Structural Equations Program Manual* can be run under DOS, without Windows, using the EQS.EXE file. This version of EQS also contains the extended features described elsewhere in this user's guide. You can implement them in the standard EQS command mode with an appropriate model file.

6

In addition to DMAS.EXE and EQS.EXE, the setup program will have installed a variety of illustrative data and model files. These are used in various chapters of this **User's Guide** to demonstrate some of the program's features.

The EQS.INI File

During installation, a file called **EQS.INI** was installed on your hard disk in the directory used for your Windows 3.1 (or higher) operating system. This file contains several lines that represent pointers to the location on your hard disk where the EQS program can be found. By default, you would find the line **EQS386=C:\EQS** in the EQS.INI file. If you used another directory, its name would be given instead. You should not move the EQS for Windows program into another directory without either updating this line in the EQS.INI file, or letting the Setup program make this adjustment for you automatically.

The EQS.INI file also contains a line **EQSLEN=?**, where the **?** is a number. This number was computed by the setup program as the number of words in memory that would be available to you during a run of the EQS.EXE modeling program. The actual number that you have depends on the physical and operating configuration of your computer, such as the amount of memory available. If you change these parameters of your computer, this number may need to be adjusted. Reinstalling EQS for Windows with the setup program would automatically adjust this number for you. You can also adjust the EQSLEN number using any text editor.

Even if you make no change in your computer, it is possible that you may need to adjust the EQSLEN value. The actual amount of memory available to EQS.EXE will depend on the amount of memory that you are using for other purposes at the time you try to run EQS. For example, if you have a lot of active windows, less memory will be available for EQS.EXE. If you find that the EQS.EXE program does not start appropriately, you could try to adjust downward the number that is given in EQSLEN.

The number given by default is computed during setup as a relatively safe number that should handle most of your jobs, given your computer configuration. If the number is, in fact, too small compared to the amount of memory actually available, the EQS.EXE program will run, but you may not be able to run a job of the maximum size that your computer could, in principle, handle. In such a case, you may want to increase the number by small amounts until you have given too large a value. If the number given is too large relative to the actual configuration of your computer, EQS.EXE will not start up appropriately, and you should adjust the number downward.

Removing EQS for Windows Files

Once you are satisfied that EQS for Windows is running correctly, you may wish to remove the illustrative model and data files that were provided with the program. You can do this in the standard way, using the delete command under DOS or Windows.

Only the files DMAS.EXE, EQS.EXE, and EQSFLIB.DLL cannot be removed with a file delete command. Their attributes have been set during installation to prevent you from accidentally removing these files. If you really do want to delete EQS for Windows from your computer by deleting all of its files, you have to modify the file attributes of these three files.

To remove DMAS.EXE, EQS.EXE, and EQSFLIB.DLL, go to the directory containing the files and type:
> **ATTRIB -R DMAS.EXE**
> **ATTRIB -R EQS.EXE**
> **ATTRIB -R EQSFLIB.DLL**

After you have changed the file attributes, they can be deleted. Of course, you should not delete these files unless you are sure that you still have the original installation disks provided by Multivariate Software.

Converting V4.x ESS files to V5 ESS

EQS for Windows can read most of the files created by EQS/Windows version 4. The only exception is the system file type. EQS for Windows version 5 cannot read the system files from earlier versions of EQS/Windows. If you have such files, you must convert them. To start converting old EQS/Windows Version 4 system files, double click on the **EQS for Windows Convertor** icon.

EQS for Windows
Convertor

Figure 1.6 Convertor Icon

The convertor main window will appear, as shown in Figure 1.7.

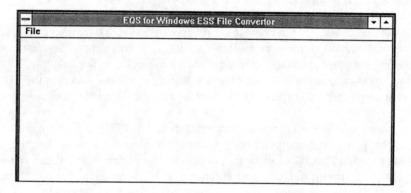

Figure 1.7 Convertor Main Window

Click on the **File** menu, then on the **Convert** option to bring up the **Converting Dmas Data Files** dialog box.

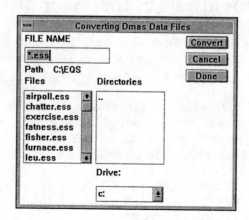

Figure 1.8 Converting Dmas Data Files Dialog Box

You can use this dialog box to convert all of the files in your directory at one time, or you can convert a single file. Follow the simple directions below.

Converting all Version 4.x ess Files in the Directory

To convert all EQS system data files in the directory:

1. Confirm that all EQS system data files in the directory have the **.ess** extension. If any EQS system data files have a different extension, rename the files with the **.ess** extension.

2. Double click on the **EQS for Windows Convertor** icon, then verify the drive and directory, changing if necessary. The list of *.ess files will appear in the **Files** list box.

3. Click on the **Convert** button. The Convertor will automatically convert every file in the specified directory.

4. The new Version 5 files will carry the file names assigned in step 1. The old Version 4 files will be renamed with the **.bak** extension.

Converting a Single Version 4.x ess File in the Directory

To convert a single EQS system data file:

1. Confirm that the desired EQS system data file in the directory has the **.ess** extension. If the file has a different extension, rename the file with the **.ess** extension.

2. Double click on the **EQS for Windows Convertor** icon, then verify the drive and directory, changing if necessary. The list of *.ess files will appear in the **Files** list box.

3. Highlight the file in the **Files** list box.

4. Click on the **Convert** button. The Convertor will automatically convert the selected file in the specified directory.

5. The new Version 5 file will carry the file name assigned in step 1. The old Version 4 file will be renamed with the **.bak** extension.

Where to Go from Here

Now you can begin to explore EQS for Windows. You can do this on your own, or by following along with the examples given in the various chapters. We suggest the latter approach, starting with Chapter 2, **A Quick Start to EQS for Windows**. But no matter how you approach the program, you'll find it to be a lot of fun!

2. A QUICK START TO EQS FOR WINDOWS

In the next several chapters of this user's guide, we will provide detailed instructions on the use of various features of this program. In this chapter we provide you with an introduction to the program without going into a lot of technical details.

It is quite easy to get started with the program, as we will show you with a few "hands on" examples. After you complete these examples, we hope that you will have such a good idea about the basic operations of EQS for Windows that you can do real-world data analysis without reading this user's guide any further. Please take a few moments to complete all three examples shown below.

Step 1: Run EQS for Windows

> *Note*: If you are using Windows 95, see chapter 11 for details on starting EQS in Windows 95. If you are using Windows 3.1, continue reading this section.

To start running EQS for Windows, double click on the EQS icon. It looks like this:

EQS for
Windows 5.0

Figure 2.1 The EQS for Windows Icon

Two windows appear, one on top of the other, as shown in Figure 2.2.

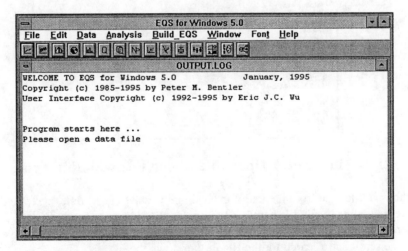

Figure 2.2 Menu and OUTPUT.LOG

First there is the main menu, which contains eight menus. Below the menu bar, you will find a series of tools for various plotting functions. Below that, there is a window called **output.log** which welcomes you to the program. It asks you, as the first step, to open a data file. Since EQS is data-analysis oriented, this is always the first step in any analysis.

Step 2: Open a Data File

Click **File** in the upper left corner of the main menu. Then select **Open** from the File menu to bring up the dialog box shown in Figure 2.3.

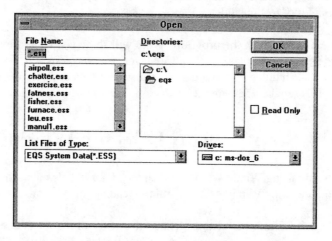

Figure 2.3 Open File Dialog Box with Data Files

Click on the down arrow in the **List Files of Type** box to bring up the list of file types.

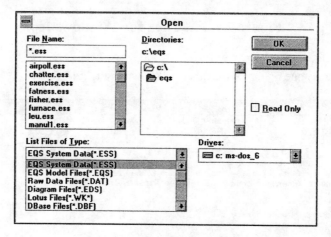

Figure 2.4 Open File Dialog Box with File Types

You can choose a file type from the list of extensions, ***.ess, *.eqs, *.dat, *.txt, *.eds, *.wk*, *.db***. In this context, * refers to any file name. You can specify file names in upper case, lower case, or any combination of upper and lower case. If you do not see any particular file, you can click on the down arrow ↓ in the scroll batto search for the file farther down the list.

Note that the **Open** file dialog box lists only those files that are known to EQS for Windows. For example, it will recognize all text files and files created by EQS for Windows. However, it will not recognize a file created by Microsoft Word, unless you actually save the file as a text file with line breaks.

File Types

In EQS for Windows, the file type is identified by the file extension, three letters after the period (.). We use this format to maintain consistency across various EQS programs for other computer systems. Although there are several other choices, the types of files that you will use most often in data analysis and EQS runs are the following:

- ***.eqs** files are EQS model files that are input to a structural modeling run
- ***.ess** files are EQS raw or covariance data system files have been processed by EQS to add identifying and labeling information
- ***.dat** files are raw text data files containing scores of subjects on variables.
- ***.eds** files are diagram files created by **Diagrammer**.
- ***.out** files are output files created by EQS.

You should open a raw text data file in this example. That will be a file with the suffix ***.dat**, so choose ***.dat** in the **List Files of Type** box, as shown in Figure 2.5.

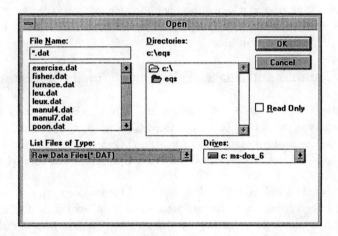

Figure 2.5 Open Dialog Box with Raw Data Files

Double click on file name **chatter.dat** in this dialog box. Alternatively, you can click the file name and then click the **OK** button to open this raw data file. After double-clicking on the name of the file, or clicking the **OK** button, you will see the **Raw Data File Information** dialog box in Figure 2.6.

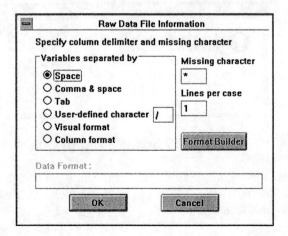

Figure 2.6 Raw Data File Information

Format

The **Raw Data File Information** dialog box in Figure 2.6 requires information on the format of your data file. It is assumed that the data are organized in such a way that one or more rows or records of the file first describe case number 1, across all variables; that the second case's scores on the variables are next; and so on. You can also specify a format to read the data in the file. There are two possible types of format:

- Free format
- Fixed format

Free Format

A data file in free format has at least one delimiter between the numerical values for any adjacent variables. In such a file, you plan to read in every score for every case or subject. The delimiter can be a space, a tab, a comma and a space, or any character that you specify. If your data file is in free format, chose **Variables separated by Space**, **Comma & space**, **Tab**, or **User-defined character**. You have no need for **Format Builder**.

Space, Commas and Space, Tab, User-defined Character

The default in the **Raw Data File Information** dialog box in Figure 2.6 is **Variables separated by Space**. You can accept the default or choose from **Comma & space**, **Tab**, **User defined-character**, **Visual format** or **Column format**. When you need detailed information on fixed format and the fixed format options, **Visual format** and **Column format**, read **Data Import and Export**, chapter 4.

If your data file contains only variable data separated by a space, you can simply accept the default, **Space**. The number of lines per case are vital to EQS in analyzing the data. In addition to the number of lines per case, you can specify the character(s) that designate the missing values.

Free Format Example

For **chatter.dat**, accept the defaults of **1 Lines per Case** and **Space**. Click **OK**. The **String** prompt box in Figure 2.7 appears.

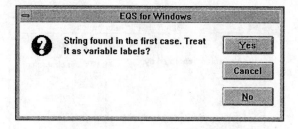

Figure 2.7 String Prompt Box

EQS for Windows found a string in the first case of the **chatter.dat** data file, so you see the **String Prompt** box. You get this box because EQS can read complex ASCII files in which the first case actually contains the variable names.

If you did not want EQS to treat the string as variable labels, you would click **NO**. However, since the first case contains the names of the variables in **chatter.dat**, click **YES**. Click **YES** for this example, and the data file appears.

Data File in Data Editor

Actually, the file that you see in the **Data Editor** is a copy of the raw data file, so that your original file remains intact. This file is named **chatter.ess**, since it is now treated as a system file. The file appears on your screen with default variable names: V1, V2, V3, etc. Typically, you would now go to the **Data** menu and pull down the **Information** dialog box so that you could assign some identifying labels to the variables. But we shall save this step till later. (You can, of course, explore it now by yourself.)

Figure 2.8, shows the file brought up in the EQS Data Editor.

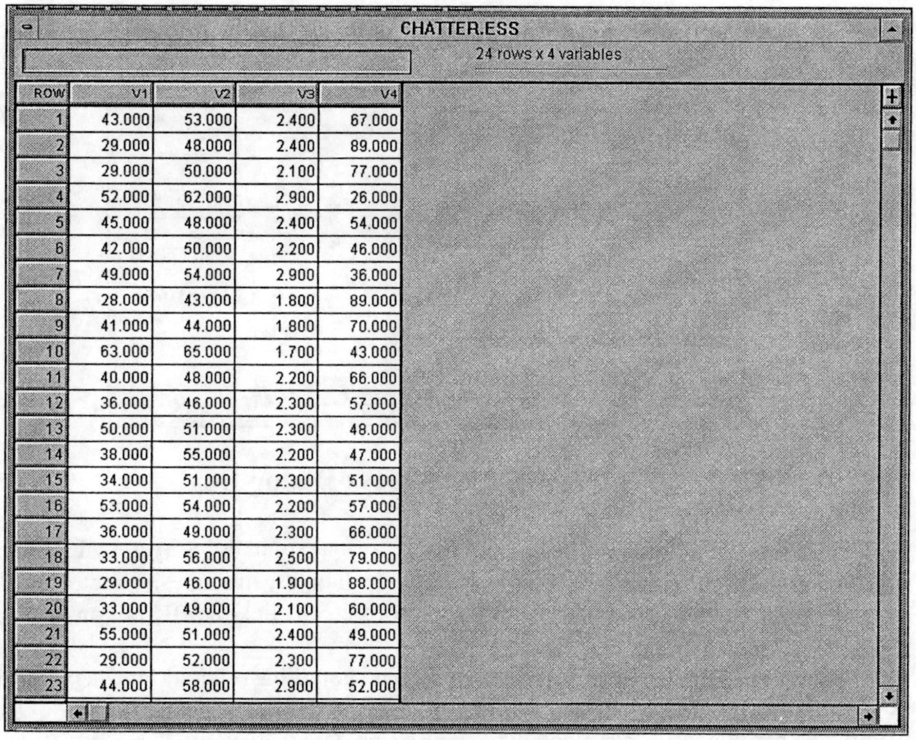

CHATTER.ESS			
		24 rows x 4 variables	

ROW	V1	V2	V3	V4
1	43.000	53.000	2.400	67.000
2	29.000	48.000	2.400	89.000
3	29.000	50.000	2.100	77.000
4	52.000	62.000	2.900	26.000
5	45.000	48.000	2.400	54.000
6	42.000	50.000	2.200	46.000
7	49.000	54.000	2.900	36.000
8	28.000	43.000	1.800	89.000
9	41.000	44.000	1.800	70.000
10	63.000	65.000	1.700	43.000
11	40.000	48.000	2.200	66.000
12	36.000	46.000	2.300	57.000
13	50.000	51.000	2.300	48.000
14	38.000	55.000	2.200	47.000
15	34.000	51.000	2.300	51.000
16	53.000	54.000	2.200	57.000
17	36.000	49.000	2.300	66.000
18	33.000	56.000	2.500	79.000
19	29.000	46.000	1.900	88.000
20	33.000	49.000	2.100	60.000
21	55.000	51.000	2.400	49.000
22	29.000	52.000	2.300	77.000
23	44.000	58.000	2.900	52.000

Figure 2.8 Chatter.ess in EQS for Windows Data Editor

The rows along the left give the subject, or case, numbers. The columns give the variable default names, V1, V2, and so on. Each entry, of course, gives the raw data score of a case on a variable.

> *Note: A data file must be visible and active before you can perform any meaningful function.*

We have purposely created the EQS for Windows program to be data-oriented. All procedures available in EQS for Windows are based on a dataset being available in the Data Editor. Thus, you must have an open dataset in the Data Editor in order to continue processing. If you have no data in an existing file, you must create a new data file by clicking the **File** menu, selecting **New**, and typing in the numbers yourself. These numbers are entered cell by cell into the spreadsheet Data Editor so that the data file resembles Figure 2.8.

As you probably know, you can keep several screens active in EQS for Windows. Thus, after some work, you may find that you have opened screens dealing with data, plots, computational results, and so on. At various points, you may be unable to continue data analysis because the relevant data matrix is not active. For example, if **output.log** is active rather than **chatter.ess**, the options in the Analysis menu will be grayed out. To activate **chatter.ess**, go to **Window** in the main menu. Choose **chatter.ess**, and you can then choose an option on the **Analysis** menu.

Saving As

Before we go on to other analyses, it might be a good idea to save the data file which is now an EQS System (*.ess) file. An EQS System file includes such file information as: tables, number of cases, variable names, format definitions, etc. The next time the file is opened, it will be retrieved as an *.ess file, so that all of this information will be automatically available to you.

Choose the **File** menu and select **Save As**. A Save As dialog box will appear as shown below in Figure 2.9.

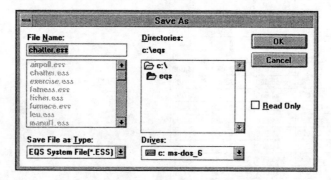

Figure 2.9 Save As Dialog Box

When this box appears, it automatically has the file format set as **EQS System File**. The dialog box has **chatter.ess** in the **File Name** box. You can make changes, in names, directories, drives, as you like. In this situation, there seems to be nothing to correct, so click the **OK** button to save the file.

If you have gone through the steps just discussed, you should have found that EQS did not allow you to save this file as **chatter.ess**, because a file with that name already exists in the directory. Instead, it asks you whether you want to replace the existing file. Don't do that; click **NO**. Then press **Cancel** in the **Save As** dialog box. You will go back to the file in the Data Editor. You cannot by mistake overwrite an existing file.

To discard this file, double click on the small gray square in the upper left corner of the **chatter.ess** file window. Now you should be out of the data file and back to the main EQS for Windows screen shown in Figure 2.2. If you are not at the main screen, use the **Window** menu to choose **output.log** to navigate back to this point. Otherwise, quit EQS for Windows, and restart the program.

We are now ready to do some real data analysis. Finally!

Step 3. Activate a Program Function

To activate a program function, we must open a data file. Retrieve the **fisher.ess** file by going to the **File** menu, selecting **Open**, and clicking on **fisher.ess**. The **fisher.ess** file contains numbers along with a label for each of the variables. Previously, another researcher entered these labels via the **Data** menu, using the **Information** selection.

The program permits a variety of data analytic procedures and manipulations, but here we start with an example based on a histogram. Then we turn to a regression analysis and build an EQS model.

Plotting a Histogram

After you have opened a data file, you can access many data manipulation procedures easily. Please note that there are 15 icons right below the EQS for Windows main menu. These icons are as follows:

Figure 2.10 EQS for Windows Plot Function Icons

The first 13 icons are the plot icon tools in EQS for Windows. The last two icons on the right are the Missing Data plot icon and the icon for Diagrammer. Once the data file is in the Data Editor, you can access all of the plotting functions through these icons.

Let's choose the third plot option, the histogram. A histogram provides a nice graphical way to show the distribution of scores on a variable. A histogram also provides visual information that is relevant to evaluating model assumptions such as normality.

Use your mouse to move the selector arrow to the histogram icon tool and click on it. The dialog box that serves the histogram option will open, as shown in Figure 2.11 below. You will see some options that we need not use here.

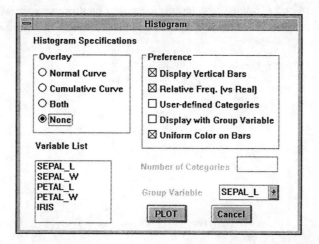

Figure 2.11 Histogram Specification Dialog Box

Click on the variable **SEPAL_W** in the list box, and then click the **PLOT** button. The histogram shown in Figure 2.12 will appear.

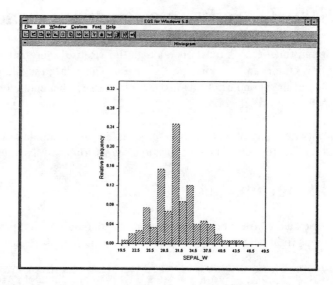

Figure 2.12 Histogram Plot

Note: Your version will have a black background. To improve the quality of the printing, we have switched the background color for all plots in this manual.

There are other possibilities for further actions available within this window, using the **Custom** menu for the histogram plot. We shall not pursue these now. Instead we will explore one of the other functions available on the EQS for Windows main menu (shown in Figure 2.2).

Window Menu

EQS for Windows provides the **Window** menu so that you can easily activate one screen after another. When you click on **Window** on the menu, you get a listing of the screens that currently exist in the program's memory. These are all of the screens, including data, documents, and plots, except those which you have specifically closed so that they have been eliminated from memory. Now that you have opened **fisher.ess** and created a histogram, there will be three screens available in the **Window**. Note that Histogram is checked, because it is the active screen. The Window menu looks like this:

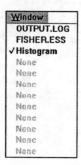

Figure 2.13 Window Menu

The original data file, **fisher.ess**, is there as well, as is the **output.log** file (to be discussed further below). If you do not want to change to another screen, click again on the mouse button while the cursor is on the word **Window**. The list of available screens will disappear.

However, you should experiment a bit with moving between various screens. Move the pointer in the **Window** list to the **fisher.ess** file and release the mouse button. The Window selections disappear, and the **fisher.ess** data file becomes the active screen that you see. EQS marks the active screen with a check mark in the **Window** menu, while an inactive screen has no check mark.

Go back to **Window** and click on **output.log**. You will see Figure 2.2. Finally, go back to **Window** and click on **Histogram**. Figure 2.12 will reappear.

Printing a Plot

EQS for Windows will print a hard copy of any plot that is in an active window. If the graphic display of your histogram is important to you, you might want to create a paper copy. Pull down the **File** menu and click the **Print** command. The histogram will be sent to the printer automatically. Only the histogram itself will be printed. The frame of the screen will be ignored.

Of course, we assume that you set up your printer correctly when you initialized Windows. We would expect that, if there is a printing problem, it will almost certainly be in the general Windows environment or your hardware, and not in EQS for Windows.

You might want to use a plot in a different program, such as a wordprocessor. There are three methods that you could use to bring a plot from EQS to another program.
1. You can use the **Edit** menu **Copy** option to copy the plot to the clipboard. You can then **Paste** the plot into the new document.
2. You can use the **File** menu **Save Picture** option to create a graphics file for import into other programs.
3. You can use a screen capture program to create a graphics file of your plot. You can then insert that graphic into other PC documents. **Pizazz Plus** is a good screen capture program for Windows. It is published by Application Techniques, Inc., 10 Lomar Park Drive, Pepperell, MA 01463.

Summary

The above steps of reading a dataset, saving the raw data in an EQS system file, generating the histogram, and getting a hard copy of the diagram have taken several pages to describe. However, the entire process takes only a few clicks or double clicks of the mouse, and very few keyboard actions. You will find, in general, that the actions you might take will be clearly visible to you at all times by way of graphical choices. While you should know what you are attempting to do with your data, you need to remember very little about the program itself. EQS for Windows aims to be easy and intuitive no matter what you want to accomplish. Doing statistics, you will see, can be fun!

Discarding Windows and Files

If you have been following this tutorial carefully, you will have only three screens available for study and analysis. The number and their content is shown in the **Window** menu. However, this is a good place to point out that you can have a maximum of 12 windows active at once. It is usually worthwhile to close or discard datasets and windows that have no meaning to you.

You can save and close most datasets. After you save a dataset as a file, click on the box in the upper left corner to close the dataset window. That dataset is removed from the list in **Window**.

You can save plots by using the **File** menu **Save Picture** option. You can also print or discard plots. To discard a plot, close its screen. When you close the plot screen, that screen disappears from the **Window** menu.

Output.log

The **output.log** is one file that you cannot discard. It is always required when running EQS for Windows. Based on our prior actions, this file contains no information of use right now. But in general, when you run a statistical analysis, some textual and numerical results will be obtained. That output is placed into the **output.log** file. As you do additional analyses, the new results are simply appended to the previously-existing **output.log**. Thus, this one file may contain information from many different analyses that you conducted.

You can selectively discard material within the **output.log** file by using the **Edit** feature of main menu. For example, you can highlight the file and then cut it. When you quit EQS for Windows, you will be asked whether you want to save **output.log**. If it contains important results, you will want to save it.

A Multiple Regression Analysis

Now we can turn to one of the most widely used methods for data analysis, linear regression. A standard problem in data analysis is predicting the scores on one variable from the scores on other variables. This is a problem in multiple regression. To illustrate the method, we will use an EQS system file called **airpoll.ess**. As usual, you must bring up the data.

After activating EQS for Windows, pull down the **File** menu from the main menu and select the Open option to get the **Open** dialog box for opening a file.

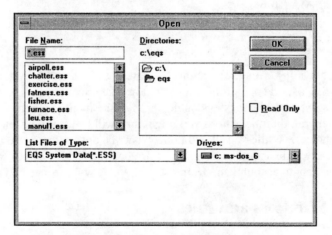

Figure 2.14 File Open Dialog Box

Select the data file name, **airpoll.ess**. Then click on **OK**, press the <Enter> key, or double click on **airpoll.ess** to bring the file into the Data Editor.

At this point, the data file is placed into the active screen, and you can proceed to the analysis. So far we have not told you what information the **airpoll.ess** dataset actually contains. In order to find out, you should open the data information dialog box. To get it, you pull down the **Data** menu and select **Information**. The information dialog box will appear as in Figure 2.15.

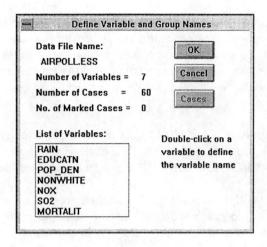

Figure 2.15 Data Information Dialog Box

This dialog box gives information on the file as it was created. The box shows that the file is based on 7 variables and 60 cases. It also shows how many cases in the Data Editor are marked or selected.

In EQS for Windows, it is possible to select certain cases for a particular analysis or further action. For example, you might want to perform an analysis on only one random half of all cases. In this example, we are using all cases in the data file, and none are marked.

The **List of Variables** shows either the default variable names or any existing specific names. If you were to make changes to these names, the new names would be automatically transferred to the **airpoll.ess** system file.

When you press **Cancel** in the dialog box of Figure 2.15, the box disappears, and the Data Editor with the dataset becomes the active window again. You are now ready to specify the regression model.

To specify a regression model, start by pulling down the **Analysis** menu from the main menu. Select the **Regression** option. A regression analysis specification dialog box will appear as shown in Figure 2.16.

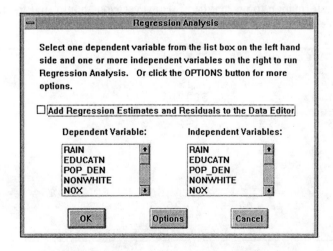

Figure 2.16 Regression Analysis Dialog Box

The box is self-explanatory. You should pick one variable from the left column, and one or more variables from the right column, depending on whether you are doing bivariate or multiple regression. Notice that you can add two columns of numbers to your input data file, namely, the regression estimates based on the optimal prediction equation, and the residuals, for each case. When you add these numbers to the file, they are available for further analysis or plotting. In this example, we will skip this feature.

We will do a simple regression using **MORTALIT** as the dependent variable to be predicted. Search the **Dependent Variable** list until you find it, then click on it. In the **Independent Variables** list, click on **EDUCATN**, **POP_DEN**, and **NONWHITE** to select the independent, or predictor, variables.

> *Note*: To select multiple noncontiguous variables from the list, hold down the <Ctrl> key while clicking on each variable. To select multiple contiguous variables from the list, drag the cursor over each variable, or hold down the <Shift>> key while clicking on each variable.

After you specify these variables with mouse clicks, press the <Enter> key or click the **OK** button to run the regression analysis program. After you press **OK**, wait a few moments. A note box will pop up to inform you that the analysis is done. Click **OK**, you can review the regression analysis output.

As stated above, the output of all statistical computations in EQS for Windows are stored in the **output.log** file. This file opens automatically when the EQS program starts, though it is empty until you do some analyses. However, at the end of a computation, this output file will automatically become the active window. You can scroll through the output to examine the results of your analysis.

You can review the **output.log** file at any time in a text window. You can access the **output.log** text window by selecting **output.log** from **Window** of the main menu. In the case of regression, the **output.log** file has five parts, consisting of:

1. Analysis of variance of the regression
2. Statistics for the regression
3. Multiple regression equation (unstandardized)
4. Standardized regression equation
5. Test statistics for the regression coefficients

This is too much information to present here. However, you should find the key parts of the results, namely the multiple correlation and the multiple regression equation shown in Figure 2.17.

```
Dependent Variable  =    MORTALIT
Number of obs.      =          60
Multiple R          =      0.7713
R-square            =      0.5949
Adjusted R-square   =      0.5732
F( 3,     56)       =     27.4162
Prob > F            =      0.0000
Std. Error of Est.  =     40.6418
Durbin-Watson Stat. =      1.7809


          =======MULTIPLE REGRESSION EQUATION=======
MORTALIT =     1142.047 +     -25.507*EDUCATN   +       0.008*POP_DEN

                +        4.000*NONWHITE   + ERROR;
```

Figure 2.17 Part of Output.log Showing Regression Equation

Although there is a lot more to discuss, for the sake of brevity, this concludes the regression example. If you wish, you may now delete all windows except the **output.log**. You can also delete material from the **output.log**. First, make **output.log** the active window via **Window** or by clicking in the **output.log** window itself. Then drag the mouse to block all the unwanted text, and go to the **Edit** menu to **Cut** this material. Now the file will not be cluttered by material that you do not want, and it is ready for new output. Let us turn to a structural equation model.

Create and Run an EQS Model

Let's use a confirmatory factor analysis model, the example from page 117 of the *EQS Structural Equations Program Manual*. It uses a raw score dataset called **manul7.ess**, which is stored as an EQS system file. This data file has six variables. We want to show you how to build a six-variable, two-factor confirmatory factor model. We will develop the model based on an input of the raw data. If the file were the covariance or correlation matrix for these data, we would use a virtually identical procedure.

> *Note:* If you prefer, you can use **manul7a.ess** rather than **manul7.ess**. **Manul7a.ess** is nearly identical to **manul7.ess**, but missing one case deleted as an outlier.

First, of course, you have to activate the EQS for Windows program if it is not already active, and open the appropriate data file. Pull down the **File** menu from the main menu and select the **Open** option to get a file open dialog box. The dialog box shows the list of files. Select **manul7.ess** and click **OK** or press the <Enter> key. If you prefer, you can double-click **manul7.ess** to bring the file to the Data Editor.

We can start building the EQS model after deciding on the dataset. To build an EQS model in the conventional way, you type in the equations, variances, and covariances, character by character using a text editor. EQS for Windows provides two more advanced ways to build the equations.

1. The **Building EQS Model Using the Diagrammer** section of this chapter illustrates how you can build a model by simply drawing a diagram on the screen and letting the program generate the model for you.
2. The **Building EQS Model by Equation Table** section of this chapter shows that you can create a table consisting of the components of the equations. Then fill in the free parameters by clicking the cells with your mouse.

Either method will substantially reduce the time required to build a model.

1. Building EQS Model Using the Diagrammer

You must open the **Draw Diagram** to draw a structural equation diagram. To do this, click the **Diagrammer** icon, the rightmost icon in the icon row on your screen.

The **Draw Diagram** window will appear (Figure 2.18).

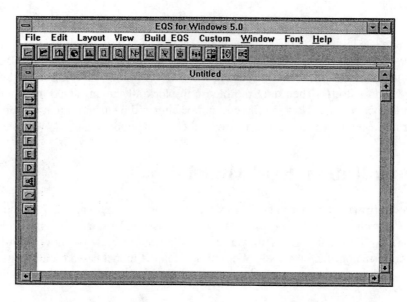

Figure 2.18 The Draw Diagram Window

On the left side of the **Diagrammer** window, there is a vertical tool bar with ten icon tools. You can use these icon tools to create the diagram. The top icon of the icon tools has the character **A** on it. It is a **text tool**. By clicking this icon once and moving the mouse cursor to the draw window, you can add labels or comments to your diagram.

The second and third icons in the column are two **arrow tools** for creating factor loadings and covariances. After the arrow tools are four **variable tools** for creating V, F, E, and D variables. After the variable tools there is a **factor structure tool**. This factor structure tool is probably the most important tool of all. It allows a you to create a factor loading structure with only a few clicks.

The last two icons are **freehand arrow tools**. They allow you to connect two diagram objects (i.e. two factor structures, two variables, or one variable and one factor structure) by drawing freely. Then it will recalculate the path you have drawn and smooth the path.

Create a Factor Structure

Since we want to create a two factor confirmatory factor model, we can use the factor structure icon tool to do it.

Click the factor structure icon tool once and move the mouse to the draw window. Note that the mouse cursor changes to a crosshair.

Click the mouse pointer once on the draw window when the mouse pointer is positioned where you want the factor structure. The Factor Structure Specification dialog box in Figure 2.19 will appear. The dialog box shows the default F1 for factor name and factor label.

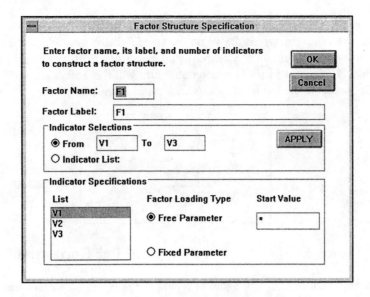

Figure 2.19 Factor Structure Specification Dialog Box

Indicator Selections

There are two radio buttons in the **Indicator Selections** section of the dialog box. The default button is the top button marking the indicators V1 to V3. For this example, click **OK** to accept the default.

When you are drawing a different model, you can change the indicator list by clicking on the **Indicator List** radio button. When the new field box appears, enter the indicator names (i.e. V1, V3, V4, V7, etc.). Be sure to use a comma to separate indicators.

After you change the factor indicators, you must click on the **APPLY** button. That forces the program to take your specified number of variables and list them in the **List** box. You can verify your indicators by viewing the **Indicator Specifications List** box in the lower left corner of the dialog box.

Indicator Specifications

You can use the two radio buttons in the **Indicator Specifications** section to specify your preferred type of indicator specifications. The default specifies free parameters with the starting value noted as an asterisk (*). The * tells the program to estimate the best starting value for you.

To change the parameter type from free to fixed on the factor loading, click on your chosen variable in the list box. Then click on the radio button to select the parameter type. You can accept the default **Start Value** of 1.0 or enter a new value. After entering all of the information necessary to construct a factor structure, click on the **OK** button to create the factor structure.

For the example using defaults, EQS for Windows draws the factor structure as shown in Figure 2.20.

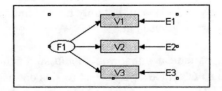

Figure 2.20 First Factor Structure

Please note that, when the structure is drawn on the screen, the arrows on the factor loadings point to the right. To change the orientation, you must pull down the **Edit** menu from the Draw Diagram window and select **Horizontal Flip**. The factor structure will flip 180 degrees. Thus, the direction of the factor loading points to the left hand side as shown in Figure 2.21.

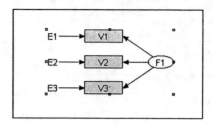

Figure 2.21 First Factor Structure after Horizontal Flip

Click on the factor structure icon tool again to repeat the previous step and create the second factor structure. This time you do not have to flip the factor structure.

When you see the second factor structure, click the two-way freehand arrow tool and move the mouse to draw a curve between F1 and F2. Be sure to start with your mouse pointer inside one factor oval, and end with your mouse pointer inside the other factor oval. After you release the mouse pointer, EQS will redraw the curve and you will have the diagram as shown in Figure 2.22.

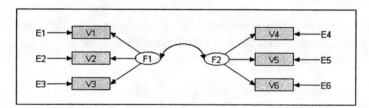

Figure 2.22 Complete Two Factors CFA Model

Note that your two factor structures may not align themselves nicely. If that is the case, you can click on one of the structures to select it. Then hold down the mouse button while you move the structure to a better position. Release the mouse button when you have brought the structure to a good position.

If you make a mistake, you can click on the portion of the diagram that you want to correct. Then click on **Edit** and choose **Cut**. The chosen portion will disappear, and you can try again.

Build EQS Model

After you have properly opened the data file and drawn the diagram, you are ready to build the EQS model. First, click the **Build_EQS** selection from the main menu. You can see from the drop-down menu that there are many items in this menu, but only three items are active. The active options are black, while the inactive options are grayed out.

This choice of only two options indicates that you should start with the item on top of the menu, **Title/Specifications,** to build an EQS model. By selecting this option, you can see a new dialog box:

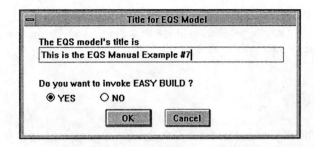

Figure 2.23 Build EQS Model Title Dialog Box

You should type in the EQS model title in the edit box shown in Figure 2.23. This title will be used as the EQS job title.

Notice that the dialog box also asks you if you want to invoke the **EASY BUILD** facility. The default is **YES**. The **EASY BUILD** facility will ask you a series of questions. Your responses build the specific model that you want in the form of a ***.eqs** file that is used as input to the computational part of the EQS program. Let's use the default by clicking the **OK** button.

After you click on **OK**, the program will automatically generate that part of the model file containing the title. A new dialog box called **EQS Model Specifications** will appear as shown in Figure 2.24.

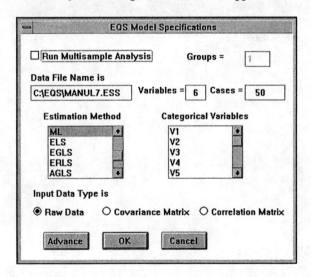

Figure 2.24 EQS Model Specifications Dialog Box

This box has the information that is needed in the /SPECIFICATIONS paragraph of the EQS program. By default, it automatically has most of the information you need to specify a model. Some of the default information is from the ***.ess** file (here, **manul7.ess**), and some reflects choices typically made in structural modeling. The file name, number of variables, number of cases, method of analysis, and type of input data (raw data, covariance matrix, etc.) have been set by defaults.

For many analyses, these defaults probably will meet your needs. Notice that you can specify a multiple group model, and that you can define certain variables in your file as being **categorical** variables for the polychoric-polyserial methodology in EQS. After you finish with the model specifications dialog box, the relevant information is transferred automatically to the ***.eqs** model file that is being built.

For our illustration, there is no reason to change anything in this dialog box. Therefore, click the **OK** button without changing anything. You will see that the EQS model instructions will be written to a text window. **You are now ready to run EQS.**

EQS Model File

Whether or not you build your model from a diagram or an equation table, you complete building an EQS model with the **Build_EQS** feature. As this is done, you can see that the EQS command language is built line by line and is written onto the background window. The file that is created is called **work.eqs** by default. When the cursor returns to the **work.eqs** window, your model is complete, and you are ready to run EQS. Experienced EQS users may wonder where the /END statement is. Don't worry, it will be attached automatically before the model is run. The following shows an example of part of the model file that is created.

```
/TITLE
This is the EQS Manual Example #7
/SPECIFICATIONS
DATA=' C:\EQS\MANUL7.ESS'; VARIABLES=  6; CASES=    50;
METHODS=ML;
MATRIX=RAW;
/LABELS
V1=V1; V2=V2; V3=V3; V4=V4; V5=V5;
V6=V6;
/EQUATIONS
V1 =  + *F1  + E1;
V2 =  + *F1  + E2;
V3 =  + *F1  + E3;
V4 =  + *F2  + E4;
V5 =  + *F2  + E5;
V6 =  + *F2  + E6;
/VARIANCES
F1 = 1;
F2 = 1;
E1 = *;
E2 = *;
E3 = *;
E4 = *;
E5 = *;
E6 = *;
/COVARIANCES
F2 , F1 = *;
```

If you made a mistake in the file, or if you change your mind about any of the specifications, you can move your cursor into the window that contains the **work.eqs** file. Then you can edit this file using the usual Windows editing features. For example, you can highlight a section by holding down the mouse button and dragging the mouse. Hitting any key then deletes the highlighted material. (Clicking in another section of the screen removes the highlighting.)

Run EQS

To run EQS, go back to the **Build_EQS** menu and select **Run EQS/386** to run EQS.

Before the program actually runs the EQS job, it displays a **Save As** dialog box as in Figure 2.25. For safety's sake, you must save your EQS model file before running it.

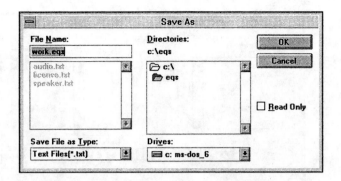

Figure 2.25 EQS Model Save As Dialog Box

We have been working on the **manul7.ess** data, but the default file name for an EQS model is **work.eqs**. In naming your file, set the file name to something like **manul7.eqs** so that you will more easily remember what the job actually is.

The output from the run will have your specified file name, with the ***.out** extension. So, **work.eqs** will yield **work.out** as the output file, and **manul7.eqs** will yield **manul7.out,** and **model1** will yield **model1.out**.

Enter the name you prefer, confirm that **Save File as Type** is ***.txt**, and press **OK**. EQS for Windows will save the model file and go to DOS to run the EQS program. This job should not take much time. However, it may take from a few seconds to several hours to complete an EQS job, depending on the size of your model and the speed of your computer. If it is a long job, you can switch to another task, such as typing a paper using a word processing program. How to switch between tasks will be discussed later.

Examine the EQS Output File

When the program has finished running, the EQS analysis is complete. You will want to bring the output file back to your screen so that you can examine it conveniently.

If you are using Windows 95, the DOS window will remain open. Click on the **Cross** button in the corner of the window shown in Figure 11.6 to close the DOS window and bring up the **Open an EQS Output File** dialog box.

If you are using Windows 3.1, the DOS window will close automatically. As shown in Figure 2.26, the **Open an EQS Output File** dialog box will appear.

The **Open an EQS Output File** dialog box displays ***.out** in the **File Name** edit box, and it has the file type correctly set. You must click on the **OK** button to bring the file name into the list. Then double click on the file name to open the output file.

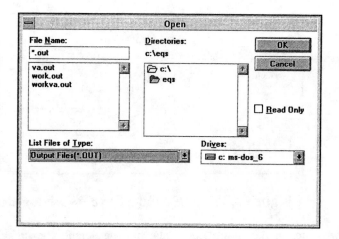

Figure 2.26 Open an EQS Output File Dialog Box

Note: You <u>must</u> click on **OK** in this dialog box to refresh the screen and bring your new output file to the list. Then you can double click on the file name to bring it up in the usual way.

The first part of the output will echo your input file, so that you can verify what job was actually run. Beyond that, the output file includes all the standard results from a structural modeling run. We do not describe this output any further, however, because it is fully documented in the *EQS Structural Equations Program Manual*.

Examine EQS Output on Diagram

If you have created the EQS model using the diagram method, the parameter estimates will be brought to the diagram when the job is done. When building an EQS model file using diagram, the program will create an /OUTPUT section automatically. The /OUTPUT command will write all estimates to an external file called **eqsout&.ets**. The **Diagrammer** can read those estimates later, after the EQS job is done.

To review the parameter estimates from the diagram, choose **Window** and **Draw Diagram** in the main menu. Then choose the **Draw Diagram View** menu and select **Estimates** and **Parameter estimates**. The diagram window will be redrawn with parameter estimates embedded in the paths (Figure 2.27).

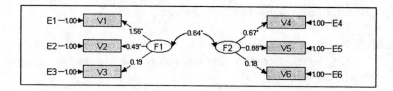

Figure 2.27 Path Diagram with Embedded Parameter Estimates

Now close the diagram window, and let's try doing the same thing a different way.

2. Building EQS Model by Equation Table

Remember that you must first activate EQS for Windows, pull down the **File** menu from the main menu, and select the **Open** option to get the **Open** dialog box for opening a file. Select the **manul7.ess** data file and click on **OK** to bring the file into the Data Editor.

After you bring the desired data into the Data Editor, you are ready to build the EQS model. First, click the **Build_EQS** selection from the main menu. You can see that there are many items in this menu, but only two items are active. The active options are black, while the inactive options are grayed out.

This choice of only two options indicates that you should start with the item on top of the menu, **Title/Specifications,** to build an EQS model. After you select this option, you see a new dialog box:

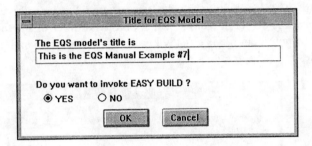

Figure 2.28 Build EQS Model Title Dialog Box

Type the EQS model title in the edit box shown in Figure 2.28. This title will be used as the EQS job title. Notice that the dialog box also asks you if you want to invoke the **EASY BUILD** facility. The default is **YES**. The EASY BUILD facility will ask you a series of questions. Your responses build the specific model that you want in the form of an ***.eqs** file that is used as input to the computational part of the EQS program. Let's use the default by clicking the **OK** button.

After you have clicked on **OK**, the program will automatically generate that part of the model file containing the title. Figure 2.29 displays a new dialog box called **EQS Model Specifications**.

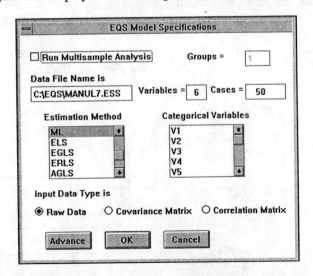

Figure 2.29 EQS Model Specifications Dialog Box

This box has the information that is needed in the /SPECIFICATIONS paragraph of the EQS program. By default, it automatically has most of the information you need to specify a model. Some of the default information is from the *.ess file (here, **manul7.ess**), and some reflects choices typically made in structural modeling. The file name, number of variables, number of cases, method of analysis, and type of input data (raw data, covariance matrix, etc.) have been set by defaults.

For many analyses, these defaults probably will meet your needs. Notice that you can specify a multiple group model, and that you can define certain variables in your file as being categorical variables for the new polychoric-polyserial methodology in EQS. After you complete the model specifications dialog box, the relevant information is transferred automatically to the *.EQS model file that is being built.

For our illustration, there is no reason to change anything in this dialog box. Therefore, click the **OK** button without changing anything. Next, you will be given the dialog box called **Build Equations** as shown in Figure 2.30. This box builds the heart of your model. Typically, you will be doing a latent variable model that uses a number of factors. Click on the **Number of Factors field** and type **2**. The number of variables in your data file is already known by the program and already exists in the field **Number of Variables**.

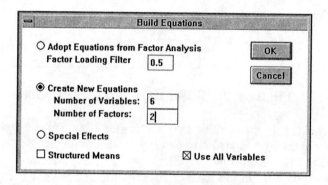

Figure 2.30 Build Equations Dialog Box

As you can see in the first line of Figure 2.30, if we had run a preliminary factor analysis, the number of factors would already be known, and the equations could be built automatically from the factor analysis results. In our case, we must enter the number **2** for the number of factors.

After you have done this, click the **OK** button to continue to build the EQS model. The **Create New Equations** dialog box will appear. This dialog box, shown in Figure 2.31, has a table-like entry field with the number of variables (**Vs**) and number of factors (**Fs**) listed in both rows and columns.

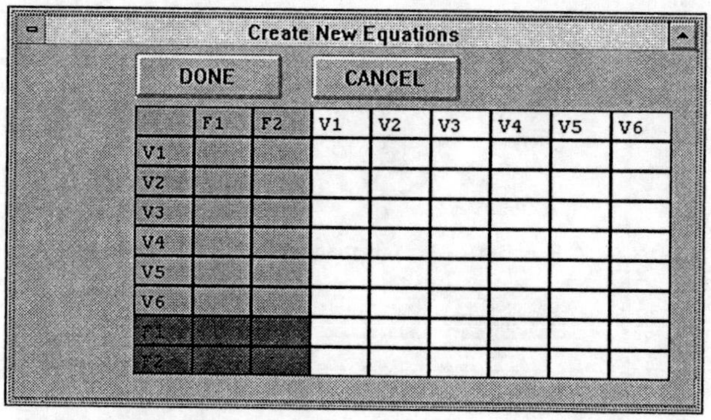

Figure 2.31 Create New Equations Dialog Box

The row variables are the dependent variables, while the column variables are the predictor variables that might be used in your model. Each row corresponds to a dependent variable in your path diagram, i.e., a variable with one or more one-way arrows aimed at it. Thus, each row corresponds to a possible equation that you might build. Each column gives one of the possible predictors of that variable.

The dialog box purposely omits residual independent variables: these will be created automatically when the actual equations are created. Thus, there are no **E** or **D** variables listed in the columns. In a factor analysis model, every measured variable is a dependent variable, and requires an equation. The factors are the only independent variables needed to specify the model, since the **E** residuals will be created automatically when the results are transferred to the model file. For a discussion of **V**, **F**, **E**, and **D** variables, see Chapter 7 of this user's guide.

There are two simple ways to specify your equations.

1. Use your mouse to click on each aqua-colored cell that should be a free parameter in the model. As you click on a cell, an asterisk will appear.

2. As an alternative, you can use click and drag. Position your mouse pointer in the upper left cell, just above V1 and to the left of F1. Click your mouse button, and hold down the button and drag the pointer so that it terminates in the upper-left part of the V4,F2 cell. The idea is to surround the top three cells under F1 by an active rectangle created by a dotted line. Now, release your mouse button.
   a. You will see that three asterisks shown under F1 in Figure 2.32 appear all at once.
   b. Note that, if you enclosed cells that already contain an asterisk using this approach, the result would be to deselect or remove the asterisks.

In this example, variables 1-3 are indicators of Factor 1, and V4-V6 are indicators of Factor 2. Make the relevant selections now. If you make a mistake, you can click again on a cell to unselect a parameter that was previously selected. You should get a result that looks like Figure 2.32.

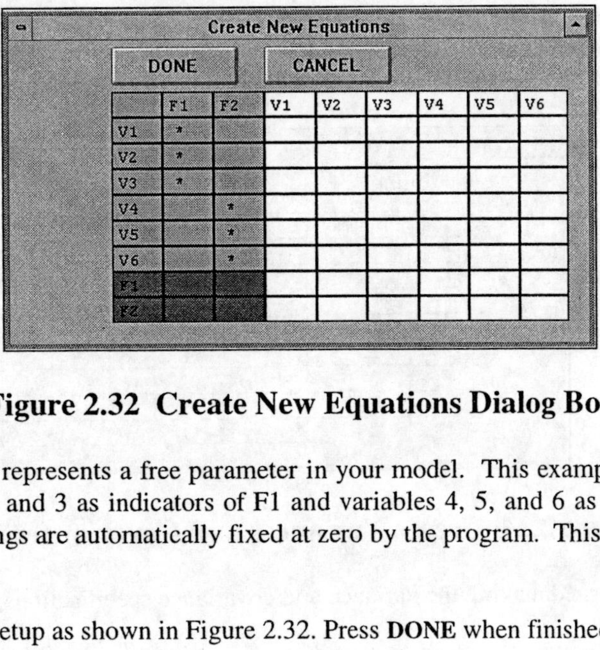

Figure 2.32 Create New Equations Dialog Box

Each asterisk in a cell represents a free parameter in your model. This example shows that we want to have variables 1, 2, and 3 as indicators of F1 and variables 4, 5, and 6 as indicators of F2. The unmarked factor loadings are automatically fixed at zero by the program. This completes the setup of equations.

You should leave the setup as shown in Figure 2.32. Press **DONE** when finished with the dialog box.

Of course, a model consists of variances and covariances of independent variables as well as equations. So, next we need to specify these parameters. The **Create Variances/Covariances** dialog box appears next, as shown in Figure 2.33.

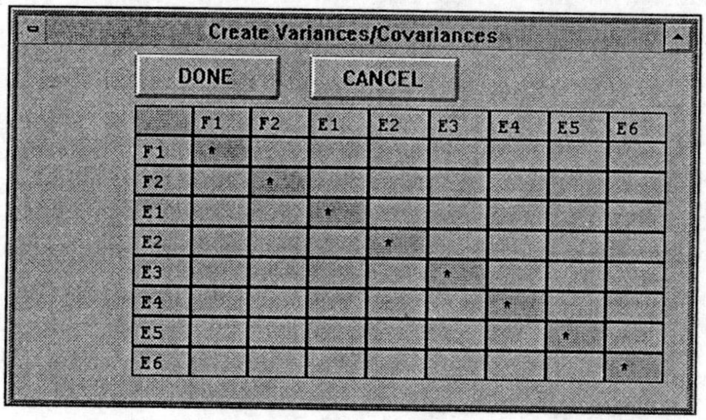

	F1	F2	E1	E2	E3	E4	E5	E6
F1	*							
F2		*						
E1			*					
E2				*				
E3					*			
E4						*		
E5							*	
E6								*

Create Variances/Covariances — DONE CANCEL

Figure 2.33 Create Variances and Covariances Dialog Box

In this box, blank entries are fixed parameters, while entries that will become free parameters must be specified with an asterisk. The diagonals of this matrix represent the variances of the variables, while the off-diagonals deal with the covariances or correlations between pairs of variables.

When the dialog box appears on the screen, the independent variables from the equations box, plus the implied residual variables, are shown as the independent variables in the model. Each diagonal cell contains an asterisk, indicating that the variances of F1, F2, E1, ..., E6 are taken to be free parameters. This may or may not be the correct specification that you have in mind, so you should adjust the box to meet your specific model needs.

Since we have marked all the factor loadings as free parameters, for identification purposes we need to fix the variances of the factors. So, we unselect these by clicking the diagonal cells marked F1,F1 and F2,F2. The effect of not having an asterisk in the variance section is to yield a fixed parameter with the fixed value of 1.0.

We also want to let the two factors correlate, so we place an asterisk in the F2,F1 cell. The result will look like Figure 2.34. (We could also have made these three changes at once by moving the pointer above and left of the F1,F1 position, clicking, dragging into the E1,E1 position, and then releasing.)

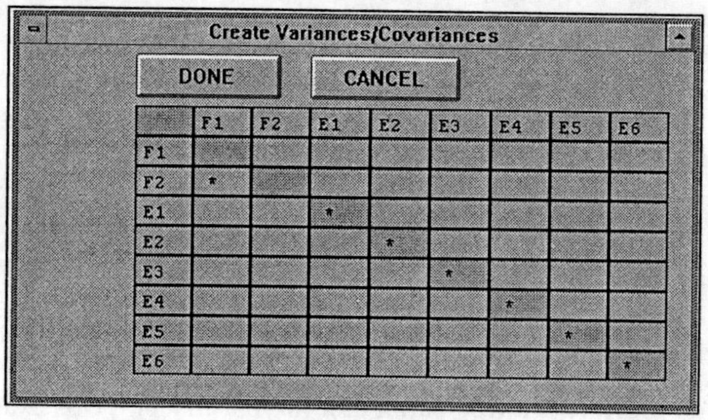

	F1	F2	E1	E2	E3	E4	E5	E6
F1								
F2	*							
E1			*					
E2				*				
E3					*			
E4						*		
E5							*	
E6								*

Create Variances/Covariances — DONE CANCEL

Figure 2.34 Create Variances and Covariances Dialog Box

Now that we are finished making the variance and covariance specifications, press the **DONE** button.

EQS Model File

Whether or not you build your model from a diagram or an equation table, you complete building an EQS model with the **Build_EQS** feature. As this is done, you can see that the EQS command language is built line by line and is written onto the background window. The file that is created is called **work.eqs** by default. When the cursor returns to the **work.eqs** window, your model is complete, and you are ready to run EQS. Experienced EQS users may wonder where the /END statement is. Don't worry, it is attached automatically before the model is run. The following shows an example of part of the model file which is created.

```
/TITLE
This is the EQS Manual Example #7
/SPECIFICATIONS
DATA=' C:\EQS\MANUL7.ESS'; VARIABLES=  6; CASES=    50;
METHODS=ML;
MATRIX=RAW;
/LABELS
V1=V1; V2=V2; V3=V3; V4=V4; V5=V5;
V6=V6;
/EQUATIONS
V1  =   + *F1   + E1;
V2  =   + *F1   + E2;
V3  =   + *F1   + E3;
V4  =   + *F2   + E4;
V5  =   + *F2   + E5;
V6  =   + *F2   + E6;
/VARIANCES
F1  = 1;
F2  = 1;
E1  = *;
E2  = *;
E3  = *;
E4  = *;
E5  = *;
E6  = *;
/COVARIANCES
F2 , F1 = *;
```

If you made a mistake in the file, or if you change your mind about any of the specifications, you can move your cursor into the window that contains the **work.eqs** file. Then you can edit this file using the usual Windows editing features, including **Find**. For example, you can highlight a section by holding down the mouse button and dragging the mouse. Hitting the <Delete> key then deletes the highlighted material. (Clicking in another section of the screen removes the highlighting.)

Run EQS

To run EQS, go back to the **Build_EQS** menu and select **Run EQS/386** to run EQS.

Before the program actually runs the EQS job, a **Save As** dialog box will appear as in Figure 2.35. For safety's sake, you must save your EQS model file before running it.

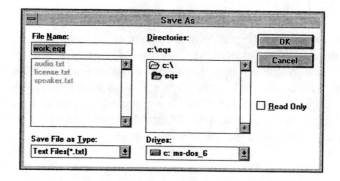

Figure 2.35 EQS Model Save As Dialog Box

We have been working on the **manul7.ess** data, but the default file name for an EQS model is **work.eqs**. If this name is not meaningful, here is your chance to change the file name to something like **manul7.eqs** so that you will more easily remember what the job actually is.

The output from the run will have the same file name, with ***.out** replacing the ***.eqs** extension. So, **work.eqs** will yield **work.out** as the output file, and **manul7.eqs** will yield **manul7.out**, and **model1** will yield **model1.out**.

After you have entered the name, confirm that **Save File as Type** is ***.txt** and press **OK**. The program will save the file and run the EQS program in the DOS environment. This job should not take much time. However, it may take from a few seconds to several hours to complete an EQS job, depending on the size of your model and the speed of your computer. If it is a long job, you can switch to another task, such as typing a paper using a word processing program. Later we will discuss how to switch between tasks.

Examine the EQS Output File

When the program has finished running, the EQS analysis is complete and saved to a file. You will want to bring the output file back to your screen so that you can examine it conveniently. As shown in Figure 2.36, the **Open** dialog box will appear with ***.out** in the **File Name** edit box and the file type correctly set. (In Windows 95, you must close the DOS window before the Open dialog box appears. See Chapter 11 for details.)

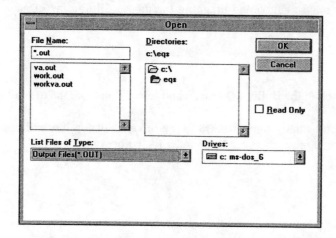

Figure 2.36 Open an EQS Output File Dialog Box

36

You will want to bring the output file back to your screen so that you can examine it conveniently. In the Open dialog box, you must go through two steps:

1. Click on the OK button to bring the file name into the list.
2. Double click on the file name in the list to open the file.

> *Note*: You <u>must</u> click on **OK** in this dialog box to refresh the screen and bring your new output file into the list. Then double click on the file name to bring the file up in the usual way.

The name of the output file is always the input file name, with **.out** replacing **.eqs**. We do not describe this output any further, because it is fully documented in the *EQS Structural Equations Program Manual*.

Hot Key Specifications

When you start using EQS for Windows, you will probably prefer to use the menu options to perform your tasks. When you are ready to save time by using hot keys, you can use them with the **File** and **Edit** menus.

<u>File Menu</u>		<u>Edit Menu</u>	
<u>Option</u>	<u>Hot Key</u>	<u>Option</u>	<u>Hot Key</u>
New	<Ctrl>-N	Cut	<Ctrl>-X
Open	<Ctrl>-O	Copy	<Ctrl>-C
Close	<Ctrl>-W	Paste	<Ctrl>-V
Save	<Ctrl>-S	Find	<Ctrl>-F (for text window only)
Print	<Ctrl>-P	Goto	<Ctrl>-G (for data window only)
Quit	<Ctrl>-Q		

This completes our overview of EQS for Windows. Have fun exploring the program on your own! While it is not necessary for you to read the subsequent chapters in this *EQS for Windows User's Guide*, they provide additional documentation that you will probably find interesting and pertinent.

3. DATA PREPARATION & MANAGEMENT

EQS for Windows has various facilities for entering, cleaning, manipulating, and filtering your data to make it ready for plotting or other statistical analyses including EQS structural modeling runs. You can import and export files with the **File** option of the main menu bar. You'll find procedures to help you in preparing data for analysis in the **Data** selection of the main menu bar. We shall discuss these procedures for data handling in a logical sequence, beginning with data entry.

Creating a New Dataset File

Remember that, before taking any actions in EQS for Windows, you must make some data file active, whether the file consists of existing data or you build a new data file. In this section, we shall create a new dataset using a data entry procedure that helps you to enter this data in a convenient and systematic way. When the file is complete, you can use it for data analysis.

To create a new data file, you must select the **File** menu from the **Main** Window menu bar and select the **New** option. You will see the **Open a New File** dialog box shown in Figure 3.1.

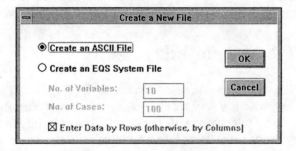

Figure 3.1 Create a New File Dialog Box

There are two circled choice options, sometimes called radio buttons, in this dialog box. One is **Create an ASCII File**, while the other is **Create an EQS System File**. When the dialog box appears, the ASCII file button will be selected, as indicated by a heavy dot inside its radio button. If you wanted to create a plain ASCII or text file, you would choose this option, which helps you to edit a standard text file.

Creating an ASCII File

If you were to press **OK** with **Create an ASCII File** selected, you would be given a plain screen with nothing in it. You can write on this screen as you like to create your new text document. The default name for the text document file is **untitled.txt** until you change its name. As you enter characters in this file, you may make mistakes and may want to make corrections and modifications. You can do this using the usual Windows conventions, such as the **Cut** or **Paste** features of the **Edit** menu in the main menu.

When you are creating an ASCII file, the Edit menu displays one additional option, **Find/Replace**. To use this option, place your cursor in the upper left corner of the data window. Choose **Edit** and **Find/Replace**. The **Find and Replace** dialog box will appear.

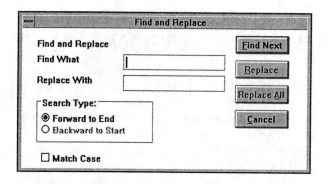

Figure 3.2 Find and Replace Dialog Box

Enter the number which you want to find in the **Find What** field. Note that the **Replace With** field will be functional in the next version. For now, you can find values, but you cannot replace them.

Since your cursor is at the beginning of the dataset, you must accept the default **Forward to End Search Type**; the **Backward to Start Search Type** will be functional in the next version. Click on **Find Next** to start the search. When the program highlights one of the chosen numbers, this dialog box disappears.

We will say no more about ASCII files, because their use is self-explanatory.

Creating an EQS System File

To create a raw data file in EQS format, select **Create an EQS System File** by clicking your mouse on its radio button. The previously gray area indicating **Number of Variables** and **Number of Cases** will be activated with the default numbers **10** and **100**. You must modify these numbers to make them consistent with the number of variables and the number of subjects or cases that you plan to use.

Suppose that you want to create a file with 5 variables and 20 cases. Double click on the **No. of variables** field and type **5**, to replace 10. Then press the <Tab> key or double click on the **No. of Cases** field and enter **20**.

When you have selected **Create an EQS System File**, the **Enter Data by Rows** option becomes active. You can now select the direction for data entry. The default is **Enter Data by Rows**, indicated by an **x** in the checkbox.

If you wanted to **Enter Data by Columns**, you would click on the checkbox to remove the **x**, thus switching from **Enter Data by Rows** to **by Columns**. For this example, do not remove the **x**. After you have finished your selections, click the **OK** button.

A blank spreadsheet-like **Data Editor** will open, as shown in Figure 3.3. It contains case numbers down the left and the variable numbers V1, V2, ... above the columns. The main part of the screen will contain no numbers, since this is a new file. By default, the file is called **untitled.ess.**

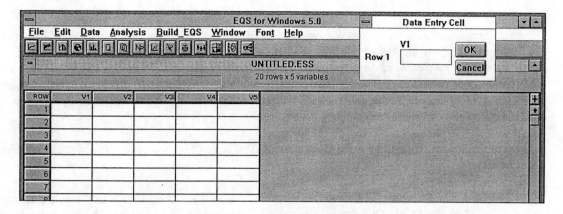

Figure 3.3 Data Editor

> *Note:* You can enter data only for the number of cases and number of variables that you have specified. The Data Editor that you see on your screen may show only a part of the specified variables and cases. This does not matter, because you will be entering your data in the **Data Entry Cell** in the upper right of your screen. After data entry, you can scroll through the full Data Editor to review the data.

Data Entry Cell

With 20 rows and 5 columns, there will be 100 numbers to enter in this data matrix, so there is substantial room for making errors during data entry. In order to minimize these errors, you need not enter the numbers in the data matrix itself. Rather, we provide you with a small data entry box, as shown in Figure 3.4, which appears in the upper right corner of the screen.

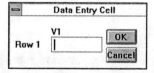

Figure 3.4 Data Entry Cell

You enter one number in this cell. If you want to enter missing data, type an asterisk (*) in the data entry cell. The program treats the missing data character as a system-wide missing data value. For a full discusion of missing data, including variable-related missing data, see the next section, Missing Data Code.

After you enter the number, press the <Enter> key or click **OK**. The next cell will appear in turn.

In Figure 3.4, the **Data Entry Cell** shows that you are ready to enter the data value of case #1 (Row 1) on variable #1 (V1). The cursor is located in that cell so that you can immediately enter the number you want. Please practice by entering a number now. Press <Enter> on your keyboard, or click **OK**, when you have done this. The number you just entered will be placed in the case 1, variable 1 position in the upper left corner of the new data matrix. Since you kept the default of row-wise data entry, the **Data Entry Cell** will read **Row 1, V2**, indicating that you should enter the case 1 score for variable 2.

As you continue entering additional numbers, the information in each cell will be placed in turn into the Data Editor row by row. The **Data Entry Cell** will keep track of where you are. It always shows the current status, indicating which particular cell you are working on at any given time.

The numbers that you enter should use the same format for all cases on each variable. The numbers are written into the Data Editor as right-justified (flush right). While you have the default variable column width, *only eight characters (plus the decimal place) will appear* in any cell of the matrix even if the number you entered is larger than eight characters. Of course, the dataset manipulated by EQS for Windows accepts any number of characters and utilizes the entire number, whether the number is completely displayed in the Data Editor or not.

If your numbers include more than eight characters, you have two choices for viewing the numbers in the Data Editor:

1. If you want to retain the default column width, it is possible to view any single data entry. Go to that cell in the Data Editor and click on the cell. You can then move the cursor with the arrow key to show the rest of the number.

2. To increase the width of the variable column, move your cursor to the border between the label for that variable and the variable to its right. Click on the border and the cursor changes. Drag the border to the right. If you make the variable column too wide, you can click on the border and drag it to the left.

To return to entering your data in the Data Entry Cell, first note that you have made Data Editor the active window, bringing it in front of the Data Entry Cell. You can see the top of the Data Entry Cell on the upper right of your screen, partially overlapping the Error Bar Chart, Multi-Plot, Missing Data Plot, and **Diagrammer** icons. Click on the top of the Data Entry Cell to make it active again.

Note: You can enter your data directly into the Data Editor, if you prefer. Click on the small square in the upper left corner of the Data Entry Cell window to close that window. Click on the next cell awaiting data and enter that data.

Missing Data Code

If some scores are not available in a variable, you have some missing data, and you must let the Data Editor know about this. There are two ways to enter a missing data code during data entry:

1. Enter an asterisk to represent the missing cell data. This method creates a global missing data code. If you enter an asterisk during data entry, the EQS for Windows program recognizes the asterisk as your missing data code. The program will convert the missing character to a missing value automatically. The Data Editor will display the missing data cell as blank.

2. Enter a number to represent the missing cell data. This method creates either a series of individual variable codes, or a global missing data code. If you enter a number, such as 999, during data entry, the EQS for Windows program will display that number in the cell, because it cannot yet differentiate between your missing data number code and your data. To specify your missing data number(s) as missing data code(s) in EQS for Windows, you can enter your missing data code number in either of two ways:
   a. You can use the **Variable Definition** dialog box to enter one missing data code for one variable.
   b. You can use the **Variable Missing Value Specifications** dialog box to enter one missing data code for all variables or one missing data code for each variable.

Missing Data Code for One Variable

After you have entered all of your data, you must tell EQS which number you have chosen to represent the missing cell data for each variable. To do that for a single variable, double click on the variable name to bring up the variable definition dialog box.

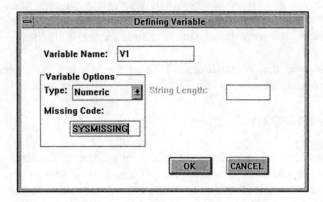

Figure 3.5 Variable Definition Dialog Box

In the **Missing Code** field, enter the number that you chose to represent the missing cell data for this variable. You can change the variable **Type** from **Numeric** to **String** or **Boolean**, if necessary. Click **OK** when you have finished. Repeat this procedure for each variable containing missing data. You will see later that various statistical procedures will be available to help you deal thoughtfully with your missing data.

Missing Data Code for Several Variables

To specify the number that you have chosen to represent the missing data for several variables, choose **Data** on the main menu. Then select the **Missing Values** option. The Variable Missing Values Specifications dialog box will appear.

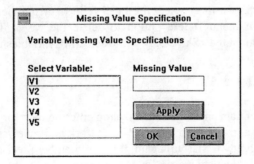

Figure 3.6 Variable Missing Value Specifications Dialog Box

In the **Select Variable** list box, click on a variable to select it. (If all variables have the same missing value number, click on the first variable, then hold down the <Shift> key while clicking on the last variable to select all.)

> *Note*: To select multiple noncontiguous variables from the list, hold down the <Ctrl> key while clicking on each variable. To select multiple contiguous variables from the list, you can simply drag the cursor over each variable, or hold down the <Shift> key while clicking on each variable.

In the **Missing Value** field, enter the number that represents the missing value for that variable. After you have selected each variable and entered the number representing the missing value, click on **Apply**.

> *Note*: When you enter the data, you can see, in any missing data cell on the screen, the number which you have chosen as your missing code. You can still see the missing code after you enter the missing data code for each variable.

> *Note:* Please read the **Visualizing and Treating Missing Data** section in this chapter for more details on how EQS for Windows treats missing data.

Adding Variables or Cases

If you later want to add variables or cases for scores for additional subjects, you must create a second data file to contain the additions. You can then use the **Join** or **Merge** option in the **Data** menu to combine your files into a single file. You have two procedures to choose from:

1. If you are adding cases, create the new file containing all of the new cases, then use the **Merge** option described later in this chapter to merge the new cases with the cases in the earlier file.
2. If you are adding variables, create the new file containing all of the new variables, then use the **Join** option described later in this chapter to join the new variables with the variables in the earlier file.

Deleting Variables or Cases

You can use the **Delete** option from the **Edit** menu to delete variables or cases. To delete a variable, click on the label field of the variable to highlight the variable. Pull down the **Edit** menu and select the **Delete** option to delete the variable.

Likewise, to delete a case, you must select the label field (row number) of the case to highlight the case. Then use the **Edit** menu **Delete** option to delete the case. To delete multiple contiguous variables or cases, hold down the <Shift> key while selecting variables or cases.

Interrupting Data Entry

If you are in the middle of data entry, but want to stop entering data for any reason, EQS for Windows makes it easy for you. It allows you to interrupt your work and save your file. Then, at some time in the future, when you are ready to start up again, it will remember precisely where you left off and will take you to that position in the data matrix for further entry.

Let us continue the example of 5 variables and 20 cases. Go ahead and enter a few numbers as explained above. Now let us assume that you want to interrupt data entry. Instead of entering a number in the **Data Entry Cell**, click on **Cancel**. This will remove the Data Entry Cell and take you back to the data matrix you are creating. You should now save the file for safety before you perform various other actions.

Saving Your New File

Saving your work will be an important part of what you do, since you will not want to duplicate work that you have previously done. In this case, we want to save the file, and possibly quit the program. You can do this by going to the small square in the upper left corner of the current window, the window called **untitled.ess**. Double click on the square to close the window. The **Save As** dialog box will appear. Alternatively, you can go to the main menu and select **File,** then select **Save As** to get the relevant dialog box. You may be prompted to click on the Data Editor file **untitled.ess** to make it the active window.

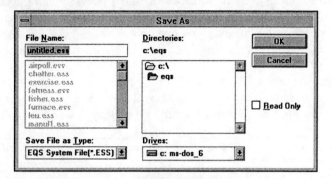

Figure 3.7 Save As Dialog Box

In the **Save As** dialog box, enter the name for your new file in the **File Name** field. Enter the name **test.ess**. This is a file of type * .ess.

In the this **Save File as Type** field, click on **EQS System File**, because this file will be a system file. Click **OK**. The program brings up a dialog box asking whether you want to save not-selected, selected, or all cases.

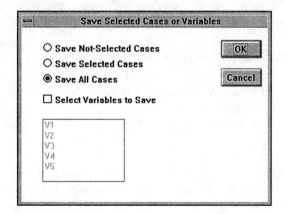

Figure 3.8 Save As Case Selection Dialog Box

Accept the default of **Save All Cases** even though you may not have entered data for all cases. Click **OK**.

You should now get back to the initial EQS for Windows screen. If you want to eliminate the data file from the screen, do so now with the **Close** option.

Saving System and Text Files

Whether or not you are finished entering all of your data, you can save your work at any time. There are two major **file types** that you could use to save data: **EQS System Files** and **Text Files**. When you get the **Save As** dialog box, you should choose the correct file type.

EQS System Files

You can label your files in any way that you want, but we cannot emphasize strongly enough that *you should generally label an EQS System File as an *.ess file*. A system file contains information that you specified about the data, such as the number of variables and cases, along with any labels that you provided for the variables. Whenever you open an existing ***.ess** file, the program brings to the screen not only the raw data, but also the descriptive information on the data.

> *Note:* When you save a file, the choice of file type that you made in Figure 3.1 determines the type of file which the EQS program will save, *even if you use a file name that implies a different file type*. Table 3.1 specifies the file type saved for each choice.

New File Choice	File Type Created	Recommended Extension	Usage
Text Data File	80-Column Text	.txt	Email, etc.
Text File/ Tab Delimiter	Continuous Text	.txt	Excel, etc.
EQS System File	EQS System File	.ess	EQS

Table 3.1

In the example under the **Saving Your Data** section, if you had decided to use the file name **test.dat** instead of the designation **test.ess**, while choosing the **EQS System File** option, the file would still be saved as an EQS System File. However, an EQS System File named test.dat is misleading. You will complicate your use of EQS if you save data files without an appropriate extension. Alternatively, if you use the correct extension, you will know the file type for any file that you might want to open.

How File Names Affect File Opening

When you are opening a file, and you do not know its file type, you can type ***.*** in the **File Name** field in the upper left of the **Open** dialog box to get a list of all files. Otherwise, EQS for Windows provides a list for each recognizable file: ***.ess, *.eqs, *.dat, *.eds, *.wk*, *.dbf, *.out, *.cov, *.sav, *.txt**.

1. If you want to open an EQS System File, click on the **File** menu **Open** option to ask for a listing of EQS System Files. If you choose an EQS System File, the program will recognize its own EQS System File and open it with no further questions. This is true even when the system file is a covariance or correlation file.

2. Choose the **File Type** to get a listing of the desired file types. Regarding text files:
   a) If you have chosen a regular text file that was saved as an ***.eqs** or ***.out** file, click **OK**, and EQS will open the file with no further prompting.
   b) If you have chosen a raw data file saved as a ***.dat** file, click **OK**, and you will be prompted to specify the column delimiter and the missing character. When the file appears on the screen, EQS will have changed the file extension to **.ess**.

c) If you have chosen a Covariance/Correlation matrix file, click **OK**, and you will be prompted to specify the **Input Matrix Type** and **Number of Observations**.

In short, when you name your data files, use extensions that allow you to differentiate among the types of files. Data entered via EQS for Windows data entry are best saved with the ***.ess** extension and the **System File** option. See the **File Types** section of this chapter for further discussion of this topic.

Restarting Interrupted Data Entry

Now, back to the new data file. To show how you can get back to the correct position in a data file you were creating, let's open the **test.ess** file that you just saved. First, select **File** from the menu bar. Select **Open**. All of the directory files, including EQS System Files with an **.ess** extension, will be displayed in the list box. Double click on **test.ess** to select the **test.ess** file. You will get a dialog box similar to that shown in Figure 3.9.

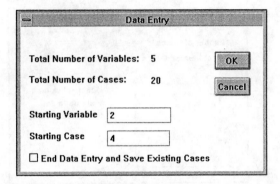

Figure 3.9 Data Entry Information Dialog Box

This figure shows the number of variables and cases in your data file. You click on **End Data Entry and Save Existing Cases** if you want to finish your file with the current number of variables and complete cases. If you clicked on **End Data Entry and Save Existing Cases** in Figure 3.9, you would create a file with five variables and three complete cases. This action terminates data entry for the current file, and precludes any further data entry in the file.

If you do not click on **End Data Entry and Save Existing Cases**, but only click on **OK**, the program will start data entry where you left off. In the example in the figure, this is with variable #2, case #4. If you stopped at a different cell, your screen will show a different starting place. Click the **OK** button to confirm that you want to continue data entry at the specified variable and case.

You will be in the data entry mode as shown in Figure 3.3, with the **Data Entry Cell** showing Row 4, V2 (or your relevant cell number). You can continue with data entry as described before. When you have filled in all cells of the data matrix, the procedure will stop, and the **Data Entry Cell** will disappear. When you are done, you can go on to another task, or save the file.

Remember, you can end data entry at any time by clicking on **Cancel** in the Data Entry Cell shown in Figure 3.4. This action will terminate data entry in the file for the present time. Be sure to save any important file after entering the data. Let's start a new task, giving the variables some new names.

Adding Variable Labels

EQS assumes that variables are named V1, V2, and so on, in sequence. It would be a good idea for you to replace the default labels with mnemonic labels. This manual includes some examples using variables with default names, and some examples using variables with descriptive names.

While the data matrix is active (visible) go to the menu bar and select **Data**. Then, click on **Information**. This brings up the dialog box called **Define Variable and Group Names** shown in Figure 3.10.

You can see that the dialog box shows you the name of the data file as well as the data file size. No cases are marked in the Data Editor. The marking feature is described further in other sections, particularly in the section on Case Selection later in this chapter.

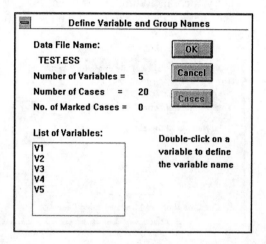

Figure 3.10 Define Variable and Group Names Dialog Box

Follow the instructions in this box: double-click on one of the variables in the list. The box shown in Figure 3.11 will appear with the selected variable shown in a box.

Note: To force EQS to read the codes and their names, click on the box beside **Categorical Variable**. Click a second time beside **Categorical Variable** to gray out the codes.

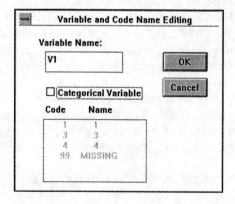

Figure 3.11 Variable and Code Name Editing Dialog Box

Note: Labels are limited to eight characters and cannot include spaces.

You can simply type a new name for the given variable name (V1, in Figure 3.11), but be careful that your number of characters does not exceed eight for any variable. Press **OK** when you are done. You return to the previous screen and you can continue in this way for all variables in turn, or until you decide that you are done.

Code in Figure 3.11 lists the various scores or values of the chosen variable that actually appear in the data file. You see that the numbers 1, 3, 4, and missing are the only score values for V1 in the data, i.e., no subject had a score of 0 or 2, or any other nonlisted number. The numbers shown under **Code** are always shown as integer values. This may accurately represent the coding of the data, or it may represent truncated values for non-integer numbers (that is, a 2.35 would be shown here as 2). **Code** gives a quick way to evaluate whether the numbers in the data file are about as expected, or if there is a serious miscode that needs to be corrected.

If you want to treat a variable as a categorical variable for analysis purposes, as would be desirable when you are doing modeling with some variables that you want to treat as categorical, mark the **Categorical Variable** option box with an **x** by clicking on it. This darkens the **Code** and **Name** columns. Then you could double click on a code number to bring up another dialog box that permits you to provide a label for that category of the variable.

Figure 3.12 Category Label Dialog Box

You can provide a label for each code. These labels replace the existing numerical codes in the **Name** column.

Press **OK** when you are finished. You will see that new variable names appear in the **Variable and Code Name Editing** dialog box. When you save the file as an ***.ess** file, these labels will be saved along with the remaining information. Whenever you open the file, the labels will be part of the file.

Editing *.ess Data Files

After you have created a data file, you may want to edit it. It is always wise to verify each number that was entered, perhaps by comparing a printout of the file as entered with the original source data material. In any case, you may want to change some of the numbers in the file. In this case, you must go to **File**, click **Open**, and select the desired ***.ess** file from the file list.

When the data matrix window appears, you can refresh your memory concerning file details. Just click on **Data** in the menu bar, then click on **Information.**

You will see that the numbers in the file show up in the Data Editor as right-justified. Again, numbers with more than eight characters will not be totally visible. Make any necessary changes in the file, then save it using the **File** menu **Save** option.

You can, of course, use the process just described to edit any existing EQS System File. This holds for raw data as well as covariance matrices that have been saved in the ***.ess** format.

Creating a Correlation or Covariance Matrix

In general, it is a good idea to provide EQS with raw data so that you can use the program's analytic capabilities on these data. You can also analyze derived matrices such as correlation or covariance matrices that EQS can compute for you. The previous section showed you how to enter raw data into EQS by creating an EQS System File using the Data Editor. There may be times, however, when the raw data are not available. For example, you may want to duplicate an analysis given in a publication providing only the covariance matrix.

To create a correlation or covariance matrix directly, do not use the EQS Data Editor. Rather, you should use the EQS for Windows text editor or another text editor to create and save the file as an ASCII (text) file. Then you can read the file and import it into EQS for use as an EQS System (***.ess**) File.

To create the file as a text file in EQS for Windows, select the **File** menu **New** option. The **Create a New File** dialog box, shown in Figure 3.1, appears. Select the **Create an ASCII File** option.

Press **OK** with **Create an ASCII File** selected, and you will see a plain screen with nothing in it. Enter the matrix on this screen to create your new text file. The default name for the text document file is **untitled.txt** until you change its name. As you enter characters in this file, you may make mistakes and may want to make corrections and modifications. You can do this using the usual Windows conventions, such as the **Cut** or **Paste** features of the **Edit** menu in the main menu.

Type in the entries of the covariance (correlation) matrix using either full matrix or lower triangular matrix formatting. The lower triangular matrix is quicker, since you only type in the entries on the diagonal and below the diagonal of the matrix. In full matrix style, you enter the entire matrix, row by row, including the upper and lower triangular parts. Either way, you should be consistent about leaving one or more spaces between entries to distinguish them. You should have an equal number of rows and columns.

When you have finished entering the data, save the results as a text file. We recommend that you use the **.cov** extension on your file, since this is the file type that EQS for Windows recognizes as a covariance or correlation matrix.

To save the file in EQS for Windows, select the **File** menu **Save As** option. Then verify that **the Save File as Type** option is set to **Text Data Files (*.txt)**. Enter the file name with a **cov** extension, and click on **OK**.

When you want to analyze the covariance (correlation) matrix in EQS for Windows, you will import the file. See the Data Import section below for details on importing these files.

Visualizing and Treating Missing Data

If your dataset, whether created as a new dataset or imported as a data file, is complete with no missing cells, you can start to perform a variety of descriptive and inferential statistical procedures on these data. Then you do not need the features described in this section.

Frequently, however, data matrices contain entries that do not represent scores but represent the fact that the data in the cells are missing.

> *Note:* You should not do any data analysis on such matrices unless the procedure you use has a feature that explicitly takes into account the fact that data are missing.

You have three main options:

1. Delete cases that contain any missing data.
2. Impute or estimate values for these missing numbers.
3. Use a statistical procedure that has a built-in feature that ignores cases on which data are missing.

All three alternatives are available in EQS and will be discussed below. Before we can get into those details, though, we will review some of the potential problems that occur when one ignores the distinction between real data and missing data. Then we will describe the EQS for Windows plotting, selection, and imputation procedures that make it possible to evaluate and deal with missing data in an effective way.

Some Dangers in Ignoring Missing Data

The consequences of ignoring missing data will depend on the procedure used, and the way that you coded missingness in your data.

Numerical Missing Data Codes

If you follow normal EQS for Windows procedures for importing data, you will be working with ***.ess** system files. In such files, missing data are coded internally by EQS. Alternatively, you may be working with data that are not in ***.ess** format but contain other numerical codes for missing data, such as **9** or **9999**.

If you pretend that your data matrix has no missing data, EQS for Windows may be able to do some analyses, but the results are liable to be useless. In these cases, when you start a statistical procedure, the data can be read in, and the program will be able to perform its computations. However, the results will be somewhat distorted. The amount of distortion will depend on the extent and pattern of missing data, the particular coding that you used, and the procedure that you are invoking.

If you were to compute descriptive statistics on a file in which **9**s are treated as actual scores of cases on variables, the resulting statistics could be seriously distorted. For example, if you have a binary 0-1 scored variable with missing data, any **9**s could create means that are bigger than 1. Or, two truly uncorrelated variables might appear to be highly correlated simply because some subjects are missing pairs of scores and, thus, have high **9** scores on both variables. You might encounter this problem with modeling.

> *Note:* The EQS structural modeling program assumes that the data matrix used to compute correlations and covariances contains only meaningful scores of cases on variables.

A data matrix that is an ***.ess** file is automatically temporarily duplicated as a ***.dat** file when running EQS. So, if you have missing cells in the data file being analyzed, and you permit the program to treat these missing values as data, the resulting correlations and covariances are liable to be meaningless. Hence, your structural models are also liable to be meaningless.

In EQS for Windows, we give you several ways to create a meaningful input file for modeling. For example, you can compute a covariance matrix based on pairwise-present or complete cases, and use this matrix in modeling.

However, if you plan to do structural modeling with raw score data, e.g., to do a distribution-free estimation method, your options are severely restricted. At the point of calling the modeling program, your raw score data must be fully usable. Within the modeling program itself, if you know which case numbers are associated with any missing data, you still can eliminate those cases. In the /SPECIFICATIONS section, you can use the statement **DELETE=xx, yy, zz;** where **xx**, **yy**, and **zz** are numbers of the cases that have missing data. But this is not the simplest option, since it requires you to know the case numbers that have missing data. EQS for Windows provides several simpler data manipulation facilities that can help you to get your file into a complete data format as required for modeling.

Symbolic Missing Data Codes

Although ***.ess** files will not contain symbolic missing data codes, there may be times when you are working with other files that contain codes, such as *****, for missing data. When you attempt to do any standard method of analysis on such data, using a method that ignores the fact of missing data, the procedure will bomb. A standard procedure will not be able to perform its normal computations since the data file cannot be read.

If you run the EQS structural modeling procedure on a raw data file that contains symbolic missing data codes, EQS will ignore the case containing the non-numeric character. The sample size will be adjusted accordingly.

Selecting Complete Cases Only

Clearly, before you can do any meaningful data analysis, it is important to deal explicitly with the problem of missing data. You can do this with visualization procedures or with manipulations on the Data Editor. The simplest procedure is to create a new data matrix from the cases that have no missing data.

This example will show how to select cases that have no missing data. Please open the raw data file called **leu.ess** now.

ROW	V1	V2	V3	V4	V5	V6	V7	V8	V9
1	Lewis	1001.000	119.000	12.600	4.000	35.000	15.900	5.500	3800.000
2	Deming	1002.000		68.800		0.000	41.200	5.200	4500.000
3	Mayasich	1003.000	142.000	15.800	6.000	65.000	33.100	3.600	2500.000
4	Chen	1004.000	153.000	28.400	6.000	42.000	27.800	4.600	2576.000
5	Contreras	1005.000	171.000	116.000	5.000	34.000	42.600	6.700	5025.000
6	Jantz	1006.000	149.000	42.400		47.000	33.500	5.000	1700.000
7	Lemire	1007.000	188.000	30.400	7.000	35.000	22.000	4.500	
8	Stanfield	1008.000	172.000	23.200	5.000	44.000	21.100	3.300	2300.000
9	Mobbs	1009.000	98.000	83.800	4.000	27.000	23.600	3.300	1350.000
10	Young	1010.000	79.000	27.500	5.000	49.000	20.100	2.900	1508.000
11	Grassl	1011.000	144.000	13.900	7.000	33.000	18.700	4.200	2300.000
12	Scoffield	1012.000	242.000	19.800	0.000	29.000	28.200	6.200	3500.000
13	Winter	1013.000	181.000	14.000	5.000	38.000	24.500	3.300	1800.000
14	Rodriguez	1014.000	128.000	12.300	6.000	25.000	38.900	8.300	6500.000

LEU.ESS — 47 rows x 9 variables

Figure 3.13 LEU.ESS File with Missing Data

You should see a window similar to that in Figure 3.13. You will see some blank cells in this file. These blanks represent missing data; you should not consider them as scores of subjects on variables. If we know that there are only a few cases that have missing data, we might be satisfied with a new file that contains only cases having complete data. To create such a file, select **Data** in the main menu and then select the **Use Data** option. The dialog box shown in Figure 3.14 will appear.

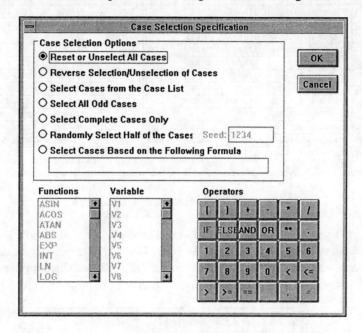

Figure 3.14 Case Selection Options Dialog Box

The Case Selection Options dialog box lists several options. For our purposes, only the fifth option, **Select Complete Cases Only** is relevant now. (The other options deal with alternative ways of selecting cases when there are no missing data.) Use the pointer and click on the option button for selecting complete cases. Then press **OK**.

The Data Editor will reappear, with added blue highlighting to mark the selected cases. These are the cases that have no missing data.

If, for some reason, the complete cases are not highlighted on your screen, the file may be not currently active. You should click on the title box of the file to make the file active. Figure 3.15 shows the window with the file, but it does not show the highlighting.

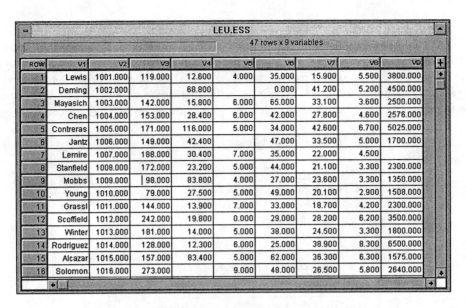

Figure 3.15 Complete Cases Selected

Now go to the **File** menu, and select **Save As**. The Save As dialog box will appear as shown previously. The cursor will be in the **Save As** box. Because you want to create a new file and not destroy the old one, you should enter a new name, such as **leu2.ess**. Click on the radio button for EQS System File. When you click **Save**, you will see the dialog box shown in Figure 3.16.

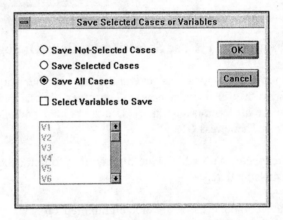

Figure 3.16 Save Selected Cases or Variables Dialog Box

This box allows you to select cases as well as variables. The default option is to **Save All Cases**, which is not appropriate now, since we would simply be duplicating our existing file. The two other options are to **Save Selected Cases,** the cases with complete data, and **Save Not Selected** Cases, the cases that have missing data. In order to understand the cases with missing data, it might be desirable to save the Not Selected cases into their own file, but we shall not pursue that point now.

For this example, mark **Save Selected Cases** and click **OK**. You have just created a file with complete data. You can use this file with any appropriate statistical method, including structural modeling.

To see what you have created, go to **File** and **Open** the **leu2.ess** file in the usual way. You will see a file similar to that in Figure 3.17.

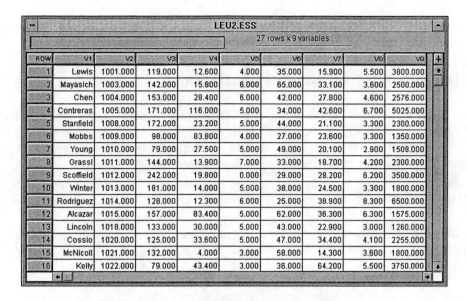

ROW	V1	V2	V3	V4	V5	V6	V7	V8	V9
1	Lewis	1001.000	119.000	12.600	4.000	35.000	15.900	5.500	3800.000
2	Mayasich	1003.000	142.000	15.800	6.000	65.000	33.100	3.600	2500.000
3	Chen	1004.000	153.000	28.400	6.000	42.000	27.800	4.600	2576.000
4	Contreras	1005.000	171.000	116.000	5.000	34.000	42.600	6.700	5025.000
5	Stanfield	1008.000	172.000	23.200	5.000	44.000	21.100	3.300	2300.000
6	Mobbs	1009.000	98.000	83.800	4.000	27.000	23.600	3.300	1350.000
7	Young	1010.000	79.000	27.500	5.000	49.000	20.100	2.900	1508.000
8	Grassl	1011.000	144.000	13.900	7.000	33.000	18.700	4.200	2300.000
9	Scoffield	1012.000	242.000	19.800	0.000	29.000	28.200	6.200	3500.000
10	Winter	1013.000	181.000	14.000	5.000	38.000	24.500	3.300	1800.000
11	Rodriguez	1014.000	128.000	12.300	6.000	25.000	38.900	8.300	6500.000
12	Alcazar	1015.000	157.000	83.400	5.000	62.000	36.300	6.300	1575.000
13	Lincoln	1018.000	133.000	30.000	5.000	43.000	22.900	3.000	1260.000
14	Cossio	1020.000	125.000	33.600	5.000	47.000	34.400	4.100	2255.000
15	McNicoll	1021.000	132.000	4.000	3.000	58.000	14.300	3.600	1800.000
16	Kelly	1022.000	79.000	43.400	3.000	36.000	64.200	5.500	3750.000

LEU2.ESS — 27 rows x 9 variables

Figure 3.17 File with Complete Cases

Selecting cases with complete data makes sense when:
1. The total sample size is quite large.
2. Only a small percentage of subjects have missing data.
3. There is nothing systematic about which cases have complete or missing data.

Note: Case selection based on complete data can substantially reduce the sample size.

Let us see what the effect was in the current example. To find out how many cases were selected, click on **Data** and then **Information.** You will be told that the file has nine variables and 27 cases, a substantial reduction from the 47 cases in the original file. Clearly, this simple method for handling missing data has deleted too many cases from the original file.

As is obvious, using only complete cases can be a serious problem. However, at times it provides quite a good solution to practical data analysis. Various other solutions, including working with correlation matrices based on pairwise present data, or imputing values for the missing data using one of several different approaches, also have their own advantages and disadvantages. Some of these other approaches are illustrated below.

This user's guide cannot detail the many technical issues that are involved in selecting the most appropriate method for dealing with missing data. Two excellent recent references are given in the December, 1992 issue of the *Journal of the American Statistical Association* (vol. **87**): Wang, R., Sedransk, J., & Jinn, J. H. Secondary data analysis when there are missing observations, pp. 952-961, and Little, R. J. A. Regression with missing X's: A review, pp. 1227-1237. We urge you to study these and related sources to see whether a method that is available in EQS for Windows may be appropriate to their situation.

For now, **Close** the **leu2.ess** file. The original file with missing data, **leu.ess**, should still be there. Go to the **Window** menu and click on **leu.ess** to make the file active. You will see the selected cases still highlighted in blue, since we did not undo the selection.

To undo case selection, go to **Data** and select **Use Data**. The **Case Selection Options** dialog box (Figure 3.14) will reappear. You should choose the option **Reset or Unselect All Cases**, which will eliminate the current selection. Since this is the default, click **OK**, and the **leu.ess** file will reappear without any selected cases. Let's explore some of the other available options.

Plotting Missing Data and Outliers

In general, it is not a good idea to simply select complete cases without first exploring the extent and pattern of missing data. Of course, we could just scroll through our data matrix looking for the blank cells or other missing data codes. However, when we have a large file, this is not really feasible. A compressed visual overview is likely to be much more informative.

Missing Data Plot

To obtain such an overview, there is one icon that represents questions about the missing data in the data file. This is the missing data icon, second from the right in the icon row:

Click on the missing data icon. You will get the **Missing Data Processing Specifications** dialog box as shown in Figure 3.18. This box presents options that you can use to control the visual missing data plot display that will appear subsequently. These options deal with missing data codes and outliers.

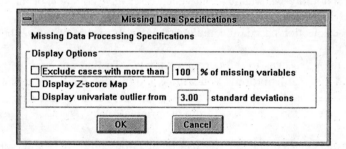

Figure 3.18 Missing Data Processing Specifications Dialog Box

You can choose one or more of the three options to specify your preferred type of missing value plot.

1. The **Exclude cases with more than 100% of missing variables** option gives you the opportunity to exclude cases from your plot when they exceed your specified percentage of missing variables.

   For example, with **leu.ess** active, click on the missing value plot icon. To choose the **Exclude cases** option, click on the square check box to the left of the option. Your click will place an **x** in in the check box, showing that the option is selected. Then click in the % field and enter the **40** in the % box to exclude all of the cases which have more than 40 percent of variables missing.

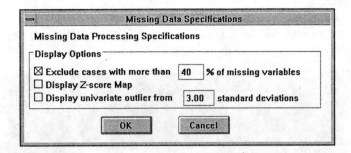

Figure 3.19 Missing Data Processing Specifications with Case Exclusion

Press the **OK** button to start the missing data plot. The missing data pattern will appear, showing a data matrix enclosed by a green rectangle with black background. The data matrix is divided by rows and columns representing cases and variables. Each missing cell is represented by a yellow rectangle. The excluded case toward the bottom of the matrix in Figure 3.20 is represented by a magenta color bar. Once the case exclusion is marked, those cases will be excluded from missing data diagnosis and missing data imputation procedures.

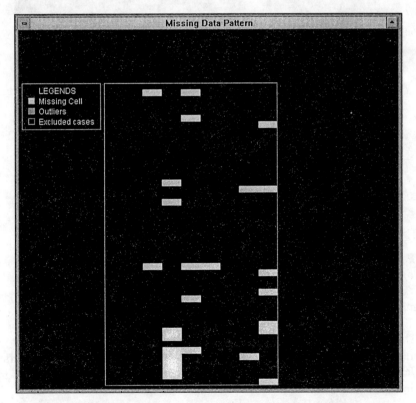

Figure 3.20 Missing Data Plot with Excluded Cases

2. The **Display Z-score Map** option will lead to the missing values plot in which each cell is colored to represent its Z-score range.

To choose this option, click on the missing data icon again. The Missing Data Processing Specifications dialog box will appear with the **Exclude cases** option checked. Enter **40** in the box again.

Click on the square check box to the left of the **Display Z-score Map** option. Your click will place an **x** in the check box, showing that the option is selected. Click on **OK** to get the resulting missing data pattern shown in Figure 3.21.

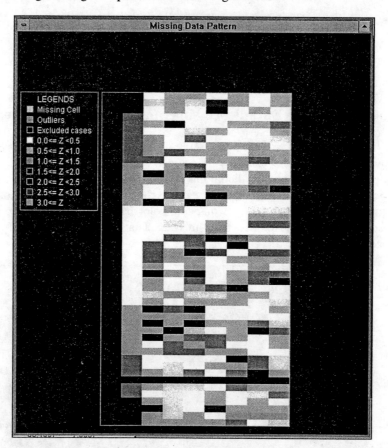

Figure 3.21 Z-score Map with Excluded Cases

You can use the Z-score Map to do preliminary screening of your data for possible outliers. The map uses color to display the absolute values of the Z-scores in 0.5 increments. The legend box on the left side of the map shows the Z-score range represented by each color. You may want to pay attention to those cells displaying a Z-score greater than 3.0. They may be due to outliers in either the positive or negative direction.

3. The **Display univariate outlier from 3.00 standard deviations** option will lead to a missing values plot displaying each outlier cell in green. Univariate outliers are defined by default as cases for each variable that are more than 3 standard deviations to either side of the mean.

To choose this option, click on the missing data icon again. The Missing Data Processing Specifications dialog box will appear with the **Exclude cases** option and the **Display Z-score** option still checked. Enter **40** in the box.

Click on the square check box to the left of the **Display Z-score Map** option to disable that option. Click on the square check box to the left of the **Display univariate outlier from 3.00 standard deviations** option.

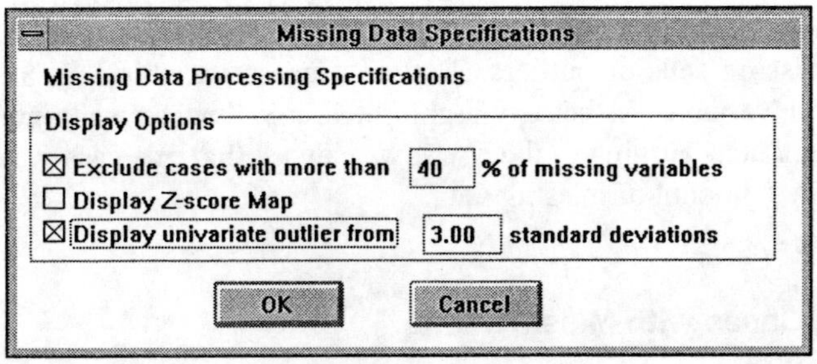

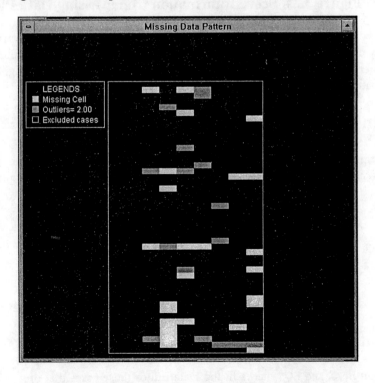

Figure 3.22 Missing Data Specification Dialog Box with Univariate Outlier

For this example, click on the standard deviations field and enter **2** for the desired number of standard deviations. Setting it to less than 3 standard deviations will show more outlying cases. Making it larger would show fewer such cases. The number of outliers shown, of course, depends on the actual distribution of the data. If the variable is not symmetrically distributed, there may be outliers in one direction of scoring, but not in the other. We will not worry about outliers now.

After clicking **OK** on the dialog box of Figure 3.22, we obtain the plot shown in Figure 3.23 below. On a color screen, missing data are shown in yellow, outliers in green, and the excluded cases in magenta. Here we have both outliers and excluded cases. The figure in the rectangle is a visual representation of the entire data matrix.

Figure 3.23 Missing Data Pattern Plot

In this case, the dataset contains 47 cases (rows) and 9 variables (columns). (Remember, you can obtain this file information by using the **Window** menu to move to the Data Editor, then choosing **Data** in the main menu, and then **Information**.) Let us focus first on the columns, and then on the rows.

While they are not distinctly visible, each column represents a variable. Thus, variable 1 has no missing cells or outliers. That is because variable 1 is a string variable. On the other hand, variable 4 is heavily highlighted in yellow, so we know that variable 4 has a lot of missing data. Turning to the rows, we can see that one case was excluded because it has a substantial amount of missing data.

Identifying Cases with Missing Data

In order to be more precise as to which case has missing data, or, for that matter, a non-missing real score, you can move the arrow pointer anywhere in the plot field and click with the mouse. The selected case/variable combination will be highlighted and a message box similar to that shown in Figure 3.24 will appear.

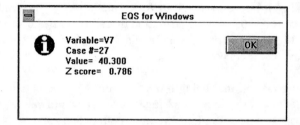

Figure 3.24 Score Information from Missing Data Plot

This message box gives you information on the particular entry in the data matrix. However, when there are many missing data cells, looking at individual cell entries may be too much of a chore to be practical. When you click **OK**, the information disappears. Click on the highlighted cell in the missing data pattern to remove the highlighting.

The Missing Data Pattern Compute Menu

While the missing data plot window is active, the top menu bar has a **Compute** menu, as shown in Figure 3.25. When you click on the **Compute** button, you have a choice of five options:

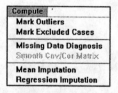

Figure 3.25 Missing Data Pattern Compute Menu

Mark Outliers

Select **Mark Outliers**, and EQS marks in the Data Editor those cases that are extreme in univariate distributions. You can work on those cases, save them separately, or specifically remove them from the data file.

To demonstrate this option, discard all plots, but keep the **leu.ess** file active. Click on the **Missing Data Values** icon to produce the **Missing Data Specifications** dialog box. To create some outliers, choose only **Display univariate outlier**, enter **2.00** in the **standard deviations** field, and click **OK**. The **Missing Data Pattern** plot will display missing cells and outliers.

In the **Missing Data Pattern** plot menu bar, select **Compute** and the **Mark Outliers** option. A message quickly appears: "Selected cases are marked in the data sheet." Click **OK**. Now you can select the **Window** menu and choose **leu.ess** to view the marked cases with outliers.

Mark Excluded Cases

Select **Mark Excluded Cases**, and EQS marks in the Data Editor the cases which you have excluded. You can work on those cases, save them separately, or specifically remove them from the data file.

Missing Data Diagnosis

Start from the **Missing Data Pattern** window. If you select the **Compute** menu **Missing Data Diagnosis** option, EQS computes a diagnostic procedure for describing the missing data pattern.

To demonstrate this option, discard all plots and choose the **leu.ess** file. Double click on the **Missing Data Values** icon to produce the **Missing Data Processing Specifications** dialog box. First, confirm that the **Exclude cases** and **Display Z-score Map** options are not checked. To create some outliers, click on **Display univariate outlier**, enter **2.00** in the **standard deviations** field, and click **OK**. The **Missing Data Pattern** plot will display missing cells and outliers.

Select the **Compute** menu **Missing Data Diagnosis** option, and the program will perform some computations, and when these are completed, you will see the **Process Done!** message. Click **OK**. The results of the analysis will be placed into the **output.log**. To see the results, go to **Window** and select the **output.log** file. You will see the **Missing Values** heading, followed by three sections of output. The output is given in Figure 3.26.

```
MISSING VALUES


9  Variables are selected from file LEU.ESS

String data found in variable  U1
Paired Frequencies for Missing Cells    n=47


              U1      U2      U3      U4      U5      U6
     U1       47
     U2       47      0
     U3       47      3       3
     U4       47     10      12      10
     U5       47      6       6      14       6
     U6       47      2       3      11       6       2
     U7       47      0       3      10       6       2
     U8       47      3       5      11       8       4
     U9       47      8      10      16      13       9

              U7      U8      U9
     U7       0
     U8       3       3
     U9       8       9       8
```
```
Percentile for Paired Missing Cells

               U1       U2       U3       U4       U5       U6
     U1     100.000
     U2     100.000    0.000
     U3     100.000    6.383    6.383
     U4     100.000   21.277   25.532   21.277
     U5     100.000   12.766   12.766   29.787   12.766
     U6     100.000    4.255    6.383   23.404   12.766    4.255
     U7     100.000    0.000    6.383   21.277   12.766    4.255
     U8     100.000    6.383   10.638   23.404   17.021    9.511
     U9     100.000   17.021   21.277   34.043   27.660   19.149

               U7       U8       U9
     U7       0.000
     U8       6.383    6.383
     U9      17.021   19.149   17.021
```

Correlation Matrix for Dichomotized Missing Data

	V1	V2	V3	V4	V5	V6
V1	1.000					
V2	0.000	1.000				
V3	0.000	0.000	1.000			
V4	0.000	0.000	0.077	1.000		
V5	0.000	0.000	0.683	0.113	1.000	
V6	0.000	0.000	0.807	0.148	0.551	1.000
V7	0.000	0.000	0.000	0.000	0.000	0.000
V8	0.000	0.000	0.288	0.290	0.161	0.376
V9	0.000	0.000	0.113	0.041	-0.004	0.185

	V7	V8	V9
V7	1.000		
V8	0.000	1.000	
V9	0.000	0.345	1.000

Figure 3.26 Missing Data Diagnosis

The Paired Frequencies for Missing Cells section is a symmetric matrix with only the lower triangle shown, like a covariance matrix. The diagonal entries give the number of cases that have missing data for that variable. In this case, all entries are missing for variable V1, since it is a string variable, while there are no missing entries for V2, three for V3, and ten for V4. If one were to compute means for variables based on cases with data present, the mean for V3 would be based on 47 - 3 = 44 cases.

Missing values make the situation worse for covariances or correlations between pairs of variables. If a case has a score missing for either variable, the case cannot be used in the computations. This information is given in the relevant off-diagonal part of the matrix. Thus, the correlation between V5 and V4, computed on pairwise present data, could only be based on 47 - 14 = 33 cases.

The second matrix in the **output.log** gives the same information in terms of percentiles. The entries in the top third of Figure 3.26 are divided by the sample size of 47 to get the percentiles. You will see that some correlations would be based on less than 2/3 of all cases, since more than 1/3 of the data are missing for some pair of variables.

The third matrix is the correlation matrix for dichotomized missing data. This is the correlation matrix computed by recoding the data matrix. If a data cell in the original data matrix is non-missing, the datum is coded 1.0. If the data cell is missing, it is replaced by 0.0. Correlations are computed based on the new recoded data matrix. If a variable has no missing data, it will have zero correlation with other dichotomized variables. Otherwise, the extent to which missingness occurs jointly among any two variables will be shown in their correlation coefficient:

1. A correlation close to zero implies that the two variables are not systematically affected by missingness.
2. A negative correlation implies that data present on one variable goes with missingness on the other variable.
3. A positive correlation implies that missing or present data occur jointly.

Smooth Cov/Cor Matrix

This option will be available in the next version.

Mean Imputation

The simplest way to adjust a data matrix is to use the sample mean of a variable to replace any missing data for that variable. When only a very few cells are missing in a large data matrix, this is a useful and reasonable way to impute data. More generally, though, unconditional mean imputation should be considered a method of last resort, since it can yield substantial bias in estimates of variances and correlations. Correcting for bias, however, takes one back to the complete case method discussed previously.

Replace by Variable Mean

To demonstrate the **Replace by Variable Mean** option, again choose the **leu.ess** file. Note that variable V1 is a string variable, so we want to eliminate V1 from this calculation. To do that, click on the **V1** name in the datasheet to highlight it. Then choose the **Edit** menu **Delete** option to remove V1 from the datasheet.

Click on the **Missing Data Values** icon to produce the **Missing Data Specifications** dialog box. Confirm that none of the check boxes have been checked and click on **OK**. The **Missing Data Pattern** plot will display missing cells. In the **Missing Data Pattern** plot menu bar, select **Compute** and the **Mean Imputation** option (see Figure 3.25). The **Mean Imputation** dialog box shown in Figure 3.27 will appear.

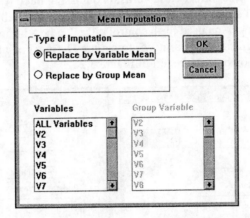

Figure 3.27 Mean Imputation Dialog Box

First you choose the type of imputation that you prefer. To replace the missing values in a variable with the mean for the variable, click on the radio button beside **Replace by Variable Mean**.

Next, you choose the variables for which you want to impute values to replace the missing values. You can replace missing data with means for any set of selected variables, or you can fill the entire matrix at the same time by choosing **ALL Variables**.

Select **All Variables** for this example and click **OK**. A **Process Done** message will appear soon after, signaling that the missing values have been replaced with estimates.

When you go to **Window** and select the **leu.ess** file, you will see that the data matrix shown partially in Figure 3.13 now contains no more blank entries. Variable means have replaced the missing numbers. You can view in the **output.log** the mean values that were computed and inserted in the file.

Please close all of your open windows, starting with the plot windows. We will use a new data file to illustrate the other imputation methods. You might also want to clean up the **output.log** to eliminate extraneous output. To do this quickly, use **File** in the main menu to **Quit** the program, following the directions to save various screens, as they occur. Then reactivate EQS for Windows for the next examples.

Replace by Group Mean

We shall use the file **werner.ess** to illustrate another method for handling missing data. The data are described in the *BMDP Statistical Software Manual* as blood chemistry data for 188 women on nine variables. Variable 5 is a categorical variable that codes whether the subject uses birth control pills or not. There are less than 1/2% of missing data, with no missing data on V5. Because blood chemistry scores may differ by birth control pill usage, replacement of missing data by a variable's grand mean may not be a good idea. It is better to replace missing data with a mean of the group to which the subject belongs. Thus, we shall replace the missing data with mean of scores on some variable, conditional on the subject's score on V5.

> *Note*: To replace the missing data with mean of scores on some variable, conditional on the subject's score on V5, in general *the group variable must be a* **categorical** *variable that has* **no** *missing* data.

First, confirm that V5 is a categorical variable with no missing data. Use **File** and **Open** to select the **werner.ess** file. You will see that V5 seems to be a categorical variable with entries that are 1 or 2, depending on whether the person used birth control pills. To be a bit more certain about V5, click on **Data,** then **Information**. Double click on V5, to get the **Define Variable and Group Names** dialog box. You will see the dialog box on the left of Figure 3.28.

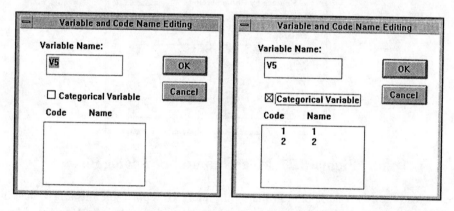

Figure 3.28 Variable and Code Name Editing Dialog Box

No codes show in the **Code** list box, because V5 was not coded as a **Categorical Variable**. Click on the box beside **Categorical Variable** to bring up the category codes as shown in the dialog box on the right of Figure 3.28. The result in the right dialog box yields good news. The scores shown under **Code** indicate that there is no **99** score, so there is no missing data value on this variable.

> *Note*: This **Define Group and Variable Names** dialog box truncates any missing data code to two digits. Thus, if your missing data code were **99999**, this box would display only **99**. However, EQS retains the assigned missing value code internally.

It is possible that the scores **1** and **2** represent integer scores for a categorical variable, but these scores also could be truncated values from non-integer numbers. To save grief, we will verify that the scores do indeed represent integers. (It would be best to correct the status of V5 by clicking **OK**. But that's not our aim here.) Let's proceed to impute the missing values, so click **Cancel** on the two dialog boxes that you have opened to return to the **werner.ess** file.

You will see that some variables have missing data, e.g., case #2 has missing data on V8. Since case #2 belongs to category 2 on V5, for that case we want to replace the missing data blank on V8 with a score that is the subgroup mean of V8 for all subjects in category 2 of V5. We can apply a similar process to other cases and variables where there are missing data.

Click on the missing data icon, 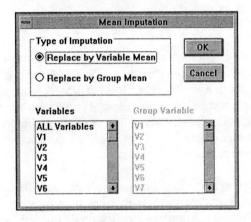, and make your selection in the default **Missing Data Specifications** dialog box (see Fig. 3.18) by clicking **OK**. You will get the visual distribution of missing data similar to that shown in the Figure 3.20 **Missing Data Pattern** plot.

Now that you have the **Missing Data Pattern**, click on **Compute** (Figure 3.25). Choose the **Mean Imputation** option. The **Mean Imputation** dialog box appears as shown in Figure 3.29.

Figure 3.29 Mean Imputation Dialog Box

To replace each missing value in a variable with the mean for its group, click on the radio button beside **Replace by Group Mean**. You will see, at the bottom of this dialog box, the two list boxes **Variables** and **Group Variable**. In the **Variables** list box, select the variables for which you want to replace missing values.

For this example, you should select **V8**, because there are three missing scores on this variable. Click on **V8** to choose it. (You would also press the <Ctrl> key while clicking on a second, third, etc. if you wanted to choose more than one variable.)

The choice **ALL Variables** is the simplest one in the **Variables** list box, although some variables have no missing data. Certainly there is no need to replace any values in the grouping variable V5. This redundancy is ignored when you select **ALL Variables**.

In the right list box, choose **V5** as the group variable. Then, click **OK**.

> *Note*: You can choose only one grouping variable.

You will get the information message **Mean Imputation Done**. Click **OK**, and the **Missing Data Pattern** will reappear, showing that all missing data cells in V8 have been filled in. You can close this plot, and you will be brought back to the **werner.ess** file. This file no longer has any missing data entries in V8. For example, the case #2, V8 entry is no longer blank. It has been filled with the group mean.

If you are satisfied, it is good practice to save this modified file with a new logical file name. You could choose to save the file as **werner2.ess**, for example. Then you would be ready to do various analyses on this file. For this example, there is no need to save this file, but go ahead and save it, if you like. Just be sure to save it with a name different from **werner.ess**.

The **output.log** lists the actual values used to fill every missing cell in **werner.ess**. Remember, you can get to that file via **Window**. You will see that the log gives the means of V1 for those in category 1 of V5, and then the mean of V1 for those in category 2 of V5. Similar group means are given for variables V2 - V9 in turn. Those were the values that EQS for Windows used to plug the missing data for variables that had missing entries.

Let's go back to the original **werner.ess** file to illustrate the regression approach to filling in missing data. **Close** the changed file without saving it, or save it with a new name.

Regression Imputation

In a sense, the group mean imputation approach just described can be considered as an example of using simple bivariate regression to plug missing values. Missing values on V9, for example, were plugged in by the expected value of V9 at each level of V5. A more general approach is to fill in the missing entries via multiple regression, in that several predictor variables can be used to estimate the scores on a dependent variable. If these variables are good predictors of the dependent variable, the imputed value will be a better estimate than one based on the unconditional mean or the conditional mean imputation procedures previously discussed.

The multiple regression approach to imputation, as currently implemented in EQS for Windows, fills in missing values for one dependent variable that has missing data. Using complete cases only, it computes a standard multiple regression equation for predicting that variable from a set of predictors. Using the estimated beta weights and scores of subjects on the predictor variables, the imputed dependent variable score is computed. When a subject also has missing data on a given predictor variable, that variable's mean is used in the prediction equation.

If several variables have missing data, you must repeat the procedure for each variable in turn. The method also requires some thought from you. Each time, you must decide:

- the dependent variable for which you want to impute missing values
- the specific predictor variables that you want to use.

Thus, the procedure is not automatic, and you will make some choices. It is not a good idea to use too few predictors if there are additional possible predictors that are highly related to the dependent variable, and yet are not too highly related to the already-chosen predictors. Using too many predictors, especially in a small sample, is not desirable if many of the correlations are spurious and would not hold up under cross-validation with new data. In small samples, we recommend using no more than three to five predictor variables. In large samples, you could use substantially more.

Ideally, you would use theory and prior research to decide on the predictors. In practice, you may need to use **Analysis** to run a preliminary correlation matrix to see which variables are highly related to a dependent variable. As an alternative, you could use **Analysis** to run a preliminary multiple regression, perhaps with a forward stepwise option. These analyses can be done with cases that have no missing data.

Open the original **werner.ess** file. We will illustrate the procedure by filling in imputed values for V9, based on predictor variables V4 and V6. After assuring that the original **werner.ess** file is active, obtain the missing data display by clicking on the **Missing Data Pattern** icon.

When you have the **Missing Data Pattern** plot for the dataset, click on **Compute** and the **Regression Imputation** option. The resulting dialog box (see Fig. 3.30) provides a list of **Variables** and a list of **Predictors**.

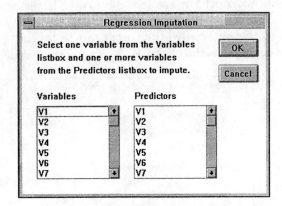

Figure 3.30 Variable Choice in Imputation by Multiple Regression

Choose V9 in the **Variables** list. Hold down the <Ctrl> key while clicking on V4 and V6 in the **Predictors** list. Press **OK**.

After you click **OK**, the program will do the regression computations, impute the missing values, update the data file, and update the missing data pattern. You will see the message **Regression Imputation Done**. Click **OK**, and click on **Window**. Choose **output.log**. After you scroll to the end of the file, you will see the message:

```
IMPUTE BY REGRESSION ESTIMATES
    VARIABLE       V9  CASE     103  IMPUTED VALUE      54.722
```

This is the value placed into the data matrix in place of a blank. You can check this by going to the appropriate place in the **werner.ess** file. If you are satisfied with the result, and do not want to do any further imputation, you should save the **werner.ess** file with a new file name.

Remember that, when you run a regression to impute missing values, the data matrix (the *.ess file) is automatically updated with the imputed scores. If you want to recover the original unmodified data matrix, or if you change your mind about the appropriateness of what you did, you must go back to a copy of the original unmodified matrix. You can do that if you close the modified ***.ess** file without saving it, or if you save the modified file under a different name. This completes our discussion of regression imputation.

Variable Selection

Quite frequently, complete data matrices contain far more information than is relevant to a particular purpose. For example, a survey may contain hundreds of variables, but only a few variables may be appropriate for a particular study. In such situations, it is useful to create a new data file that contains only the variables and, possibly, cases, relevant to the purpose at hand. **Working with a smaller data file can speed up all of your analyses substantially.**

To illustrate variable selection, **Open** the **survey.ess** file. As you can see from **Data** and **Information**, this is a large file of 37 variables and 294 cases. This file represents responses to a survey of depression and other health variables. For any particular analysis, only a few variables may be relevant. For example, variables 9-28 are depression items, and it may be of interest to see their factor structure.

To save the depression items, select **File** and then **Save As**. The dialog box prompts you for the file name to save, but it is using the current file name **survey.ess**. If you don't change this name, you will lose the original file. Generally, you will not want this to happen. So, replace the name with something logical, like **depress.ess**, and click **OK**. You will see the dialog box shown in Figure 3.31.

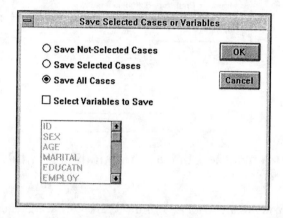

Figure 3.31 Variable Selection Using Save As

Click on the check box **Select Variables to Save**. The variable list becomes active. You will use this list to select variables V9-V12. Use the right scroll bar to make V12 visible. Then click on V9 and hold the <Shift> key down while clicking on V12. The variables from V9 to V12 will be highlighted. When you have finished, click **OK**. The selected variables will be saved in the new file.

You can close the current file without saving it. When you want to access the saved variables in your new file, click on **File** and **Open** to bring the saved variables into the Data Editor. You will see that the original variable labels are maintained in the new data file. These labels are not very informative here, since no mnemonic labels had been originally assigned to the variables.

> *Note*: You could save selected cases at the same time that you save selected variables. The next section describes how to select cases for analysis and saving.

Case Selection

Purpose of Case Selection

Most of the time you will want to analyze all of the data in your data file. There is, then, no reason to worry about case selection. But sometimes you will want to focus attention on a certain set of cases, such as only the females, or only the non-outliers, or a random half of the data. As you will see, there are many options for selecting cases in EQS for Windows, each of which can serve a different purpose. Case selection makes it easier to run analyses with a selected set of subjects. You can do analyses directly on the selected cases, or, subsequently, on a new file that contains only the selected cases.

Consider all of the options dealing with case selection as the options which change the state of a binary indicator variable that accompanies each case. This indicator is turned either on or off. When it is turned on, the case is active, or selected, and the case is included in whatever plotting or computational routine might be undertaken. When you first bring up a file, all cases are automatically selected even though you see no special marking in the file. Later, when you select particular cases, only they will be marked.

If you are in doubt about whether any cases are selected, you have two ways to tell. First, you can see the selected cases in the data file. The selected cases will have their cell contents highlighted in blue in the Data Editor. If the blue highlighting is not visible, the file may not be active; click on the title bar to make the file active. Second, you can get a summary of whether any cases are selected, and if so, how many, by going to **Data** on the main menu, selecting **Information**. The dialog box **Define Variable and Group Names** will appear, giving information about the data file. This includes a specification of the number of cases that are marked.

Analysis with Selected Cases

Once you have selected cases by any of the methods explained below, you face the question of what to do next. If your goals are limited to exploratory data analyses, you can do analyses on the selected cases quickly and immediately without first creating a new data file. The plotting and statistical procedures can be performed directly on those cases that you have selected and marked in the Data Editor. As a result you can quickly find out whether you want to pursue detailed analyses with these selected cases, which really should require first saving the cases in their own data file.

Saving Selected Cases in a New File

If you have a plan for a series of analyses with selected cases, the safest practice is to select the cases and then immediately to use the **Save As** procedure to save the selected cases under their own new file name. Then you can open that file and do what you want with it. All results will clearly refer to the precise file being used in your analyses.

Implementing Case Selection

As usual, you must have a data file active. Let us work with the **werner.ess** file again. Go to **File**, select **Open**, and make this file active in the Data Editor. Next, on the main menu, select **Data** and then the **Use Data** Option. This will activate the **Case Selection Options** dialog box.

The **Case Selection Options** dialog box is shown in Figure 3.32. You make your case selection by clicking on the relevant radio button to select one of the ready-made options, or by creating your own selection formula. We shall discuss the meaning of the various options in turn.

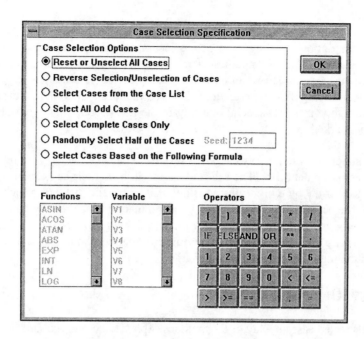

Figure 3.32 Case Selection Options Dialog Box

Reset or Unselect All Cases

In a sense, we should discuss this option last, but we place it first on the list because it is the option that you are likely to use most frequently. Suppose you had selected certain cases based on some criterion. Then these cases are marked in the Data Editor, and you can do various actions with regard to only these cases. However, you may change your mind and want to use all cases in the data file. Or, you may already have completed the analysis based on the selected cases. Thus, you may want to undo a selection. You undo it by choosing this option as long as you are still working with your original file containing all cases.

When the **Case Selection Options** dialog box first comes on the screen, the **Reset** or **Unselect All Cases** option has its radio button marked. It is the default. To use that option, just click **OK**. The selected cases become unmarked and all cases become active for the next analysis.

Reverse Selection/Unselection of Cases

Now, suppose you had marked certain cases for analysis. For example, suppose you had previously selected all of the males for some analysis, but you decide that you also want to do the same type of analysis on the females. You simply select the option to reverse the selection, and click **OK**. The effect is that previously selected cases become unselected, and unselected cases become selected. In the example, the males become unselected and the females become selected.

Remember that this option simply *reverses* the current selection. At times, this may not accomplish what you want. Suppose that, in the previous example, there were cases designated as males, others designated as females, and some cases for which gender was not known. Then, somehow, you had previously selected males only. With males currently selected, reversing the selection marks all those who are not males. This would mean that females as well as gender-unknowns become marked. Reversing the selection, thus, would not select only females in such a situation.

This option is an important workhorse that you will find to be useful in many circumstances. Suppose you want to delete outliers from an analysis. The missing data procedure permits you to mark outlier cases based on univariate criteria in a very simple way, for example. But if you want to work with the *non*outlier cases, the wrong cases are marked. Just click on **Reverse Selection/ Unselection of Cases** to select the nonoutlier cases.

Select Cases from the Case List

You may want to select certain specific subjects for analysis. This is accomplished by using the option to select cases from a list of cases. When you mark the radio button for selecting from the case list in the dialog box shown in Figure 3.32, the dialog box shown in Figure 3.33 appears.

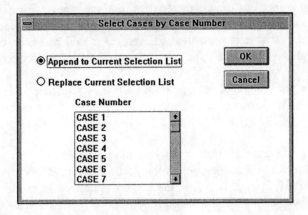

Figure 3.33 Select Cases by Case Number

As you can see, there is a list box of all cases in the currently active file, simply numbered CASE 1, CASE 2, and so on. You should scroll through this list box and click on the cases that you want to select.

By default, as you can see from the radio button **Append to Current Selection List**, the cases that you select simply get *added* to any cases that you might already have previously selected. If you had not previously selected any cases, then the newly-selected cases would be the only cases selected. If you want to ensure that the newly-selected cases are the *only* marked cases in the data file, you should click on the option **Replace Current Selection List**.

This option, like others, will be most useful when used in conjunction with other case selection procedures. Consider the current file, **werner.ess**. It has nine variables and 188 cases. Suppose that you don't trust the data on ten of these cases, so you want to select 178 cases for your analysis. True, you could go through the list box above and click 178 times on the particular cases you want to keep. But that is hard work. Your goal is more simply accomplished in two stages:

1. Choose **Data** and **Use Data** to bring up the **Case Selection Specification** dialog box of Figure 3.32 again; choose **Select Cases from the Case List** to select the 10 cases.
2. Choose **Data** and **Use Data** to bring up the **Case Selection Specification** dialog box of Figure 3.32 again; this time, choose **Reverse Selection/Unselection**.

The reversal will select the 178 cases you want. It also unselects the 10 cases initially chosen.

You might try this type of two-stage case selection with the **werner.ess** file now, to get a feel for how the procedure works in practice.

Select All Odd Cases

This option chosen from Figure 3.32 will do the obvious. It will mark every other case, starting with case #1, that is, 1, 3, 5, and so on. If your file contains cases that are in a random order when listed sequentially, selecting the odd cases will give you a random half of your data file. But be careful! Sometimes cases are listed sequentially in terms of some definable variable. If that is the situation, you will <u>not</u> get a random half of your data with this option.

A non-random selection from the data could be good or bad. It would be desirable if it helps you to get a systematic sample that has the characteristics that you want. For example, if your cases are ordered by the time it took subjects to complete a task, you may want to select one half of the sample in such a way that this variable is controlled. If you select odd cases, an equal distribution of task completion times would be obtained for the selected as well as the unselected cases.

In the **werner.ess** file, you would not get a random sample by selecting odd cases. Try it now. Make the file active, through **Window**, and then choose **Data** from the main menu. When you choose **Use Data** you will see Figure 3.32 again. Click on the **Select All Odd Cases** option, and click **OK**.

You will find that the odd cases are indeed marked, as they should be. So why is this not a random half of the data? If you will look at the column for V5 in the Data Editor, you will see that the scores in that column alternate 1, 2, 1, 2, 1... And the odd cases happen to be cases with **1** on V5. These cases are the subjects who do not take birth control pills.

Select Complete Cases Only

This option from the **Case Selection Specification** dialog box has its main use as a method for dealing with missing data. It provides a convenient way to find all those subjects that have no missing data on any variables.

To illustrate the procedure, make the file **werner.ess** the active file again. Go to **Data**, then **Use Data**, and then mark **Select Complete Cases Only** and click **OK**. If you then select **Data** and choose **Information**, you will find that 181 of the 188 cases have been marked. The remaining cases have one or more missing data entries. If you were to decide that the missing data are random, and you consider the sample size to be large enough, you might consider saving the selected cases using the **Save As** procedure. This would create a new file with complete data on 181 cases that you could use in all subsequent data analyses.

If you are not sure whether cases with complete data are systematically different from cases with some missing data, you could do some analyses to compare the two groups. Remember that you could use the option to **Reverse Selection/Unselection**. This would unselect the 181 cases with complete data, and mark the 7 cases with missing data. Their scores could then be saved in a separate file. You could, for example, compare the means of the two groups on the various variables.

> *Note*: You can obtain the same results without using the option to reverse the selection. Remember that **Save As** permits you to directly save either selected or unselected cases. So, even though the 181 cases are marked, you can use **Save As** again to save the unselected seven cases.

Randomly Select Half of the Cases

There are many reasons for wanting to obtain a random subsample from your complete data file. One application is to build a model in one half of the data, and to cross-validate it on the other half. If you use the option to **Randomly Select Half of the Cases** in the **Case Selection Option** dialog box shown in Figure 3.32 , you will get cases that are randomly selected and marked in your file.

After choosing the random selection option, you should also provide a random number in the **Seed** field, to replace the existing number. Different seed numbers will produce different selections of cases. You can save selected cases, if desired.

With a successive use of the **Save As** procedure, you can save selected and nonselected cases into two different files. As a result, you have one sample that you can use to build a structural equation model, and another sample that you can use to cross-validate the model.

One problem with random selection of cases is that any computer-generated random number procedure is not truly random. All too often, one sees clusters of selected cases that seem somehow not to be random. This is probably, technically speaking, correct, and in a certain sense rather obvious in view of the importance of the seed number. In our experience, however, the selections produced are about as random as can be obtained by standard computer routines. Furthermore, it seems that when researchers ask for a random selection of cases, often they implicitly expect to see cases marked in a somewhat more systematic fashion than a random procedure could produce. You should not expect to see, for example, more or less every other case selected. Such a systematic selection would be quite unlikely to occur by chance.

On the other hand, balance on several key variables can be critically important in selecting a subsample, as it might be in smaller samples, or when some variables have very skewed distributions. In such a situation, you might first do some systematic case selection to create new files of subsamples that have the characteristics you want. Then, if the subsamples are still large enough, you might divide these files randomly as described above.

Select Cases Based on the Following Formula

You can gain a lot of flexibility by building your own case selection formula. Figure 3.34 gives the bottom half of the **Case Selection Specification** dialog box shown fully in Figure 3.32.

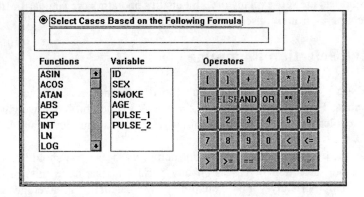

Figure 3.34 Case Selection By Formula

If you click on the radio button for **Select Cases Based on the Following Formula**, you can use your mouse to select items from **Functions, Variable**, and **Operators**. Just click on these items in logical order to produce a formula for case selection in the text box.

When you are done, click **OK**, and the chosen cases are highlighted. If there are no cases highlighted, it could be because the file is not active, in which case you should press the title bar to make it active, or because no cases met the selection criterion. You can determine how many cases met the selection criterion by selecting **Data** and then **Information**.

Case selection works in a way that is very similar to the creation of new variables, which is done with the **Transformation** option, using operators identical to those shown in Figure 3.32. As we will discuss below, new variables are developed with rules based on the same choice of functions, variables, and operators.

Functions

The available functions are typical mathematical functions, as well as statistical operations. The terminology is standard, and, for the most part, it is self-explanatory to those who know what they want to do. The functions include:

ASIN, ACOS, ATAN, ABS, EXP, INT, LN, LOG, MEAN, MIN, MAX, RANK, SIGN, SQRT, SUM, SIN, COS, RNDU, RNDG, and TAN.

In most cases, the functions are implemented on a single variable, e.g. LOG(V1) or RANK(V3), and the selection rule will compare a score to a fixed cutoff such as RANK(V3) < 10. Of course, you must use the functions with care! For example, it is not a good idea to take the log of a negative number; it can't be done, and the program may bomb.

The functions MEAN, MIN, MAX, and SUM operate on several variables given in a list. For example, MIN(V1,V3,V6) > 30, selects a case if the case has a minimum score exceeding 30 on the listed variables. RNDU and RNDG are random uniform and normal variables.

Operators

There are various useful operators. Let us discuss these by rows. The first are the parentheses ( ) which you can use to bracket ambiguous statements. Arithmetical operations are: addition, subtraction, multiplication, and division. Logical statements are: **if, else, and, or**. Exponentiation is given by ******. Numbers are self-explanatory. Inequality operators are standard. Be sure to distinguish the identity operator == from = , used in an equation.

Illustrative Selection Formulae

Let's illustrate some selection formulae using the file **werner.ess** on blood chemistry of women. **Open** this file now. For your information, V2 = age, V3 = height, V4 = weight, V5 = birth control pill usage, V6 = cholesterol level, V7 = albumin level, V8 = calcium level, and V9 = uric acid level.

We can select cases by a selection formula, but before we do so, we should recognize that if we do arithmetic, including selection of cases, on any variables that have missing data, we would be selecting cases inappropriately. For example, if we calculate an average score across several variables, the blank would get averaged in as 0. So, please, first replace the missing data in a simple way, for example with mean imputation. We'll leave that up to you. (Hint: Use the missing data icon, and follow the instructions earlier in this chapter.)

To create a selection formula, type it in the text box, or click on the relevant functions, operators, and variables. As you click on these, they appear in the text box. Typing may be faster, but you would have to remember the EQS for Windows convention for certain symbols, e.g., the operator, **AND**, which, when clicked, yields the text box equivalent, **&&**. Illustrative selection procedures are the following:
  - Select older subjects: V2 > 50

- Select women who are either tall or heavy: (V3>65)OR(V4>150)
- Select women who have high cholesterol and also do not use birth control pills:
  (V6>200)&&(V5==1)
- Select women whose average albumin, calcium, and uric acid levels are high:
  MEAN(V7,V8,V9)>70

When you click **OK**, the selected cases will appear visibly marked on the file. (To repeat: If the cases are not highlighted, it might be because the file is not active; to make it the current window, press on its title bar. Alternatively, maybe no cases meet your selection criterion.) To find the number of cases that are marked, go to **Data** and **Information**.

Error messages are given when there is an unacceptable formula or syntax, and when you use an undefined variable (V's must be in caps, for example). However, in complex situations the error decoding may be incomplete. In general, case selection should be based on relatively simple rules.

> *Note*: ***Current logical checks are incomplete and cannot verify a complicated formula***. If you are planning to use a complicated formula, it is best to first create a new variable based on the formula, and then to select cases by scores on that new variable as described here.

Joining and Merging Data Files

You may sometimes want to create a new file from two existing files. You can place the existing files side by side, or **join** them, to create a new file. Think of the first file as symbolized by **X**, and the second file as symbolized by **Y**. Then the joined file will be $Z = [X|Y]$. Typically, you would be joining two data files for the same subjects, ordered in the same sequence. For example, one file may contain the attitude scores, and the other, the personality scores. In general, the new file will contain the variables in both files, here, attitudes and personality on all the subjects. However, you may also select variables as you are joining files.

Alternatively, you may wish to take two data files and place them end to end, so that they become merged to create a new file. Think of the first file as symbolized by X, and the second file as symbolized by **Y**. Then the merged file **Z** will be

$$Z = \frac{X}{Y}$$

Typically, you will merge two data files for a given set of variables for different subjects. For example, one file may contain data from the males, and the other file, data from the females. The merged file will contain data from all subjects.

We shall illustrate joining and merging operations using the file **leu2.ess**. This file was created in the conjunction with the section **Selecting Complete Cases Only**. The file is small, having 27 cases and nine variables.

Join

To illustrate joining files, we shall first separate this file into two parts. To create two files from **leu2.ess**, bring up this file now. (We created this file earlier in the example shown in Figures 3.15 to 3.17.)

Use **Save As** to name the new file **leu2a.ess** and save it as an **EQS System File**. When you get the **Select Variables to Save** dialog box, click on **Select Variables to Save**. When the list box becomes active, click on **V1**, then, holding down the <Shift> key, click on **V5** to save variables 1-5 only in the new file called **leu2a.ess**.

Use **Save As** again to save variable 2 with variables 6-9 in the new file called **leu2b.ess**. You can bring up these files after they have been created, and use **Data** and **Information** to verify that they each contain 27 cases, the first having five variables and the second, five.

> *Note*: To select multiple noncontiguous variables from the list, hold down the <Ctrl> key while clicking on each variable. To select multiple contiguous variables from the list, you can simply drag the cursor over each variable, or hold down the <Shift> key while clicking on each variable.

Notice, in particular, that we have saved variable V2 in both files. This is a case number that varies from 1001 to 1037, and is not an actual data score. It will be an important **key** variable below.

From the main menu, select **Data** and then **Join**. You will see a window similar to that shown in Figure 3.35.

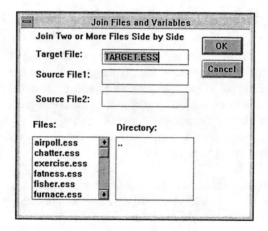

Figure 3.35 Join Files and Variables Dialog Box

When you see this figure, **target.ess** is the default name. You can change this file name to any appropriate name. We might have used the name **leu3.ess**, for example, but the default is fine for our purposes.

Initially, the text boxes **Source File 1** and **Source File 2** are empty. You should fill in the names of the two files that are to be placed side by side. Do this by moving the pointer to **leu2a.ess** under **Files** and then clicking; **leu2a.ess** will appear in the text box of **Source File 1**.

Next, you should click on **leu2b.ess**, and this name will move into the text box for **Source File 2**. After you have done this, you should click **OK**. Figure 3.36 will appear. This dialog box provides you with some options in the join operation. Basically, you can just click **OK** in this box to proceed, but this may be dangerous, as we shall explain below.

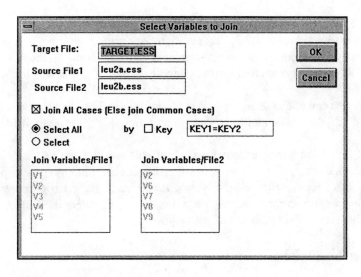

Figure 3.36 Select Variables to Join Dialog Box

The dialog box permits you to select variables and cases. You see that the default to **Join All Cases** is marked. This takes all cases from each file, which is the right thing to do in our situation. The alternative will be described below. You also see that the option **Select All** variables is chosen. If you chose to mark the other radio button **Select**, the list boxes in the bottom would be made visible and you could choose variables from each of the two files to be included in the new file, **target.ess**.

Select by Key Variables

If we were to click **OK**, the two files would be simply placed next to each other in creating the new file. This may be correct if you know that the scores for all subjects are lined up perfectly across the files. But what if, say, Joe's scores are in line 1 of file 1, but in line 20 of file 2? If you join files that are mismatched by case sequence, you would be creating a worthless—worse, a misleading—new file.

> *Note:* You should always question whether the cases in your files are lined up correctly. Even if they are not, you can match case scores across files by using a key variable.

In general, a key variable is the variable in a file that you use to identify a given case. Most data files will have an ID number that can be used as a key variable. In the **leu2.ess** file, variable V2 is the case ID number, going from 1001-1037. There are some missing numbers corresponding to cases with missing data that had previously been deleted from the original **leu.ess** file. When we created the **leu2a.ess** and **leu2b.ess** files, we included variable V2 in each file. Thus, we had case ID numbers in each file. These can be used as key variables.

Mark the **x** in the **by Key** checkbox by clicking on it. Then, in place of the default **KEY1=KEY2**, type the appropriate keying information. The left side of the = gives the name of the key variable in the first file, and the right side gives the corresponding name in the second file. In our case, you can type **V2=V2**.

> *Note:* Each key variable must be precisely given, and it must have its scores in ascending order.

In the statement **KEY1=KEY2**, each variable label must be precisely typed, with no spaces. Upper and lower case must exactly match the actual variable names. For example, V2=v2 would not work, because there is no variable v2 (lower case v) in the **leu2b.ess** file. Also on each key variable, the cases should be ordered so that scores go from low to high, i.e., they are ordered in ascending order.

The ordering is essential because the join operation does not do sorting. If your cases are not in the correct sequence, you can create the correct sequence by using **Data** on the main menu, and then the **Sort** option. This option is discussed further in another section of this chapter.

In our example, you can click **OK** in the dialog box of Figure 3.36, and the new **target.ess** file will be created on your hard drive. You will get a message stating that the joining of files is done.

Click **OK**, and **Open** the new file **target.ess**. You will see that the original file **leu2.ess** has been recreated—with one exception. The new file **target.ess** contains two copies of variable V2. Whenever you select **Key** in Figure 3.36, you will automatically get two copies of the key variable. For now, this is an extra variable that we do not want, so we delete it. But in other circumstances, this extra variable serves a valuable checking purpose.

Deleting a Variable

While viewing the opened **target.ess** file, click on the variable name of the variable that you want to delete from the file. Here, this is V2 in the middle of the file. The entire V2 column becomes highlighted in a dark color.

Go to **Edit** and click on **Delete**. The column will disappear. Then, use **Save As** to save the file without the extra variable.

Join All or Common Cases

In Figure 3.36, the check box **Join All Cases** was marked. In our illustration, this had no effect. But if your files are not perfectly matched with respect to cases, you can get very different results, depending on the choice of this option or its alternative. The choice you make should depend on your subsequent plans for analysis with the newly-created data file.

Suppose that you had two files in which the case IDs, or key variables, were sequenced as follows:

> file1: 1, 2, 3, 7, 8, 9, 10
> file2: 1, 2, 5, 6, 7, 9.

Thus file1 has 7 cases, and file2 has 6 cases. We will not worry about the number of variables are in each file. Can these files be joined? The answer is yes, but the results depend on your choice.

First, notice that if you were to join file1 and file2 without using any key variables, you would create a file with the number of cases (here, seven) given by the number in the larger file. In that file, some case scores would be aligned correctly, and other scores would be misaligned. Cases 1 and 2 in the resulting file would have their scores matched correctly, but from that point on, the data numbers would have no meaning, since scores for different cases would be placed together as if they belonged to a single case. Also, the combined file would have blank missing data entries in the file2 variable positions, since the 7th case in file2 has no data.

If you have ID numbers in each file, each of which you place into the joined file, at least you could see if the cases are aligned correctly. If you join in this manner without an ID number to check the results, you may never know about any problem that you have inadvertently created.

If you select **Join All Cases**, and you use key variables, your joined file would contain data on cases 1, 2, 3, 5, 6, 7, 8, 9, 10 in sequence, i.e., your new file would have all 9 cases. Of course, some cases have missing data in either file1 or file2, and this fact is made visible in the joined file with the blank entries.

On the other hand, if you uncheck **Join All Cases**, and you use key variables, you are selecting the alternative to **Join Common Cases**. This option would create a new file consisting of data for subjects 1, 2, 7, 9 only. That is, your new file would have four cases. Of course, this is a file with complete data. Necessarily, this means that the data for some subjects is excluded from the file.

Actions Recorded in Output.log

As you will have noted, in all but the simplest situations, joining files can lead to perplexing results. You must be aware of the options available to you and the differing results that will occur under these various options. If you have identifying variables in each file, whether or not these variables are used as key variables, it is worthwhile to move these variables to the new file. Then you should check to see whether the cases have aligned in the way that you intended. You can perform such a check in the new file. But you can also check the **output.log** file for a record of actions taken.

As you join files, the actions taken are recorded in **output.log**. A partial listing of output based on the above example is given below. As you see, you get a list of the files that were joined, and their characteristics, the newly created file, as well as the key variables that may have been used. In addition, the listing under JOINING RECORDS provides a case by case analysis of the new record number and where its data came from in each of the two files.

```
JOINING FILES
FILE NAME                 # OF VAR.   # OF CASES     KEY VAR.
TARGET.ESS
LEU2A.ESS                     5           27            V2
LEU2B.ESS                     5           27            V2

JOINING RECORDS

  rec=    1        key1= 1001      key2= 1001
  rec=    2        key1= 1003      key2= 1003
  rec=    3        key1= 1004      key2= 1004
```

Merge

Placing files end to end creates some of the same opportunities and complexities as placing them side by side. In the simplest case, the procedure is completely transparent and almost trivial to implement. To demonstrate this, let us again create two files from **leu2.ess**. Open **leu2.ess** now.

On the main menu, select **Data** and then **Use Data**. In the dialog box, mark the option to **Select All Odd Cases** and click **OK**. You will see that the odd cases are now marked in the Data Editor.

Use **Save As** and name the file **leu2c.ess**. When prompted by the dialog box, choose **Save Selected Cases** and click on **OK**. Then, use **Save As** again and name the file **leu2d.ess**. Choose **Save Not-Selected Cases** and click on **OK**. These are the files that we will merge.

To merge these files, go to **Data** and then click on **Merge**. You will be given the option box shown in the left half of Figure 3.37. As before, the **Target File** is defaulted to **target.ess**, and you click in source files order on the files in the file list to select choices for **Source File 1** and **Source File 2**.

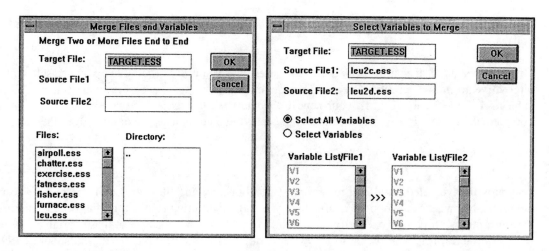

Figure 3.37 Merge Files and Select Variables to Merge Dialog Boxes

In the example shown on the left of Figure 3.37, the **leu2c.ess** and **leu2d.ess** files still need to be selected. After doing that, click **OK**. The right side of Figure 3.37 displays the second **Merge** dialog box with the default setting, the radio button **Select All Variables** marked.

If you use the default and click **OK**, a message will appear, telling you that the merge is done. When you examine **target.ess**, you will see that you have reconstructed the entire data file **leu2.ess**, except that the cases have been rearranged. They are rearranged, because the odd cases were sorted into file **leu2c.ess**, and those scores are given first. The even cases from the original file are given below those in the new file.

If you mark **Select Variables,** as shown in the right dialog box, some very complicated alternatives become possible. The two list/files shown in the right box become active, and you can click on any variable in either list. The actual variable names in either list will determine the number of variables that appear in the target file, and whether there are any missing data blank entries. Some examples are:

1. Suppose that you select V1-V9 in File1, and V1-V9 in File2. This duplicates the previous result and creates one file with nine variables and all 27 cases.

2. Suppose that you select V1-V4 in File1 and also V1-V4 in File2. You will create a combined file with four variables and 27 cases.

3. Suppose that you select V1-V4 in File1 and V5-V9 in File2. This also creates a file with 27 cases, but missing data entries will appear. In the schematic below, the two rows represent two sets of cases from the two files, and the two columns represent two sets of variables:

V1- V4 from File1	Missing Data blanks
Missing Data blanks	V5-V9 from File2

The missing data codes are created because V5-V9 scores were not selected from File1, and because V1-V4 scores were not selected from File2. A blank will appear in each cell where a variable was not chosen.

As stated above, the actual list of variable names will determine the outcome of the merge operation. As a result, by the clever use of renaming strategies, you can achieve unusual results that may be useful from time to time.

For example, if you want two seemingly unrelated variables to line up below each other in a new file, you could create variable names that are identical in the two files and then merge. Having the same variable name, the corresponding scores will stack end to end. Sequential manipulations of this sort will create some special results. Remember that you can delete any undesired variables that you might create as shown above.

> *Note*: When you do these types of special applications, and perhaps in general, you should be sure to work with copies of your original files instead of the original files, so that if your procedure fails to have the desired effect, you will not have destroyed any valuable data.

Variable Transformation

In the section on Case Selection, above, we discussed the EQS for Windows approach to selecting cases based on a variety of possible rules and procedures. Very similar procedures are available for creating a new variable that is a transformation of an existing variable. The transformed variable can be based on a simple mathematical function of one variable, or it can be a more complex function of several variables.

In general, you start with the following steps to create a transformed variable.
1. Open the data file with the original variables. As an example, make this the **airpoll.ess** file.
2. Select **Data** on the main menu bar, and click on **Transformation** on the list box.

This will bring up a dialog box as shown in Figure 3.38.

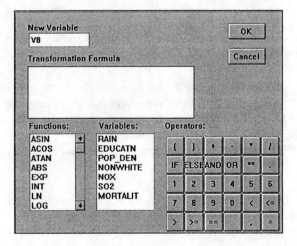

Figure 3.38 Variable Transformations Dialog Box

In this file, there are seven variables as shown in the **Variable** list box. You can create a **New Variable** V8 by taking some action based on the **Functions** shown in the lower left list box and the **Operators** shown in the lower right array. Of course, you can call the new variable anything you want; V8 is just the default. (If your file had eight variables already, this new variable would be V9.)

Transformation Functions

The functions available to you are the following:

81

ASIN, ACOS, ATAN, ABS, EXP, INT, LN, LOG, MEAN, MIN, MAX, RANK, SIGN, SQRT, SUM, SIN, COS, RNDU, RNDG, and TAN.

These functions are basically self-explanatory. They are mathematical functions to be applied to a single variable, in general. Please see the discussion under **Functions** in this chapter for more information.

The operators in Figure 3.38 are self-explanatory. They include numbers, mathematical operators, and logical operators. See the section titled **Operators** in this chapter for more information.

Creating a Transformed Variable

To create a new transformed variable, click on a function, operator, or a variable in a logical sequence. As you click on these alternatives, a line specifying the transformation is built up in the text box called **Transformation Formula**. The resulting formula should be a generally recognizable mathematical or logical statement. It cannot, at this time, be too complex, since the program does not yet have an extended logic for decoding the entire range of complex statements that could be generated. But standard statistical transformations can be carried out easily. This section illustrates a few transformations.

Suppose that you want to use the formula V8 = EDUCATN + POP_DEN - NONWHITE in the **airpoll.ess** dataset. Then you don't need the **Functions**. Click on **EDUCATN**, click on the **+ Operator** button, click on **POP_DEN**, click on the **- Operator** button, and click on **NONWHITE**. You will see that you have created EDUCATN + POP_DEN - NONWHITE inside the **Transformation Formula** text box. Then click **OK**. The new variable V8 will appear as a column of data in your input file.

> *Note*: The transformation is case-sensitive. If your variable name is all upper case in the data sheet, it must be all upper case in the transformation.

As another example, you may want to do a poor man's ordinal data analysis by using the rank order of a variable rather than its actual scores in some analysis. You can create the ranked variable by clicking on **RANK** from the **Functions** list, EDUCATN, and) to create the statement RANK(EDUCATN). If you do this now, when you click **OK** you will have created the new variable V9, since you created V8 earlier. V9 contains numbers representing the rank of the original scores, from low to high.

Or, suppose you are interested in extremity ratings. You may have a categorical variable and want to recode it in terms of extremity. **V3** in the **pancake.ess** file has four score categories ranging from 0 to 4. You could create a new variable as ABS(V3 - 2) for example. Note, however, that you can more easily recode using the **Group** option available under **Data**.

Creating a Conditional Transformation

To create a conditional transformation, you can either click on the operators **IF** and **ELSE**, or you can type them in upper case in the Transformation Formula box. The following is a set of formulas for a conditional transformation for the **RAIN** variable in the **airpoll.ess** dataset. Enter the first formula and press <Enter>, enter the next formula and press <Enter>, etc. Enter all of these formulas now, line by line, in the **Transformation Formula** box. Be sure to add a space between ELSE and IF.

        IF (RAIN>45) V8=-2
        ELSE IF (RAIN>35 && RAIN<=45) V8=2

ELSE IF (RAIN>20 && RAIN <=35) V8=-1
ELSE IF (RAIN>15 && RAIN <=20) V8=1
ELSE V8=0

After you enter all of the conditional transformations in the Transformation Formula box, click OK. The program will create and display the new variable in your data sheet. If any data cell in RAIN is not defined in the formula shown above, a system missing value will be entered in the equivalent cell in the new variable. That is, the new variable will display a blank cell for any missing data.

Displaying a Transformation Formula

The EQS for Windows Data Editor remembers the formula(s) that you use to create a variable. To display the formula(s), hold down the <Ctrl> key while clicking on the variable name in the data sheet. The formula(s) for the selected variable will appear in the transformation formula box in the upper left of your data sheet, as shown in Figure 3.39.

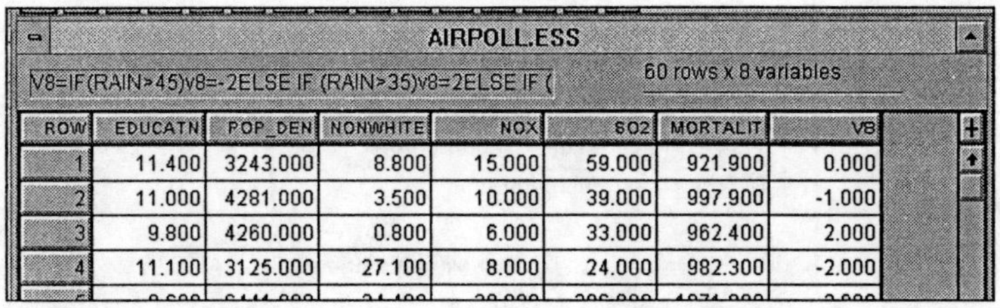

ROW	EDUCATN	POP_DEN	NONWHITE	NOX	SO2	MORTALIT	V8
1	11.400	3243.000	8.800	15.000	59.000	921.900	0.000
2	11.000	4281.000	3.500	10.000	39.000	997.900	-1.000
3	9.800	4260.000	0.800	6.000	33.000	962.400	2.000
4	11.100	3125.000	27.100	8.000	24.000	982.300	-2.000

Figure 3.39 Transformation Formula Box

When you have a set of formulas for a transformation, you cannot see all of them in the transformation formula box. However, you can bring the rest of the formulas into view. First, click on the transformation formula box to place your cursor in the box. Then press the right arrow several times to move the cursor to the right, bringing up the rest of the formulas.

Saving a File with New Variables

When you save a file with new variables, click on **Save As**, giving the file a new name. Then you are asked to fill out the **Save Selected Cases or Variables** dialog box, and you can click the box **Select Variables to Save**. This action highlights all of the variables in your current file, and you click on all old as well as new variables that you want to save. Then you click **OK**, and the new file is created. The variables that you did not want are not part of the new file. Of course, you would then close and open the various files for further work in the usual way.

It is obvious from Figure 3.38 that there are many other transformation options that you could explore and find relevant in a particular context. We shall leave these options to your creativity. Just don't get too fancy for the program! And, as a reminder, it is always a useful habit to save your work regularly. If you save frequently, you would lose only a small part of your work in the case of a system problem or power surge.

Group or Recode Variables

Occasionally, when doing data analysis, you may want to collapse one or more variables into a smaller, more manageable number of categories. We call this process grouping or recoding variables. For grouping, you must specify a range for each category in a source variable so that the program can put one code into the new variable for each source variable case within the range.

EQS for Windows provides a simple and logical way to regroup variables, creating up to 15 groups. You can form two, three, or four groups of equal or near-equal size if you click on the appropriate **Grouping Options** as shown in Figure 3.40. Then select the relevant variable and give the new variable a name. To do more complex grouping, use the **Create customized groups** option.

Creating Groups in a Variable

For this example, use **exercise.ess**. It is a six variable dataset including the AGE variable, the age of the subjects. We want to regroup AGE into three categories using cutpoints of 30 and 35.

To start the grouping process, choose **Data** from the main menu bar, and select **Group**. A dialog box similar to Figure 3.40 will appear.

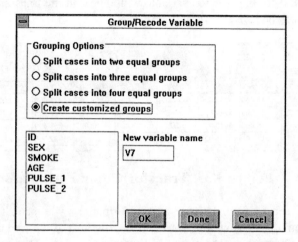

Figure 3.40 Grouping Variable Dialog Box

The **Group/Recode Variable** dialog box includes an edit box labeled **New variable name** with the default **V7**. Change V7 to **AGEGRP** since the new variable will be the age group. Then select the variable **AGE** from the list box, because you are regrouping AGE. Click the **OK** button when you have finished the specifications. The next dialog box, shown in Figure 3.41, shows two edit boxes, **Category Code** and **Code Name**. You can change both the **Category Code** and the **Code Name** for each group for which you define a range.

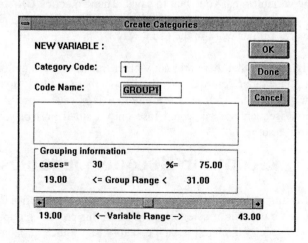

Figure 3.41 Grouping Code Dialog Box

The list box in the middle of the dialog box displays the groups that you create. The list box starts empty and has an inactive scroll bar as long as you can view all contents without scrolling. The bottom line gives the full variable range, which is 19.00 to 43.00. Immediately above the range is a slider for your use in specifying the range of a specific category.

Adding Categories

By default, the first **NEW VARIABLE Category Code** is **1**, and the **Code Name** for the first group is **Group1**. Use your cursor and the mouse button to drag the slider to the approximate boundary between Group1 and Group2. Slide quickly by using the mouse to move the "thumb" of the slider (the square box between the <- and -> marks). Use the left or the right arrow for incremental moves.

When you release the mouse button, the Group Range will appear in the Grouping Information box. At that point, you can evaluate the range. In Figure 3.41, 30 cases fall in the range from 19 to any number less than 31. You may adjust the slider again to include cases with a score of 30, or to any bound you like. Click on **OK** to accept the **Group Range**.

Your new code appears in the list box. The first line of the list box shows category code, its name, the number of cases at that code, the percent, and the range, 19.00 to 30.00, as shown in Figure 3.42.

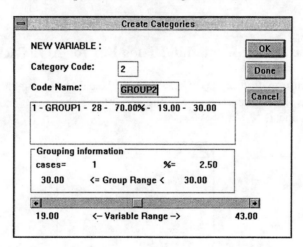

Figure 3.42 Grouping Code Dialog Box

After you click the **OK** button for the first group, the dialog box prepares for the next group. Use the slider to set the next upper bound, 35.00. Click the **OK** button, and the code information for the second group will appear in the list box. For the third group, move the slider thumb to to the right end. When the thumb touches the rightmost boundary, click **OK** to view the third group. Click the **DONE** button.

Removing Categories

If you want to change your selection before clicking **DONE**, you can remove the groups one by one. First double click on the last group, then double click on the next group, etc. After you remove a group from the list box, the slider will go back to its position for the previous group.

When you get to the first group, double clicking will not remove it. Just click on **Cancel** in the **Grouping Code** dialog box to return to the previous dialog box without having created any groups.

Finishing Grouping

After clicking the **DONE** button, you will go back to Figure 3.40. You can select another variable and click **OK**, or you can click **DONE** to go back to the Data Editor. If you go back to the Data Editor, you will see a new variable, AGEGRP, added to the last column of the Data Editor.

You can verify the results using the **Data** menu and **Information**. When you get the Information dialog box for the data file, double click on **AGEGRP** to bring up the information on that new variable. Note that the newly created variable is defined as a categorical variable.

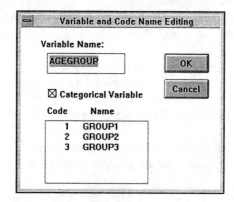

Figure 3.43 Information Dialog Box for AGEGRP Variable

While viewing the information on **AGEGRP**, you may decide to change a group name. You can do that easily by double clicking on the name of the group to be changed. The **Group** dialog box shown in Figure 3.44 will appear.

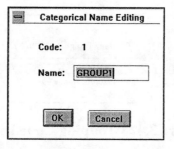

Figure 3.44 Group Dialog Box

The group name will be highlighted. Simply type in the new group name and click **OK**. You will return to the Information dialog box for the variable. There you can follow the above instructions for the other groups, or you can click **OK** to return to the Information dialog box for the data file. Click **OK** to finalize your choices and close the Information dialog box for the data file.

Reverse Group Code

There are times when you might want to reverse the current coding on a certain variable. For example, if the original coding is 1, 2, and 3, representing three different age groups, you might want to recode them to 3, 2, and 1. You might do this, for example, if you were expecting a positive correlation between the target variable and another variable, but you have a negative correlation. In most statistical packages, it is necessary to use variable transformations and lots of IF and ELSE statements. However, EQS for Windows lets you reverse all codes with a single click.

Use the variable **AGEGRP** which you created in the section above. To reverse the variable code, click on the **Data** menu from the main menu bar and select **Reverse** to obtain the dialog box shown in Figure 3.45.

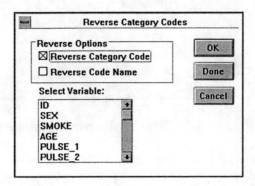

Figure 3.45 Reversing Group Codes Dialog Box

The **Reverse** dialog box provides two options. By default, the program reverses only the numerical code, **Reverse Category Code**. However, you can also reverse the code names by selecting **Reverse Code Name**. Your options are applied when you select a variable and click **OK**. Select the **AGEGRP** variable from the list box and click **OK**.

After you click **OK**, you remain in the box so that you can choose another categorical variable for code reversal. Click **DONE** to reverse the group codes on all chosen variables.

Sort Records

There are times when you want to sort records or cases. For example, before you perform join and merge with keys, you have to sort your key variable in ascending order. If the key is in a random order, the program may not be able to join or merge correctly. Therefore, we provide a simple and logical way to sort.

Use the **exercise.ess** data file. Let's assume that you want to sort the data file by SEX and SMOKE in ascending order. Click on the **Data** menu from the main menu, and select the **Sort** option. Figure 3.46 will appear. Select the **SEX** variable from the first list box and the **SMOKE** variable from the second list box.

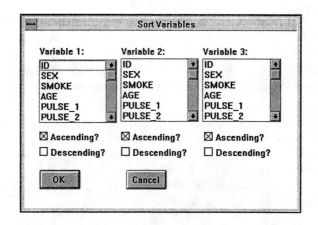

Figure 3.46 Sorting Records Dialog Box

Below each list box, you can click in the checkbox to choose between ascending order or descending order for your sort. In this example, we retain the default, **Ascending**. After you have finished the specifications, press the **OK** button. The rows in the Data Editor will be sorted. Be sure to check the results.

Data Smoother—Moving Average

You may want to smooth a dataset, such as a time series, that fluctuates over time. One of the simplest and most commonly-used data smoothing techniques is the moving average. The moving average method averages data from consecutive cases using a specific time lag. For example, for time lag t, the moving average takes $Y_i=(X_i + X_{i+1}+...X_{i+t-1})/t$, where X is the data, i is the sequence of the data, and Y_i is the resulting data.

The data file is **furnace.ess**. More description on this dataset can be found in the Line Plot section of Chapter 5. To start the moving average, click on **Data** in the main menu and select **Moving Average**. A dialog box like Figure 3.47 will appear.

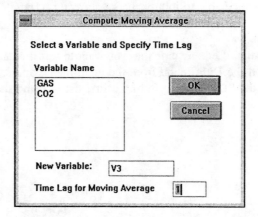

Figure 3.47 Moving Average Dialog Box

The two variables in the data file are listed in the list box. Click on the **CO2** variable to select it.

The **New Variable** edit box has a default variable, **V3**. Change that variable name to **MoveCO2**.

Note: When doing moving average, the program always creates a new variable for you so that you can compare the two variables side by side.

Since the data are monthly and fluctuate annually, we use a time lag of 12. After entering **12**, click the **OK** button.

The program will compute the moving average and send the data back to the Data Editor case by case, starting from case one. Note that, for *n* cases and a *t* lag moving average, you will get *n-t* cases. For the cases between case *n-t+1* and case *n*, EQS for Windows will enter missing values.

When you are ready to display the plot of the CO2 variable and the MoveCO2 variable, remember that you have missing data. First, choose the **Data** menu and select **Use Data** and **choose Select Complete Cases Only** for plotting.

To create the plot, click on the Line Plot icon.

Hold the <Shift> key while clicking on the **CO2** and **MoveCO2** variables. Then clock on **PLOT** to create a line plot similar to that shown in Figure 3.48. The original variable CO2 is shown in one color, and the new variable MoveCO2 is shown in another color.

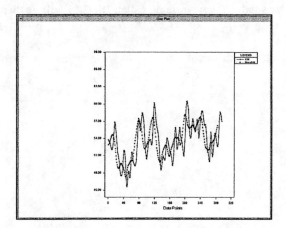

Figure 3.48 Line Plot for CO2 and MoveCO2

Difference Your Data—To Remove Autocorrelation

There are many types of data distributions. In some situations, observations are totally independent, while in other situations, data are dependent on each other. When you have dependent data, there are autocorrelations within the data. When you do a regression analysis on dependent data, there may be intercorrelated residuals. This violates the assumption of regression analysis that the residuals are uncorrelated.

To remove the autocorrelations, you might want to try differencing your data. In differencing, we subtract a later case from an earlier case to create a new variable. For example you can take

$$Y_t = X_t - X_{t-1},$$

where X is the variable and *t* is the lag for differences. This operation is especially useful when your cases represent time-ordered observations. Please consult a good time series book for details on the theory and use of the method of differences.

This example uses **furnace.ess**. Click on the **Data** menu from the main menu, and select **Differences** to get the dialog box as shown in Figure 3.49.

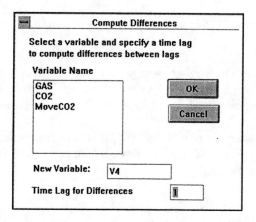

Figure 3.49 Computing Differences Dialog Box

Choose the **GAS** variable for differencing from the list box. Then enter **DIFGAS** in the **New Variable** edit box, and accept the default of 1 in the **Time Lag for Differences** box. Click the **OK** button when you have finished. A new variable called DIFGAS will be displayed at the last column of the Data Editor.

In practice, you may need to try different time lags to see whether you have appropriately removed the dependencies.

4. DATA IMPORT AND EXPORT

Often, a dataset already exists, and you do not need or want to reenter the data into EQS. You simply want to import the existing data file into EQS for further analysis. You can always do this with raw data files. Such files can be produced by virtually all types of computer programs, including editors, word processors, and statistical applications programs.

However, many programs create their files in a default proprietary format, and EQS for Windows does not read those formats. You must use your application to create an ASCII file for EQS. Almost all programs will write out a file in a simple ASCII or text format for use by other programs, including EQS for Windows.

File Types

There are dozens of different data formats in daily use, but EQS for Windows will read only a few of the more common types, as well as some universal types. In the previous sections of this chapter, we have already encountered Raw Data Files and EQS System Files. Let's review the options that are available when you use EQS for Windows to import a file.

The Importance of File Extensions

When using EQS for Windows to analyze your data, whether you are running a structural equation program, exploring your data using data plots, or performing general statistics, you will be dealing with a number of files of different types. You will want to distinguish among the different types of files, some of which may display the same icon. You can do that by using file extensions. If you use file extensions, you will find it easy to distinguish files today and at any time in the future when you return to the analysis.

File extensions are necessary for exact file identification in the EQS for Windows Open file dialog box. You can choose your own file extensions or use the following recommended extensions:

File Type	Extension	Description of File Type
EQS System Data	*.ess	Binary files created by EQS for Windows
EQS Diagram Files	*.eds	Binary files created by EQS for Windows
EQS Model Files	*.eqs	Text files created by EQS for Windows
Raw Data Files	*.dat	Plain ASCII files containing numbers arranged in a data matrix
Output Files	*.out	Text files created by EQS for Windows
Covariance Matrix	*.cov	Full symmetric or lower triangular covariance matrix in free format ASCII
BMDP Files	*.sav	Binary files created by BMDP/PC, PC-90, and 386 Dynamic
Lotus Files	*.wk*	Binary files created by Lotus 1-2-3 version 2.2 or earlier
dBase Files	*.dbf	Binary files created by dBase III Plus and earlier versions

Table 4.1 File Extensions

A file name will consist of several characters, indicated by the * above, followed by a period and then a specific extension consisting of three characters. Although you can save a file with almost any combination of characters, saving it with a specific extension classifies the file as belonging to a particular file type that is frequently used.

EQS for Windows uses the five file types shown above for grouping files. The first three types of files have been discussed previously, and some additional thoughts are presented below for the sake of completeness.

You can view and edit text and ASCII files with ordinary editors and word processors. Binary files, such as the *.ess files, are program-specific files that are stored in a compressed form in machine language format. They typically contain special codings for file attributes to permit rapid re-creation of complicated formats. The proprietary program can read in and write out such files quickly. However, you cannot readily view or edit them without special decoding (as is done in EQS for Windows for its own type).

EQS for Windows recognizes five types of binary files: the *.ess system files, the *.eds diagram files, the *.sav BMDP files, the *.wk* Lotus files, and the *.dbf dBase files. You will see those files listed in the **Open** dialog box, along with the text and ASCII files.

. Files

There may be times when you want to import a file but do not remember much about the file. You may not even remember the file name or type. If that situation arises, you can choose All Files (*.* in the List Files of Type list box. If you prefer, you can type *.* in the **File Name** field in the upper left of the Figure 4.1 **Open** dialog box. When you click **OK**, your *.* overrides the **List Files of Type** designation, and you will get a listing of all files in your current directory. This wildcard search feature can help you to locate a particular file. Once you have located the file, if the file is stored as a particular file type, you should set the **List Files of Type** field to the correct file type.

You should remember that files may reside in various directories and drives, and you may find it necessary to search several directories to locate a particular file. You can obtain choices by using the vertical scroll bars in the Drives field, shown in the lower right of Figure 4.1. For hints on organizing the storage of files, so that you can easily find them again, see any good Windows or DOS book.

Standard EQS File Types

EQS System Data

When you start the EQS for Windows program, you are asked to open a data file. In order to make this process as easy and painless as possible, EQS for Windows has developed the EQS System File format. We use the *.ess designation to identify those files.

EQS System Files are assumed to have been created by EQS for Windows and are stored in a special binary format that permits bringing onto the screen the data and associated attributes, such as the number of variables and cases, labels for the variables, grouping codes, and other previously-established information about the data. This standard format makes it possible for you to start work with a minimum of fuss.

Note: This special file format is used for raw data as well as for covariance or correlation matrices stored in the ***.ess** format.

Select **File** from the main menu, and then **Open**. You will see an **Open** dialog box similar to Figure 4.1. As you see, this box lists all files in the chosen directory (here, EQS is on the C: drive).

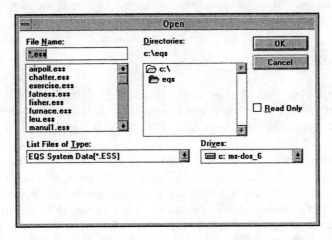

Figure 4.1 Open Dialog Box

You can choose to work with any existing file by clicking on your particular choice. If the list of files is longer than can be shown at once, you will scroll through the list box to find the file of interest to you. You can also type the first letter of a file name to bring it up into the viewable part of the list. When you open an EQS System File, all of the associated file information will be in place.

To make this file format work effectively for you, you should save data files with the ***.ess** file extension name. You can use a different extension, but this is not advisable. As discussed above, it is possible for you to save EQS System Data with other file extensions, such as ***.esd**, but you must keep track of your choices. If you do not maintain a key listing for your file extensions, you might have trouble locating a file that you had worked on previously.

For ease of locating the proper file, you should try to develop a naming convention that would permit you to distinguish between those ***.ess** files that represent raw data and those that represent covariance matrices. For example, you could use names of the form ***C.ess** for covariance matrices.

When actually viewing an **.ess** data file, you can easily differentiate between raw data and a covariance matrix. If the **.ess** file contains raw data, the case label will be a sequence number such as 1, 2, 3, etc. If the file contains a covariance matrix, the case label will be the variable name you entered.

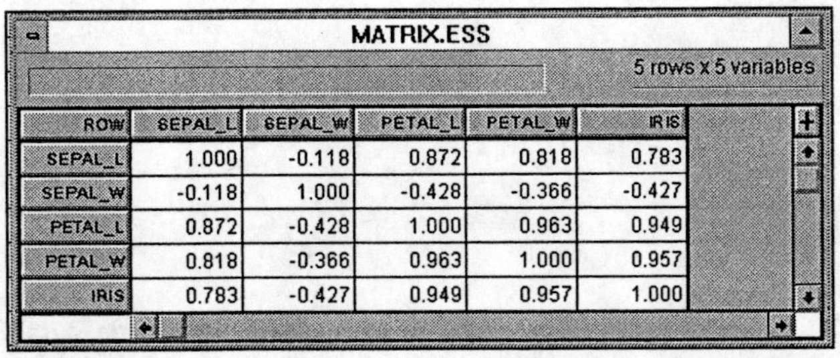

ROW	SEPAL_L	SEPAL_W	PETAL_L	PETAL_W	IRIS
SEPAL_L	1.000	-0.118	0.872	0.818	0.783
SEPAL_W	-0.118	1.000	-0.428	-0.366	-0.427
PETAL_L	0.872	-0.428	1.000	0.963	0.949
PETAL_W	0.818	-0.366	0.963	1.000	0.957
IRIS	0.783	-0.427	0.949	0.957	1.000

MATRIX.ESS — 5 rows x 5 variables

Figure 4.2 Matrix.ess, a Covariance Matrix File

Figure 4.2 gives an example of a covariance matrix file in ***.ess** format. This covariance matrix was created by the covariance computation in EQS for Windows, saved to the Data Editor, and then saved as a file. When you open the file, the variable labels come up along with the data.

Other programs will not be able to read ***.ess** files. If you are planning to export a file to another program, you should use one of the exporting procedures discussed later in this chapter in the section called **Saving and Exporting Data and Other Files**.

EQS Model Files

EQS Model Files are plain text files that could, in principle, be stored with any other file extension, but we suggest that you use the unique ***.eqs** extension. This is a convenient way of locating all EQS model files from the potentially very large list of files that you might have in a directory.

If you work entirely within the Windows environment, you will probably create your ***.eqs** files with the **Build_EQS** procedure available in the main menu. However, you can also create such files in other ways. You can create a ***.eqs** file with any word processor or editor, provided that you store the file as a plain ASCII file with no special characters or file format information. To be useful, such a file should contain the paragraphs and sentences needed to run an EQS job, as described in the *EQS Structural Equations Program Manual*. The model file should be able to run the EQS modeling program from the Windows environment.

Output Files

When the EQS modeling program runs, its output as described in the *EQS Structural Equations Program Manual* is placed into a plain text file. The default file name given to these output files is ***.out**, where * is the designation taken from the corresponding ***.eqs** input file name. These files are editable within EQS for Windows. Once saved, they are also editable by any other program that can read and work with plain text files.

When EQS for Windows has finished running, the EQS analysis is complete. The **Open an EQS Output File** dialog box will appear with ***.out** in the **File Name** edit box and the **File Type** set.

You will want to bring the output file back to your screen so that you can examine it conveniently. In the **Open an EQS Output File** dialog box, you must go through two steps:
1.   click on the **OK** button to bring the file name into the list
2.   double click on the file name in the list to open the output file.

Note: You <u>must</u> click on **OK** in this dialog box to refresh the screen and bring your new output file to the list of files. Then you can double click on the file name to bring it up in the usual way. See chapter 2 for more information on viewing your output files.

Data Import File Types

Raw Data Files

A so-called "raw" data file is the most common way of organizing one's data. Numerical scores that subjects obtain on variables are arranged in a data matrix containing as many rows as subjects and columns as variables. (In unusual situations, row and column designations are reversed.) The entries of such a data matrix will generally contain numerical values. Missing data codes may be permitted if these codes are standard ASCII characters available in Windows. In EQS for Windows, such files are called ***.dat** files. Although this extension designation is not mandatory, we suggest that you follow it to minimize confusion and allow a simple search for all raw data files that you may have.

In practice, when you import a ***.dat** file into EQS for Windows, the file is immediately duplicated as an ***.ess** file for further possible modification or action. The ***.ess** file will be displayed in the spreadsheet-type Data Editor. Notice that the original multi-character file name is maintained, but the extension **dat** is changed to **ess** in the Data Editor. The original ***.dat** file is left intact, just in case you make mistakes when working with the ***.ess** file.

BMDP *.sav Files

EQS for Windows can import data files created by BMDP's PC-90 and BMDP/386 Dynamic programs, and their subsequent versions. One advantage of this capability is that you can move data back and forth between BMDP's statistical package and EQS for Windows. The BMDP programs contain a variety of statistical analysis options that are not available within EQS.

You can import only BMDP data files involving simple data matrices, designated as ***.sav** files. You import such files by selecting the **BMDP Files** option in the **List Files of Type** section of the **Open** dialog box. Figure 4.3 provides an example of such a dialog box. As usual, you open the file by clicking on the particular file name and clicking **OK**.

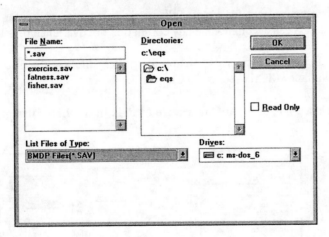

Figure 4.3 Open Dialog Box for BMDP Files

After you have brought the file to the screen in EQS for Windows, the program will change the file name into the relevant ***.ess** file format. The original BMDP file remains intact. You should save the new ***.ess** file immediately.

Lotus 1-2-3 *.wk* Files

EQS for Windows will import data files created with the Lotus 1-2-3 program. The procedure for importing such files is the same as that described under the section on importing BMDP files. That is, you start at the **Open** file dialog box. Select the appropriate file type from **List Files of Type**, then select the particular file of interest, and confirm the selection. The result will be brought to the screen as an ***.ess** EQS System File, which you should save for safety's sake.

Note: When reading Lotus 1-2-3 files, EQS:
   1. takes up to eight characters for a character variable
   2. converts blank cells as missing cells
   3. converts variable labels (names) to labels for an ESS file variable if you confirm that the first case contains labels
   4. takes up to 8,000 cases.

dBase III *.dbf Files

You can import data files created with the dBase III program into EQS for Windows. In the Open file dialog box, select the appropriate file type from the **List Files of Type** option box. Then click on the appropriate file, and click on **OK**. The original dBase file will remain intact, and you will have a system file with the ***.ess** designation on the screen for work and saving.

Note: When reading dBase III files, EQS:
   1. converts character data, numeric data, and logical variable types
   2. converts variable labels to ESS variable names automatically
   3. takes up to 8,000 cases.

Covariance Matrix Text Files

EQS can import two matrix text file types: full matrix and lower triangular matrix. This flexibility makes it likely that EQS can accommodate any correlation or covariance files that you want to read.

If you want to create a covariance or correlation matrix text file, see the discussion in the Creating a Correlation or Covariance Matrix section in Chapter 3.

To import a covariance file, click on **Covariance Matrix** in the **List Files of Type** list in the **Open** dialog box.

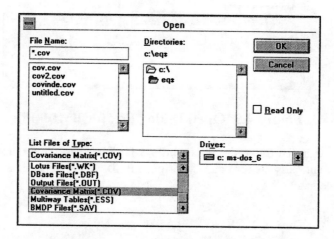

Figure 4.4 File Type Dialog Box

Choose **Covariance Matrix** (***.cov**) file in the **List Files of Type** list. When you click on your preferred matrix file and click on **OK**, the **Covariance Matrix Input Information** dialog box appears.

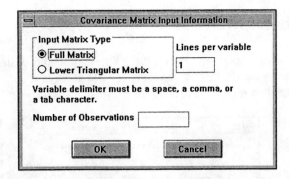

Figure 4.5 Covariance Matrix Input Information Dialog Box

This dialog box prompts you to provide information on the type of matrix. Click on the radio button for either **Full Matrix** or **Lower Triangular Matrix**. The default number of **Lines per variable** is 1. You can change that number, as necessary, to describe your data file. Enter the **Number of Observations** and click on **OK**. The matrix will appear in the **Data Editor**. After EQS reads in the file, the file in memory is identified as an ***.ess** file. When you later save the file, the variable and case information will be stored along with the file.

It is helpful to work with covariance matrices when data are normally distributed and there are many variables and/or subjects. In such a situation, it is a waste of time to recompute the covariance matrix for each modeling run. It is better to compute it once, save it, and use it repeatedly.

Importing Raw Data Files

Use the **File** option in the main menu, and then select the **Open** file dialog box. When you click on the **List Files of Type** down arrow, you will see a listing of all file types. The default selection is EQS System Data. In the **List Files of Type** list, you can choose ***.DAT** or ***.TXT** to choose a raw data file. For this example, choose ***.DAT**.

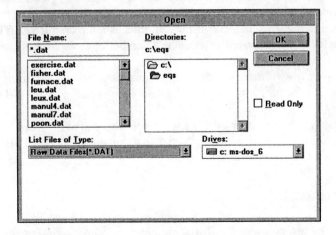

Figure 4.6 Open Dialog Box for Raw Data

Specify the File Name

The Open dialog box will display all **.DAT** files. You choose the desired raw data file by double clicking the **File Name** in the list box, or selecting the file name and clicking on **OK.** The **Raw Data File Information** dialog box appears, as shown in Figure 4.7.

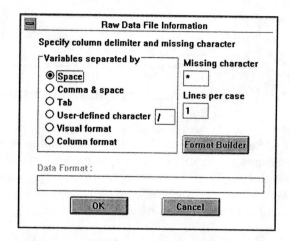

Figure 4.7 Raw Data File Information

Variable Separation

You can specify the delimiter that separates different variables in your raw data file. There are four **free format** delimiters: Space, Comma & space, Tab, and User-defined character. There are also some **fixed format** options.

Free format means that, for each case, there is at least one blank space or a designated delimiter between the numerical values for any adjacent variables. As noted above, in free format you cannot use the delimiter character to designate missing data. For example, you cannot use a space character as the missing character if the delimiter you designate is a space character. However, you can use the space character as the missing character if the delimiter is a tab character. You must have precisely as many entries in the data matrix as the product of number of cases times the number of variables.

If your data file is in free format, you don't have to choose Visual or Column format, because the program default is free format. Free format is certainly the easiest way to deal with data.

The alternative to free format is fixed format. If you chose fixed **Visual** or **Column format**, the **Format Builder** button will be enabled. You can then click on the **Format Builder** button to painlessly specify a format as described below.

Missing Character

Often enough, scores are not available for some cases on some variables. Thus, you must use the **Missing character** field to designate a single character to represent a missing cell in your data matrix. EQS for Windows uses * as the default character. That is, the * has been used in place of a score when a case does not have a score on a particular variable. If your data are coded differently, you can change the default * to any single character that represents your missing data.

Note: You can use a blank character as the missing character, ***both with free format and fixed format to read data***. If you use free format with a blank character as the missing character, you must have a different character as your delimiter.

Internally, EQS for Windows will translate any missing value into a system missing value to be used in the corresponding ***.ess*** file. This system value is internal to EQS. Thus, you see only a blank on your Data Editor where there is a missing cell.

Lines per Case

The number of lines of data for each subject or case is vital to EQS in importing ASCII data. Scores for the first subject or case may be arranged in any way on one or more lines. The scores for the next case must follow in subsequent lines using the identical format.

File Format for Raw Data Files

It is assumed that the data are organized in such a way that one or more rows or records of the file first describe case number 1, across all variables; that the second case's scores on the variables are next; and so on. You can also specify a format to read the data in the file. To repeat, there are two possible types of format, free and fixed.

Free Format

When your dataset is in free format, there is at least one delimiter between the numerical values for any adjacent variables. Also, you plan to read in every score for every case or subject. The delimiter can be a space, a tab, a comma and a space, or any character that you specify. If your data file is in free format, chose **Variables separated by Space**, **Comma & space**, **Tab**, or **User-defined character**. You have no need for **Format Builder**.

Space, Commas and Space, Tab, User-defined Character

If your data file contains only variable data separated by a space, you can simply accept the default **Space**. If the data are separated by commas and space, tab, or user-defined character, click on the radio button beside the appropriate delimiter. Click **OK**.

Free Format Example

Use **chatter.dat** for this example. Click on the **File** menu **Open** option and choose **chatter.dat**. In the **Raw Data File Information** dialog box shown in Figure 4.7, click on the radio button for **Space**. Click **OK** and the **String** prompt box appears.

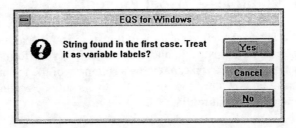

Figure 4.8 String Prompt Box

The **String Prompt** box signals that EQS for Windows found a string in the first case of the **chatter.dat** data file. You get this box because EQS can read complex ASCII files in which the first case actually contains the variable names.

If you did not want EQS to treat the string as variable labels, you would click **NO**. However, since the first case contains the names of the variables in **chatter.dat**, click **YES**. The data file appears.

Note: If variable names lie in the first line(s) of your ASCII file, there are three requirements for the file:
1. The data in such an ASCII file must be in free format.
2. The data file must have the variable names lying in a one-to-one correspondence with the data. This means:
   a. The names must be in the same order as the data.
   b. The names must span the same number of lines as one case of the data.
   c. The first line of names must correspond to the first line of the data, the second line of names with the second line of data, etc.
3. A variable name can contain a space if the variable delimiter is not a space character.

Fixed Format

If you have a **Fixed format** file, your file need not meet the requirements of free format. In a fixed format file, the numbers for each case can be anywhere in your file, separated by a delimiter or not. You must, however, be able to specify the exact locations for variables to be read and variables to be left unread. See the **Data Format Details** section later in this chapter for a discussion of fixed format coding.

Format Builder

Most programs require the user to provide a complete FORTRAN statement. EQS for Windows makes the process much easier for you. EQS for Windows provides three ways to deal with a fixed format:
- **Visual format Format Builder**, in which you define your file graphically
- **Column format Format Builder**, in which you define your file by typing specifications
- **Visual Format** or **Column Format** using **Data Format**, in which you define your file by typing the actual FORTRAN format

Thus, you can use Visual format or Column format to force EQS to write the format statement for you. Alternatively, you can enter your FORTRAN format in the **Data Format** field, if you prefer. However, you can easily enter your format by manipulating a graphical screen in Visual format or by filling in the fields of the Column format dialog box.

Fixed Format Example —Visual Format

The EQS **Visual format** is an innovative solution to the specifics of fixed format. This new method displays a complete case from the data file and lets you define your format graphically. After you have defined the format on one case, you can review a summary of the format that you have specified. In addition, you can bring up any other case in the file to visually determine whether your definition is correct for that case and for the entire file.

Let's use the **test.dat** file for this fixed format example. **Test.dat** is the test data file in Figure 4.9. It contains four variables and five cases. If you did not have this file, you could use **File**, **New**, and **Create an ASCII file** to type and save it yourself.

The number of variables read from the file depends our specification. For example, there are letters in the data, and we will want to ignore them. In the following example, we shall read **test.dat** so as to yield Figure 4.18, containing three variables with certain specified decimal places.

```
135AA123 10
341AA236 30
218AA335 40
140AA432 30
112AA517 10
```

Figure 4.9 Test.dat

Of course, the number of variables that we see when we open the file depends on our specification. For example, there are letters in the data, and we will want to ignore the variable containing the letters. In the following example, we shall read **test.dat** to yield Figure 4.18, a file with three variables displaying certain decimal places.

Select the **File** menu **Open** option and choose **test.dat**. When you see the **Raw Data File Information** dialog box, click on the radio button for **Visual format**. The **Format Builder** button becomes active. The **Raw Data File Information** dialog box will look like Figure 4.10.

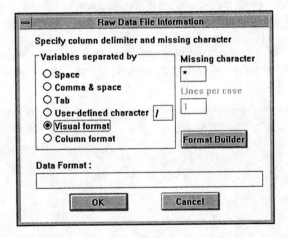

Figure 4.10 Raw Data File Information Dialog Box

Now that you have chosen **Visual format**, you have a choice of two methods to use in defining the format of the data file:

1. **Data Format**. You can click in the **Data Format** field and enter the FORTRAN fixed format for your data, as shown below. Although this method requires some knowledge of the rules of fixed format, it may be faster when you have a simple format for several variables. After you enter the format in the **Data Format** field, you can click **OK** to bring up the file.

2. **Format Builder**. You can click on the **Format Builder** button. You will see the **Case Number** dialog box in Figure 4.11, then the visual **Format Specifications** dialog box as shown in Figure 4.12. This method requires no knowledge of the rules of fixed format,

because you are entering information in a graphical way. After you enter the format in the **Format Specifications** dialog box, you can click **OK** to bring up the file. See the instructions below for details.

Format Specifications

Click on **Visual format** and **Format Builder** in the **Raw Data File Information** dialog box. You will see the **Case Number** dialog box as shown in Figure 4.11.

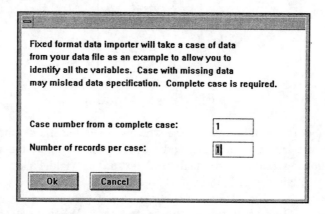

Figure 4.11 Case Number Dialog Box

Since EQS will read your designated case, enter the case number for a complete case in the data file. For this example, keep the default of **1**.

So that EQS can read the entire case, the program must know the number of records or lines per case. Keep the default **1** for this example and click on **OK** to bring up the **Format Specifications** dialog box shown in Figure 4.12.

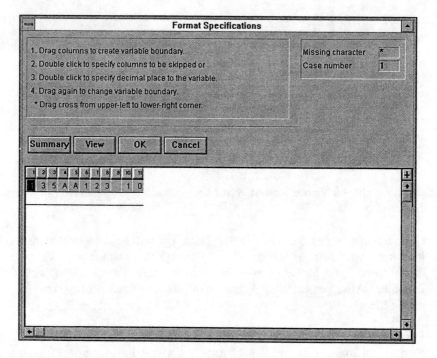

Figure 4.12 Format Specifications Dialog Box for Visual Format

The **Format Specifications** dialog box displays instructions in the top third of the box, along with the chosen missing character and the number of the displayed case. Below the instructions are four buttons: Summary, View, OK, and Cancel.

The lower part of this dialog box displays a row of squares, numbered from 1 to 11. Those squares represent the columns of data in your chosen case. Under each square, you can see the actual character or space which lies in that data column for this case. This arrangement makes it easy to identify each column and its contents. For example, in Figure 4.12, column 2 contains **3**, and column 11 contains **0**.

Figure 4.12 shows that the **test.dat** data file uses 11 columns of data. Now you can use this dialog box to define the data file format exactly.

Defining Variables

The first variable lies in the first three columns of the data file. To define the first variable, move your cursor to the upper left corner of the square containing the data in the 1 column. The cursor will change to a crosshair. Drag to the lower right corner of the square under the 3 column. The three squares that you have defined will turn gray, then some dark color when you release the mouse button. (The colors may differ with various Windows color schemes.)

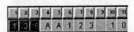

Figure 4.13 Variable 1 Area Defined in Format Specifications Dialog Box

You have specified that the first variable lies in the first three spaces of the data file. Now let's define a format for three other variables. Always dragging from the upper left corner to the lower right corner, drag from **4** to **6** and release. Drag from **7** to **9**, and then from **10** to **11**. The variable area of the **Format Specifications** dialog box will look like Figure 4.14.

Figure 4.14 Variable Areas Defined in Format Specifications Dialog Box

Now you can specify decimal places if you want. Double click on any one of the darkened squares representing variable 1. That action brings up the **Variable Skip and Decimal Specifications** dialog box in Figure 4.15.

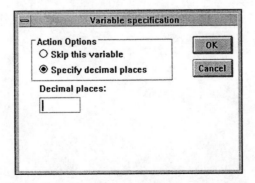

Figure 4.15 Variable Skip and Decimal Specifications Dialog Box

Specifying Decimal Places

The **Specify Decimal Places** radio button is chosen by default. Accept that default and enter **2** in the **Decimal Places** field. Click on **OK** to get back to the **Format Specifications** box which shows a decimal point in the square for the 2 column.

Note: When you specify the number of decimal places in your variable, you must start your count at the right of your defined variable area. If you specify one decimal place, only the rightmost column of your variable area will be a decimal place. If you specify two decimal places, only the two rightmost columns of your variable area will be decimal places.

Double click on one of the dark squares representing variable 3, and enter **1** in the **Decimal places** field. Double click on one of the dark squares representing variable 4, and enter **1** in the **Decimal places** field.

Note: If your data file variable contains an explicit decimal point, you will get an error message if you try to add a decimal point. There is no need to specify it here.

Omitting a Variable

The second variable is a string variable. To omit the second variable, double click on one of the dark squares under 4, 5, or 6. In the **Variable Specification** dialog box shown in Figure 4.15, click on **Skip this variable** and click **OK**. The variable-defining area will appear as shown in Figure 4.16. Note that the squares representing the second variable are lighter, showing that you are omitting that variable.

Figure 4.16 Variable Areas in Format Specifications Dialog Box

Reviewing the Summary

You can review a summary of your choices for this data file. Click on the **Summary** button in the **Format Specifications** dialog box. The **Fixed Format Summary** table in Figure 4.17 will appear.

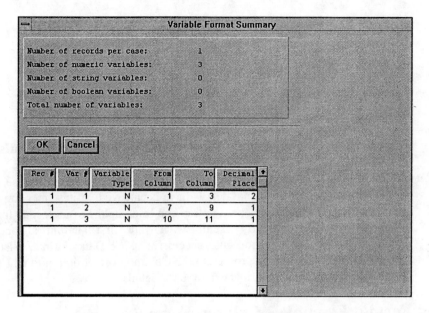

Figure 4.17 Fixed Format Summary Table

Note that the table states that you have three numeric variables. The table specifies the starting and ending column for each variable, as well as the number of decimal places. Click **OK** to go back to the **Format Specifications** dialog box.

Viewing Another Case

Now that you have finished specifying the **test.dat** data file, you can bring up another case from the file to confirm that your settings are correct. Just enter the number of the desired case in the **Case Number** field. For this example, enter **3** and click on the **View** button to bring up the **Format Specifications** dialog box displaying the case number 3. You can confirm that your settings are correct.

When you have fully specified the file format, click on **OK** to bring up the data file as an EQS System File. Figure 4.18 shows **test.ess** as a system file.

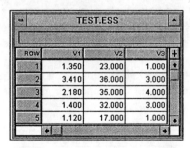

Figure 4.18 Test.ess

After you have brought up **test.ess**, you can still view the exact format of this file. The **output.log** window contains a description of the file format. To get to the **output.log** window, click on the **Windows** menu, then choose **output.log**. The window will resemble Figure 4.19.

```
Input raw data file name : C:\EQS\TEST.DAT

    Rec #  Var seq.      From col.       To col.      Format

        1      1            1               3         F3.2
        1      3            7               9         F3.1
        1      4           10              11         F2.1
```

Figure 4.19 Output.log Window with File Format Details

Note: EQS for Windows saves these file format details for possible later use in the Column
Format. Since the file format details have been saved, at any later time you can open
test.dat with the Column Format option and bring up the exact format for editing. This
feature will be particularly useful when your first attempt at opening a large,
complicated data file is not fully successful using Data Format, Visual Format, or
Column Format. You can proceed to the Column Format option to edit the file format.
See the second Column Format example for details.

Fixed Format Example—Column Format

This example of fixed format using the **Column format** method uses the **test.dat** file in Figure 4.9.
Select the **File** menu **Open** option and choose **test.dat**. When you see the **Raw Data File
Information** dialog box, click on the radio button for **Column format**.

Now that you have chosen **Column format**, you have a choice of two methods to use in defining the
format of the data file:

1. **Data Format**. You can click in the **Data Format** field and enter the FORTRAN fixed
   format for your data as shown below. Although this method requires some knowledge of
   the rules of fixed format, it may be faster when you have a simple format for several
   variables. After you enter the format in the **Data Format** field, you click **OK** to bring up
   the file.

2. **Format Builder**. You can click on the **Format Builder** button to bring up the column
   Format Generator dialog box as shown in Figure 4.21. This method requires little
   knowledge of the rules of fixed format, because you are entering information in descriptive
   fields. After you enter the format in the **Format Specifications** dialog box, you can click
   OK to bring up the file. See the instructions below for details.

Click on the **Format Builder** button to start generating the format for this file. Since you ran the
Visual Format example, you see a dialog box concerning the file format specified for this file in the
Visual Format example.

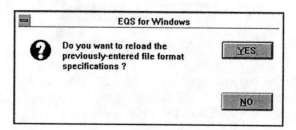

Figure 4.20 File Format Reload Dialog Box

Press **NO**, and the **Format Generator** dialog box will look like Figure 4.21.

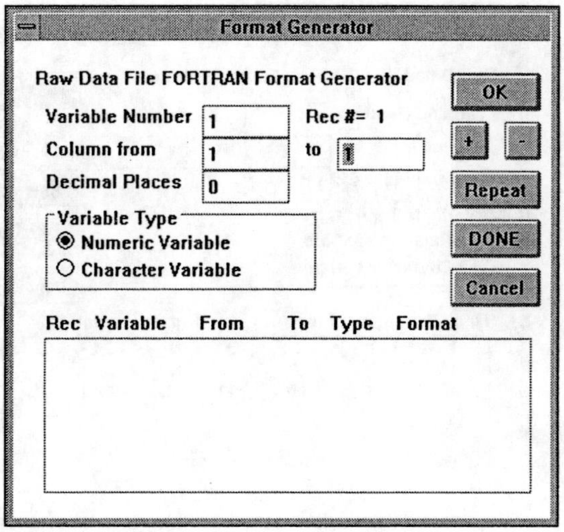

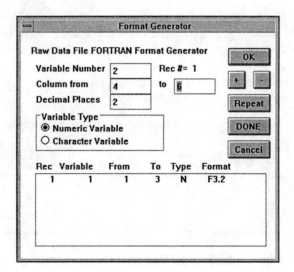

Figure 4.21 FORTRAN Format Generator Dialog Box

This dialog box comes up with **Variable Number 1**, starting at **Column from 1**. We must tell the **Format Generator** exactly how the data are situated.

Enter **3** in the **to** field to specify that variable 1 lies in columns 1 through 3. Then enter **2** in the **Decimal Places** field. Click on **OK**.

Figure 4.22 FORTRAN Format Generator Dialog Box

The dialog box will list the characteristics of variable 1 in the list box in the lower part of the screen. Then the dialog box will show **Variable Number 2** in **Column from 4 to 6** and **Decimal Places 2** automatically. This is because EQS assumes that succeeding variables are similar to the preceding variables.

We want to skip the actual second variable in **test.dat**. Thus, for variable 2 in the new file, change **Decimal Places** to **1** and **Column from 7 to 9**. Click on **OK**.

For variable 3, change **Column from 10 to 11**. Click on **OK**.

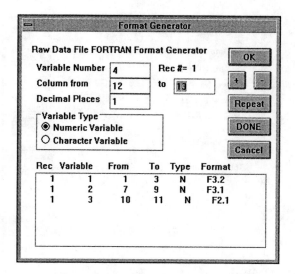

Figure 4.23 Format Generator Dialog Box

You have finished defining the format for the **test.dat** dataset. Click on **DONE**, and the test data file will be displayed as **test.ess** in the spreadsheet-like Data Editor.

Fixed Format Example—Column Format—Editing & Repeating

This example of fixed format using the **Column format** method uses the **test.dat** file from Figure 4.9 again.   Select the **File** menu **Open** option and choose **test.dat**. When you see the **Raw Data File Information** dialog box, click on the radio button for **Column format**.

Click on the **Format Builder** button to start generating the format for this file. You see a dialog box concerning the file format specified for this file in the earlier example.

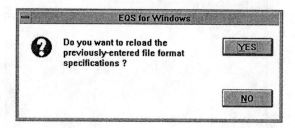

Figure 4.24 File Format Reload Dialog Box

Press **YES**, and the **Format Generator** dialog box will look like Figure 4.25.

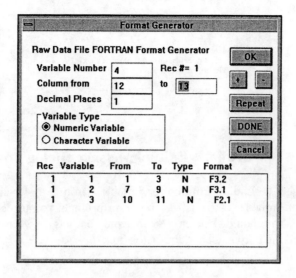

Figure 4.25 Format Generator Dialog Box

This dialog box includes the format which you specified when you opened **test.ess** using the Visual Format. Now that you have three variables formatted in this dialog box, you can edit the formatting.

Editing in the Format Generator Dialog Box

You know that you can delete the last format line in the Format Generator dialog box list box by double clicking on it. In contrast, double clicking on any other line in the list box has a different effect. You can double click on any line other than the bottom line to bring up an editing dialog box for that line.

To edit variable 1 in record 1, double click on the variable 1 format line in the list box. The Format Editor dialog box will appear.

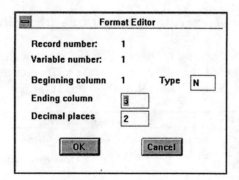

Figure 4.26 Format Editor Dialog Box

Change the **Ending Column** to **4** and the **Decimal Places** to **1**. Click on **OK**, and you will see a new message.

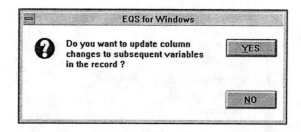

Figure 4.27 Editing Message Dialog Box

Since you have changed the Ending Column for variable 1 from 3 to **4**, variable 1 would extend into the space reserved for variable 2. Thus, the program prompts you to decide whether to move all succeeding variables. You should click on **YES** to avoid conflicts between variables. After you click **YES**, you will return to the Format Generator dialog box.

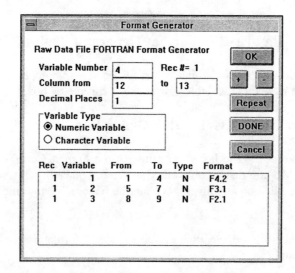

Figure 4.28 Format Generator Dialog Box with Edited Variable Columns

This dialog box displays your editing changes. You can see how the expansion of variable 1 from column 3 to column 4 affected the other two variables. To prepare for the next section of this example, click on **Cancel** to get back to the **Raw Data File Information Dialog Box**.

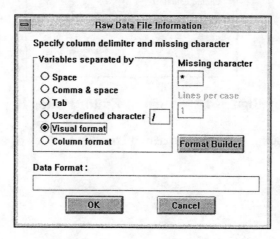

Figure 4.29 Raw Data File Information Dialog Box

110

In the **Raw Data File Information Dialog Box**, click on the **Format Builder** button, and click on **YES** in the **File Format Reload** dialog box. This action will bring up the Format Generator dialog box with the format set for the **test.dat** data file. You will use these settings to learn about the Repeat option.

Repeat Option

The Repeat option allows you to repeat the format for the last specified variable one or more times. This option is valuable when you have several variables with the same format. In the Format Generator, click on the **Repeat** button to bring up the **Format Repeater** dialog box.

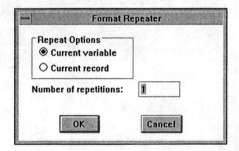

Figure 4.30 Format Repeater Dialog Box

Repeat Current Variable

Note that you can choose the Current variable or the Current record. Let's keep the **Current variable** choice. In the **Number of repetitions** field, enter **4**. Click **OK**, and the Format Generator dialog box will display four more defined variables.

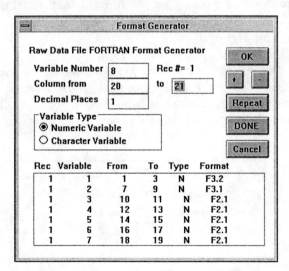

Figure 4.31 Format Generator Dialog Box with Variable Repetitions

Let's remove the last four variable specifications so that we can review the Repeat option for records. To remove the specifications for the last variable, double click on the bottom line in the list box. The bottom line will disappear. Perform that operation three more times. When you have finished, you should have only three lines in your list box.

Repeat Current Record

To review the Repeat option as it applies to a record, click on the **Repeat** option in the Format Generator dialog box. When you see the Repeat option dialog box, click to choose **Current record**. Enter **2** in the **Number of repetitions** field. Click **OK** to finish and get back to the Format Generator dialog box.

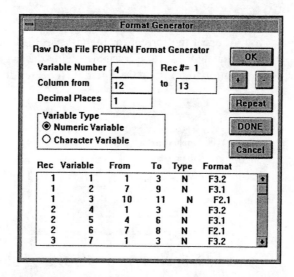

Figure 4.32 Format Generator Dialog Box with Record Repetitions

You can see that you have specified three identical records for a single case. This Repeat option makes it easy for you to specify the format for many variables or several records making up a single case. Starting at the bottom line, double click on each of the bottom four lines in the list box to delete those lines. Your Format Generator dialog box will be ready for the next part of this example.

Specifying A New Record

If your file had more than one record per case, you could use the Format Generator dialog box to define the format for those additional records. Just click on the + button to toggle up through other possible record numbers. Click three times on the + button, and you will see the **Record# =** field change from **1** to **4** in the Format Generator dialog box. Click twice on the **-** button to move back down to **Record# = 2**.

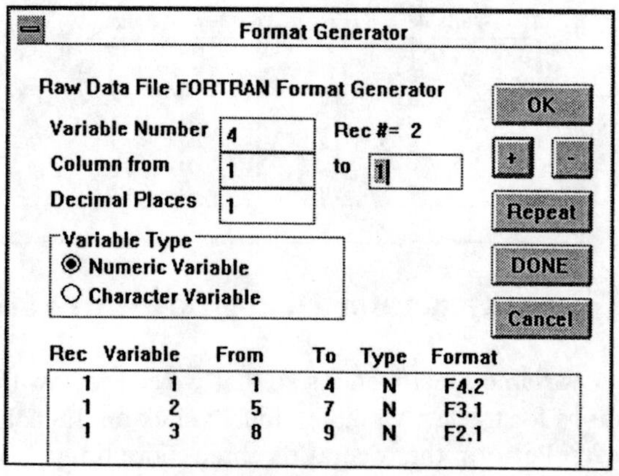

Figure 4.33 Format Generator Set for Record #2

Note that the Format Generator dialog box displays **Column from 1 to 1** for **Record# = 2**. Now that you have chosen a different record, you can enter the specifications for this record. Click on the **OK** button when you finish the specifications for each variable in record 2. Click on **DONE** when you have finished specifying the records for the data file.

This example demonstrated the use of the options for editing and repeating variable and record format specifications. It also showed you how to specify another record in your file.

Data Format Details

When adjacent numbers in your dataset are not separated by a delimiter, you must use a fixed format to read the data correctly. A fixed format consists of a series of statements enclosed in parentheses, such as **(5x, 3f1.0, f10.3/20f3.1)**, and represents instructions for finding and skipping data for any case. To get the result of Figure 4.18 based on test.dat, we would have used the Data Format, typing in (F3.2, 3X, F2.0, 1X, F2.1).

Since EQS for Windows provides the **FORTRAN Format Generator**, it is **not** necessary for you to know the specifics of writing fixed format specifications. We include some specifics here for completeness.

Fixed format data require a FORTRAN format statement to define the layout of your raw data. The FORTRAN format uses **fm.n** to designate the format. The **f** means that the data are in floating point format; **m** gives the length of the variable in number of characters (including decimal point); and **n** refers to the number of characters after the decimal point.

For example, **f10.4** means this particular variable is 10 characters in length and there are four digits after the decimal point. The **(5F3.0)** format means that there are five variables in the data file, each occupies 3 characters, and none of these variables have numbers after the decimal point.

You can use upper and lower case letters as you like. If you want to skip a blank space, you must place an **x** in the format, e.g., **10x** means skip 10 characters. A slash **/** means that you want to skip to the next line of data for that subject.

> *Note:* You must enclose a fixed format statement within a pair of parentheses. Unlike the format statement used within the DOS version of EQS, however, no quotation marks are used to delimit the format.

You can use either the Visual Format or the Column Format to enter a fixed format for your data file. After you have finished entering the format specifications, click **OK**. Your raw data file will be displayed on the spreadsheet-like **Data Editor**.

Import data by Dynamic Data Exchange (DDE)

Most Windows spreadsheet programs such as, MS Excel, Lotus 1-2-3 for Windows, Quattro Pro for Windows, support Dynamic Data Exchange (DDE). The DDE comes in two modes:

1. server mode which is supported by major spreadsheet programs
2. client mode which is supported by EQS for Windows.

The DDE server can be linked by one or more DDE clients. Whenever someone changes the data in the server (due to a transformation, an edit on a data cell, etc.), DDE automatically activates the data in its active client. If you have a commercial spreadsheet program that supports a DDE server, you can export the data to EQS dynamically. For example, your datasheet can retrieve real time data from stock exchange information. By linking EQS to your datasheet, you can get useful statistics and plots from your data immediately.

To export data to EQS by DDE, you must follow several steps:

1. Activate DDE from the Server

Open the spreadsheet from which you want to export to EQS. You can select spreadsheet data in either of two ways:
1. Select the entire variable.
2. Select a region of data cells.

After you make your selection, the selected area will be highlighted (or changed in color).

Choose the **Edit** menu and click on **Copy**. The area you have selected will be enclosed by a border. You are ready to link the selected data.

For example, you have a spreadsheet in Lotus 1-2-3 for Windows with 6 columns and 50 rows of data, and you want to copy the first three columns to EQS. Since Lotus is allowing the data to be copied, Lotus is acting as a file server.

2. Select Client Area

After you issue the **Copy** command in the server, you are ready to prepare the client (i.e. EQS for Windows Data Editor) to accept the data. You must activate EQS for Windows if the program is not yet running. The client area in EQS Data Editor can be a new Data Editor or an existing Data Editor.

Note: If you use the existing Data Editor, any data in the existing Data Editor client area will be lost after the linkage. It is your reponsibility to prepare the data region to receive the appropriate number of variables and cases. Specifically, **the number of variables and number of cases in your client area should be equal to, or greater than, the number of cases and variables in the server's data region.** You can prepare the file by selecting the label field for an entire variable or by dragging a region of data cells.

In this example, we want to paste the DDE data to a new EQS Data Editor. Since EQS for Windows is receiving data, it is a client.

Click on the **File** menu and select **New** to get the **Create a New File** dialog box as shown below.

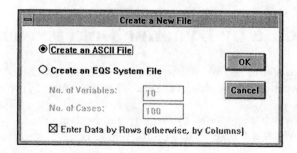

Figure 4.34 Create a New File Dialog Box

114

Click on the radio button for **Create an EQS System File**. Then change the number of variables to 3 and number of cases to 50. That is the exact amount of data which we want to import. Press the **OK** button to get the new Data Editor.

After the new Data Editor appears on the screen, you must select the client area into which you want to paste the DDE data. Thus, press down the <Ctrl> key while you click on the variable names, **V1**, **V2**, and **V3** to highlight them.

3. Issue Paste Link Command

You are ready to paste the data after you have copied the data from the server and prepared the data region in the client. To paste the data in the active client window with the selected data area, click on the EQS Data Editor **Edit** menu and select **Paste Link**. The data from the server will be pasted into the selected client area.

> *Note:* The **Paste Link** option on the **Edit** menu is different from the well-known **Paste** option. The **Paste Link** option lies near the bottom of the menu. Only **Paste Link** will activate the linkage.

4. Disconnect DDE Link

As long as the linkage between the server and the client is on, if there are any data changes on the server, the data in client area will be updated automatically. To disconnect that linkage, you can either close the server window or disable the linkage. To disable the linkage, use the EQS Data Editor **Edit** menu and select the **Links** option. You will see a dialog box as in Figure 4.35.

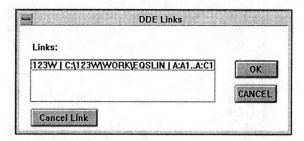

Figure 4.35 DDE Links Dialog Box

If EQS for Windows has established DDE links to other servers, those linkages will appear in the dialog box. There is a maximum number of DDE links allowed in EQS for Windows.

To disconnect the link, click to select a link in the **Links** list box and press **Cancel Link** button. The linkage will be turned off.

Import Data by Clipboard

The most convenient way of importing and exporting data is to cut (or copy) and paste data between different data sheets. When you use **Cut** or **Copy**, the chosen section goes to a Windows internal storage device called the Clipboard which can temporarily store approximately 16K, or 25 columns x 160 rows of data matrix. The data stored in the Clipboard can be repeatedly copied to another data sheet of EQS for Windows or to other Windows programs.

As an example, Open the **airpoll.ess** file. Click on the variable name for the **NONWHITE** variable to highlight it. Choose the **Edit** menu **Copy** option to copy the contents to the Clipboard.

Viewing Data in Clipboard

After you have used **Cut** or **Copy** to send information to the Clipboard, you can view the Clipboard and its contents. To move to the Clipboard:

1. Click and hold on the gray square in the upper left corner of the screen. Drag the pointer down to **Switch To....**

2. In the **Task List**, double click on the **Program Manager**. Then you have two ways to display the data in the Clipboard.
a. In the **Main** group, double click on the **Clipboard** icon. The Clipboard will appear, displaying the data that you sent.
b. If you have the **Clipboard Viewer** in the **Main** group, double click on the **Clipboard Viewer**. Click on **Window** and **Clipboard**. The data will appear.

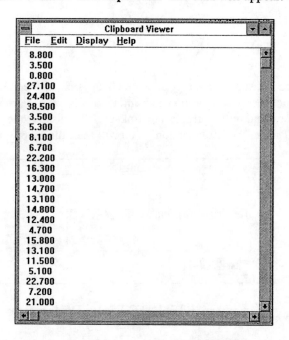

Figure 4.36 Data in Clipboard

There are two ways to import data from Clipboard to the EQS Data Editor. One way is to *paste* or cover up an area of your file, the other is to *insert* to the current Data Editor. In either case, you must know the number of rows and columns of data in the Clipboard.

To get back to EQS for Windows again, you have four choices:
1. Click on any EQS for Windows window that you can see.
2. Click and hold on the icon in the upper left corner of the screen. Choose **EQS** in the **Task List**.
3. Close any intermediate windows that you opened.
4. Click on <Alt> while repeatedly clicking <Tab> until EQS for Windows is listed. Then release both buttons.

Paste from Clipboard

Before you paste data from the Clipboard, you must create, in the recipient Data Editor, a data rectangle equal in size to, or larger than, the data in the Clipboard. You can either open a new Data Editor or use an existing data file to select the target data region.

For this example, click on the variable name to highlight the **NONWHITE** variable, then choose the **Edit** menu **Clear** option. The Data Editor display will look like Figure 4.37.

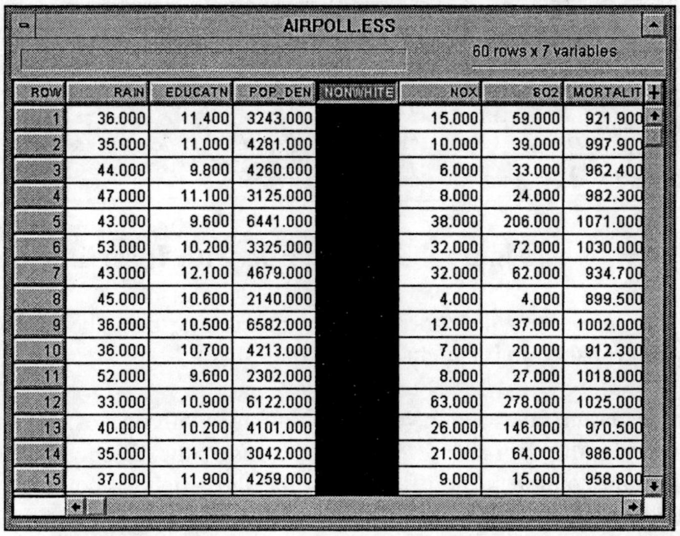

ROW	RAIN	EDUCATN	POP_DEN	NONWHITE	NOX	SO2	MORTALIT
1	36.000	11.400	3243.000		15.000	59.000	921.900
2	35.000	11.000	4281.000		10.000	39.000	997.900
3	44.000	9.800	4260.000		6.000	33.000	962.400
4	47.000	11.100	3125.000		8.000	24.000	982.300
5	43.000	9.600	6441.000		38.000	206.000	1071.000
6	53.000	10.200	3325.000		32.000	72.000	1030.000
7	43.000	12.100	4679.000		32.000	62.000	934.700
8	45.000	10.600	2140.000		4.000	4.000	899.500
9	36.000	10.500	6582.000		12.000	37.000	1002.000
10	36.000	10.700	4213.000		7.000	20.000	912.300
11	52.000	9.600	2302.000		8.000	27.000	1018.000
12	33.000	10.900	6122.000		63.000	278.000	1025.000
13	40.000	10.200	4101.000		26.000	146.000	970.500
14	35.000	11.100	3042.000		21.000	64.000	986.000
15	37.000	11.900	4259.000		9.000	15.000	958.800

AIRPOLL.ESS — 60 rows x 7 variables

Figure 4.37 Data File with Space for Pasting

Now that you have selected the target area, pull down the **Edit** menu and click on **Paste**. Those data on the clipboard will be pasted over the target area. Please note that data will be overwritten if you paste into a variable containing data.

Insert from Clipboard

As an alternative to pasting data, you can insert data from the Clipboard into your data sheet. In this case, the data in the active window will not be covered up. Rather, the data sheet will expand by the number of cells pasted.

When inserting data into your data sheet, you first create a target area for the data. Simply use your cursor to select a column of data. When you insert the data area, it will lie to the left of the selected column. If you do not select a column, the data area will be added to the left of your existing data.

Note: Click on a variable name to select the entire variable or drag a target rectangle.

In **airpoll.ess**, click on the **NOX** variable name to choose that variable as the insertion point for the Clipboard data. Choose **Edit** and **Insert** to insert the data to the left of the selected position. As you can see in Figure 4.38, you have inserted **ITEM0**, a data copy of **NONWHITE**, into the **airpoll.ess** data file. The new variable lies to the left of **NOX**, as specified.

117

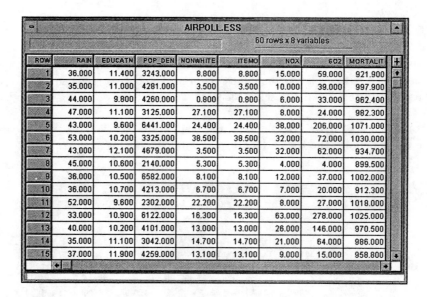

Figure 4.38 Data File with Insertion

You can insert data into a new data sheet or into an existing data sheet. In most cases, when you insert data you will probably do it into an existing data sheet.

As another example, assume that you have three columns by 50 rows of data in the Clipboard, and six columns by 50 rows in the data sheet. You want to insert the Clipboard data into your data sheet between column 3 and column 4. You first select the label field of column 4. The column will be highlighted. You then click on **Edit** and the **Insert** option. The three variables from the Clipboard will be inserted into your current data sheet. The variables will have the labels **Item0, Item1**, and **Item2** in the label field. The dimensions of your data sheet are now 9 by 50.

Saving and Exporting Data and Other Files

Whenever you choose the **Save As** dialog box from the **File** option in the main menu, you will be saving the file in one of two formats. These are: Text Files and EQS System Files.

EQS model files with the ***.eqs** extension are saved as **Text Files**. Text files are document files that contain characters and numbers. In principle, they are readable by any editor or word processor that permits the importing of plain ASCII or text files.

EQS system data files with the ***.ess** extension are saved as **EQS System Files**. As System Files, they are saved in a special format that maintains information about the dataset itself, such as number of cases and variables, and labels for the variables. These files can be read quickly by the EQS program, but are meaningless to other computer programs. Thus, if you want to save a data file for export to another statistical package, you must save the file as a text file, not an EQS system file.

When creating a text file with EQS, the file name that you use does not matter. For example, you could save it as a ***.dat** or a ***.txt** file. However you save the file, the file type designation should correspond to its intended use.

EQS for Windows provides two ways to save your text files, as you can see in Table 4.2.

Text File Type	Text File Delimiter	Recommended Usage
Data File	space-delimited and wrapped at 80 columns	files for mainframe and Email
w/ Tab Delimiter	tab-delimited without wrapping	files for MS Excel, SPSS, etc.

Table 4.2 Delimiters for Saving Text Files in EQS

To create text files in EQS for Windows, use the **File** menu **Save As** option and choose your preferred text file type. Figure 4.39 shows the two text file types in the **Save File as Type** list.

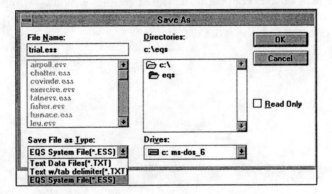

Figure 4.39 Save As Dialog Box with Text File Types

Export Data by Clipboard

You can export EQS data by using the Windows Clipboard. It is a very convenient way to import and export data between different data sheets. When exporting data to Clipboard, always keep in mind that you can copy only a relatively small amount of data to the Clipboard.

Copy data to clipboard

To copy data to clipboard, you select the target data to be copied. You can select in three ways.

Select Contents of Entire Data Editor

To select the entire Data Editor, you can pull down the **Edit** menu and click on the **Select all** option. You can see that the entire Data Editor is highlighted. The danger in selecting the entire Data Editor is that the clipboard can hold only a very small amount of data. Unless you know that you have a small amount of data, you may encounter problems when copying the data to the Clipboard.

Select some Variables

In most cases, you probably want to copy a few variables to the clipboard. Just click on the label field of each variable in the Data Editor. For each click, you highlight the entire variable. Click again to deselect a variable.

Select some Region of Data

In other circumstances, you may want to copy a subset of your data. For example, you want to copy a 3 by 4 matrix from an 8 by 8. In the Data Editor, you can simply hold down the <Shift> key while clicking on each variable which you want to copy. If you prefer, you can click and drag from upper left to lower right. The selected area will be highlighted.

After you have selected your data, click on **Edit** and the **Copy** option. The data you selected will be copied to the clipboard. You can paste or insert the data in the Clipboard to a commercial spreadsheet program, a word processor, or another Data Editor in EQS for Windows.

Note: The data on the clipboard are stored by the Windows Clipboard using an internal format. The precision of the data will be kept intact in the clipboard, although you may not be able to see the entire dataset.

5. PLOTS

A data plot helps you to efficiently present your data. The data plot not only presents your data in an organized way, but also gives you a clearer impression of the data than you can get from the raw numbers. EQS for Windows provides many types of data plots that you can use to present and diagnose your data. In this chapter, we discuss how to access the plot functions in EQS for Windows. You call up the plots through the plot icons located under the **Main Window** menu bar.

Figure 5.1 EQS for Windows Plot Icon Tools

Figure 5.1 shows all of the plot icon tools. These plot icons represent (from left to right):

1. **Line Plot**
2. **Area Plot**
3. **Histogram**
4. **Pie Chart**
5. **Bar Chart**
6. **Quantile Plot**
7. **Quantile-Quantile Plot**
8. **Normal Probability Plot**
9. **Scatter Plot (including Matrix Plot)**
10. **3D Spin Plot**
11. **Box Plot**
12. **Error Bar Chart**
13. **Multiple Plot**
14. **Missing Data Plot (with imputation functions)**
15. **Diagrammer**

This chapter discusses the functions of the first 13 plots. It does not detail the **Missing Data Plot** or the **Diagrammer**.

The **Missing Data Plot** offers you three options for creating a customized plot showing the missing data pattern in your dataset. Read Chapter 3 for a full description of the **Missing Data Plot** and the associated missing data imputation.

The **Diagrammer** is a diagram drawing function that you can use for creating a visual representation of a structural equations model. Read Chapter 8, **Build EQS by Drawing a Diagram**, for a complete description of the use and functions of the **Diagrammer**.

Start a Plot

As discussed in previous chapters, EQS for Windows is a data-oriented program. It functions only with a proper data file (i.e. ***.ess** file) in the Data Editor. If you attempt to access a plot function without a data file, you will see the following message:

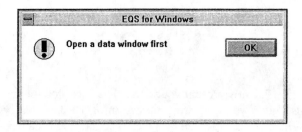

Figure 5.2 Warning Box

To work with the plot functions, go through the following steps:

Step 1: Open a Data File
Step 2: Click on a Plot Function Icon
Step 3: Specify Variable(s) and Options in the plot dialog box
Step 4: Activate the Plot
Step 5: Save the Plot

Step 1:   Open a Data File

You can use the plot function to access any EQS System (***.ess**) file presented in the Data Editor. The procedure for opening a data file was discussed in great detail in Chapter 3, Data Preparation, and will not be repeated here.

Step 2:   Select a Plot Icon

Let's assume that you have opened the **airpoll.ess** data file that came with the EQS for Windows program disk. To create a scatter plot, you select the scatter plot icon from the Plot Icon list (as shown in Figure 5.1).

In fact, the scatter plot icon looks like a scatter plot. Click on the icon once to select it.

Step 3:   Specify Variable(s) and Options from the dialog box

After you select the scatter plot icon, the **Scatter Plot** dialog box (Figure 5.3) will appear.

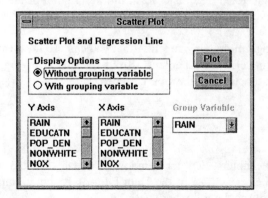

Figure 5.3 Scatter Plot Dialog Box

This dialog box gives you the choice of two display options. You can display the plot with or without a grouping variable. The default is **Without grouping variable**, so make no change now.

The dialog box contains two list boxes. The left list box is labeled **Y Axis**, while the right list box is labeled **X Axis**. Click on one variable for the **Y Axis** and one variable for the **X axis**.

For this example, click on **NONWHITE** to select that variable in the **Y Axis** box, then click on **EDUCATN** in the **X Axis** box. After you have highlighted the two variables, you have completed all specifications for a scatter plot.

The right side of the dialog box contains two buttons. Press the **Plot** button to actually create the scatter plot. You would press the **Cancel** button to return to your dataset without taking any action.

Step 4:   Activate the Plot

Click the **Plot** button to activate the scatter plot. (For clarity, this user's guide shows the plots in black against a white background.) That action creates a new window titled **Scatter Plot**. The window includes the scatter plot within a green plot frame. Notice that there are three lines within the plot frame. The center line is the bivariate regression line, while the top and bottom lines enclose the 95% confidence interval. The upper right corner of the scatter plot window displays a bivariate regression equation and its R square.

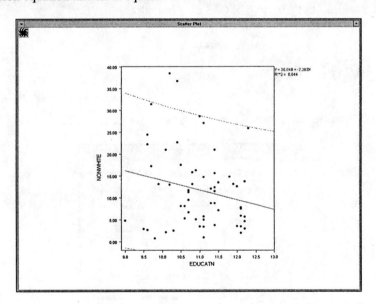

Figure 5.4 Scatter Plot Display

As you can see in Figure 5.4, there is a tool icon located on the upper left corner of the plot window. This **black hole** tool icon is unique to scatter plot. You will find detailed descriptions and instructions for using the **black hole** in the **Customize Your Plot** section later in this chapter.

You can see from this example that you can create a presentation quality plot with only a few clicks. A high quality plot will help you to present the outcome of your analysis to your audience.

Step 5: Save the Plot

When you close a plot, you will be asked whether you want to save it as a graphic file. You can save it in one of almost a dozen graphic formats. The default is ***.bmp**. Many programs can read the files saved in the various formats provided by EQS for Windows. To read a graphics file with EQS for Windows, use the **File** menu and **Open Picture** option.

In the following section, we assume that you already know how to bring a file to the Data Editor. Each plot example specifies a data file appropriate for the example. Please bring the specified file into the Data Editor before continuing with the plot example.

Line Plot

A Line Plot plots the score of a variable on the vertical axis and the sequence of the score on the horizontal axis. Since it plots the case sequence of a variable, a line plot is useful for viewing the trend of the variable across the data points (e.g., data collected at different times). The Line Plot in EQS for Windows allows you to plot up to 12 variables on the same plot. If your cases are not in order, you may want to use the **Sort** option described in Chapter 3 before creating a line plot.

Let's look at the data in **furnace.ess** on the EQS for Windows disk. **Furnace.ess** comes from Box, G. E. P. and G. M. Jenkins (1976). *Time Series Analysis: Forecasting and Control.* San Francisco: Holden Day. The data consist of two variables, GAS and CO2. GAS is the input and CO2 is the output of an industrial process. Let's try to plot GAS on a line plot.

Specifying Variables

Click on the line plot icon (as shown above) to start the plot. The Line Plot dialog box will appear.

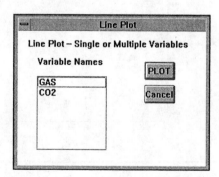

Figure 5.5 Line Plot Dialog Box

In the dialog box there are two variables, **GAS** and **CO2**. Click on **GAS** to select it. Click the **PLOT** button to plot.

Display Line Plot

As soon as you click the **PLOT** button, the line plot will appear. You can see from the plot that the Y axis is the GAS variable and the label is printed in landscape mode. The X axis just shows the sequence of the data. Note that there is a line drawn across the plot frame at the variable mean.

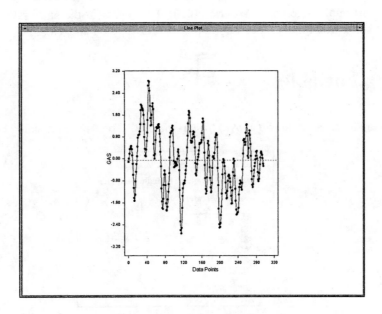

Figure 5.6 Line Plot Display

The plot in Figure 5.6 shows regular fluctuation over the data collecting period. If you want to see more than one variable on the same plot, use the Line Plot dialog box shown in Figure 5.5 to select up to 12 variables for each line plot.

> *Note*: To select multiple noncontiguous variables from the list, hold down the <Ctrl> key while clicking on each variable. To select multiple contiguous variables from the list, you can simply drag the cursor over each variable, or hold down the <Shift> key while clicking on each variable.

When drawing multiple variables, the program uses the minimum and the maximum of the specified variables as the range of the Y axis. Since all variables use the same scale, the line plot lets you see the differences between variables. Variable mean lines, however, do not appear in a multiple variable line plot.

Area Plot

An Area Plot plots the score of a variable on the vertical axis and the sequence of the score on the horizontal axis with the area under the curve filled in. Since it plots the case sequence of a variable and emphasizes the area under the curve, an area plot is useful for viewing the trend of the variable across the data points. If your cases are not in order, you may want to use the **Sort** option described in Chapter 3 before creating an area plot.

The Area Plot in EQS for Windows allows you to plot up to four variables on the same plot. For each successive variable, the program uses the plot for the previous variable as the base. EQS plots the variables in their order in the variable list. Thus, you may find it helpful to use the **Cut** and **Paste** options to rearrange your variables for an informative area plot.

Let's look at the data in **exercise.ess**. The **exercise.ess** dataset comes from the *BMDP Statistical Software Manual* Volume 1 (1993). The original data file contains eight variables. The last two variables are non-numeric variables which are not acceptable to EQS for Windows. Thus, for EQS for Windows, **exercise.ess** contains only six variables. This dataset measures pulse rate for 40 subjects before and after running one mile. We use PULSE_1 to represent the pulse rate before running and PULSE _2 for pulse after running. Let's try to plot **exercise.ess** on an area plot.

Specifying Variables

Select the Area Plot icon (as shown above) to start the plot. The Area Plot dialog box will appear.

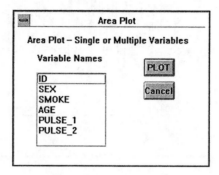

Figure 5.7 Area Plot Dialog Box

In the dialog box, click on two variables, **PULSE_1** and **PULSE_2**. Click the **PLOT** button to plot.

Display Area Plot

As soon as you click the **PLOT** button, the Area Plot will appear. You can see from the plot that the pulse rate is much higher at PULSE _2 than it is at PULSE _1.

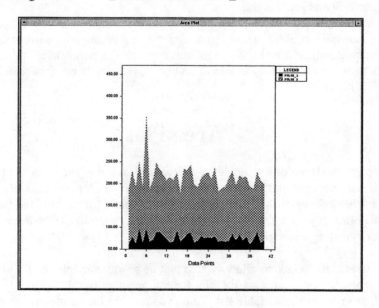

Figure 5.8 Area Plot Display

Histogram

Histograms are generally used to display the distribution of a continuous variable without requiring grouping. The data points are counted and displayed according to defined intervals which can be user-defined or computed by the program using some formula. As an example, income is a continuous variable that you might want to display as a histogram.

There are three ways to determine the grouping for the variable in the histogram. You may not be interested in the income of an individual. Rather, you may prefer to see manageable groups, such as low, medium-low, medium, medium-high, high.

You can proceed in three ways:

1. To form those groups, you can invoke the **Group** function provided in EQS for Windows (click on **Data** menu and select **Group**). If you like, you can designate each group with a meaningful name to make the display more readable. Then plot by selecting the histogram icon, clicking on your grouped variable, and pressing **PLOT**.
2. You can simply specify the number of groups which you want to display from the histogram dialog box. Start by clicking on the histogram icon, and click on the name of the variable in the dialog box as shown in Figure 5.9. Then click on the checkbox beside **User-defined Categories**. That will enable the **Number of Categories** field. Enter the number of categories and press **PLOT**. The program will divide the data into a predefined number of intervals of equal size. The data points in each interval will be counted and displayed.
3. If you want to take only a quick look at the distribution of your variable without going through the trouble of grouping your variable, you can accept the dialog box defaults and let the EQS for Windows program do the grouping for you. Just select the histogram icon, click on your grouped variable, and press **PLOT** to accept the dialog box defaults.

Specifying Variables

After you have opened the **survey.ess** dataset, click on the Histogram icon. The Histogram Specifications dialog box will appear. It includes various defaults and options as shown in Figure 5.9.

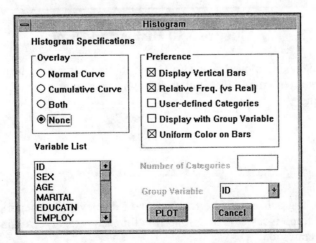

Figure 5.9 Histogram Specifications Dialog Box

You can select to overlay a **Normal** distribution **Curve**, the corresponding **Cumulative** distribution **Curve**, or **Both** or neither (**None**). These options provide a quick visual check on the normality of your data. You can also select various **Preference** items that control the presentation. The first two options, **Display** with **Vertical Bars** and **Relative Frequency** (**vs. Real**) are defaults, as is **Uniform Color on Bars**. The role of **User-defined Categories** was discussed above.

Typically, you choose a variable by clicking on the variable name in the variable list. If you also click on **Display with Group Variable**, you will get a second choice of variables in the **Group Variable** list. If you specify a group variable such as **SEX**, you will get a display in which the histograms for one group are stacked on top of histograms for the other group. This arrangement makes it easier to compare distributions.

Click on **INCOME** to choose it, then click on **PLOT** Figure 5.10 shows the histogram for the INCOME variable. We have customized the bars for greater clarity in this figure. Read the **Customizing Bars in the Histogram and Bar Chart** section later in this chapter for details on customizing the bars.

Display Histogram

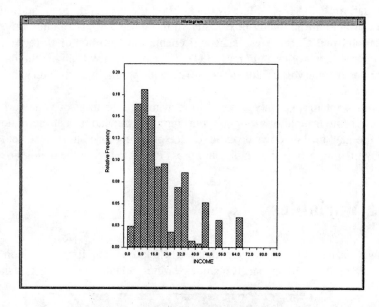

Figure 5.10 Histogram Display

Note: If you choose to overlay a normal distribution curve on a histogram to see whether the scores are normally distributed, it is important that none of the ordered categories are missing.

Pie Chart

The pie chart, or pie graph, is an alternative way of displaying a categorical variable. Unlike the histogram, the pie graph focuses on the proportion for each category. Again, we will use survey data to see the levels of education.

Specifying Variables

As usual, you must have the data file, **survey.ess** in this case, in the Data Editor, and then select the pie chart icon as shown above. A pie chart variable selection dialog box will appear (Figure 5.11). Within the dialog box, select the EDUCATN variable and click the **PLOT** button.

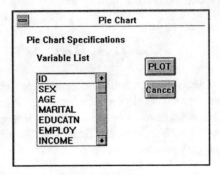

Figure 5.11 Pie Chart Dialog Box

Display Pie Chart

After you click on **PLOT**, a new window appears, displaying a pie chart. Each category in the pie is distinguished by a different color. The size of each slice represents the proportion of that category to total sample size. Note that there is a legend box on the upper right corner. The legend box marks each category with its relevant color, the name of the category (if it is defined) and the percent in each category.

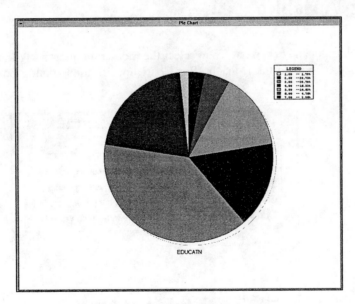

Figure 5.12 Pie Chart Display

Note: Unlike the variable name in other plots, you can move the variable name in the pie chart by dragging it. You can also modify the variable name by double clicking on it, then changing the name in the text field of the dialog box that appears.

Display Continuous Variable in Pie Chart

Since the pie chart is a member of the frequency plot family, it cannot display a continuous variable that has not been grouped. To display a continuous variable in a pie chart, you must first group the variable. To group the variable, click on the **Data** menu and select **Group**. Follow the grouping variable procedure described in Chapter 3 to create a new variable. After you have grouped the variable, select the **Pie Chart** icon to create your display.

Bar Chart

Commonly, when doing data analysis, you will encounter categorical data, such as the number of males versus females, income groups, level of education, etc. When dealing with categorical data, your interest may not be on the actual scores of the subjects. Rather, you may be more interested in the frequency or the counts for each category. Bar Chart is the plotting tool that displays the frequency with which each category score occurs.

The Bar Chart function provided in EQS for Windows allows you to display a bar chart in only a few steps. If you used the **Edit** menu **Information** option to define the variable as a categorical variable, the histogram will also display the category names. In addition, you can add a group variable so that you can compare the frequencies between groups.

The data we are using comes from the *BMDP Statistical Software Manual* (1993). The dataset is **survey.ess**. It has 37 variables and 294 cases. The file contains demographic data. We are interested in the distribution levels of education across sex.

Specifying Variables

To start a bar chart, open **survey.ess**. Then select the plot icon representing the bar chart (see above picture). After you click on the icon, the Bar Chart Specifications dialog box will appear (Figure 5.13).

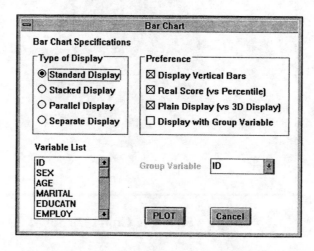

Figure 5.13 Bar Chart Dialog Box

This box provides you with choices in **Type of Display** (**Standard**, the default; **Stacked**, one on top of the other; **Parallel**, two side by side; or **Separate**) and various options in **Preference**. Preferences include **Display Vertical Bars**, use of **Real Score vs. Percentile**, and plotting in 2-D or 3-D. The 2-D option, **Plain Display**, is the default. Finally, to see the level of one variable grouped by another, you can choose **Display with Group Variable**.

Display Bar Chart

As an example, to view the histogram of education by sex, click the check box beside **Display with Group Variable**. The **Group Variable** list becomes active, so choose **SEX** as the **Group Variable** and select **EDUCATN** from the **Variable List**. Click the **PLOT** button to display the plot.

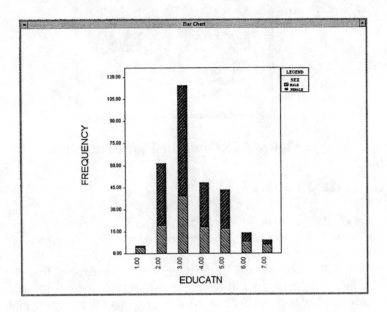

Figure 5.14 Stacked Bar Chart

Figure 5.14 shows the bar chart for the EDUCATN variable grouped by SEX. We have customized the bars for greater clarity here. Read the **Customizing Bars in the Histogram and Bar Chart** section later in this chapter for details on customizing the bars.

The plot displays seven categories of EDUCATN. Most bars contain two parts. The upper blocks are female, while the lower blocks are male. The Y axis shows the frequency of each education level. The X axis shows the code for each category. If you defined the EDUCATN variable as categorical and specified each category with a code name, the code names will replace codes on the X axis.

Quantile Plot

The Quantile plot is a tool to help you assess the distribution of your data. It plots the ordered data on the Y axis and the fraction of the data on the X axis. The formula for calculating the fraction of the data is in the BMDP Manual Volume 1 or a statistics book such as: Hamilton, L. C. (1992). *Regression with Graphics—A Second Course in Applied Statistics*. Pacific Grove, California: Brook/Cole Publishing Co.

Specifying Variables

To illustrate the Quantile Plot we use the **survey.ess** INCOME variable. To start the plot, click on the Quantile plot icon shown above. A Quantile Plot variable selection dialog box will appear (Figure 5.15). Select the INCOME variable and click the **PLOT** button.

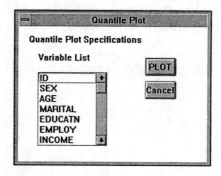

Figure 5.15 Quantile Plot Dialog Box

Display Quantile Plot

The quantile plot display is shown in Figure 5.16. The Y axis provides the data scores sorted in ascending order, and the X axis gives the fraction of the data. The fraction is calculated at $(i-0.5)/n$, where i is the sequence of the data point and n is the sample size. If the data are normally distributed, the plot will be bow-shaped. If the points lie on the diagonal line, the data are uniformly distributed. Again, we do not intend to replace a statistical textbook with this user's guide. You should refer to any standard textbook for a detailed discussion of the Quantile plot.

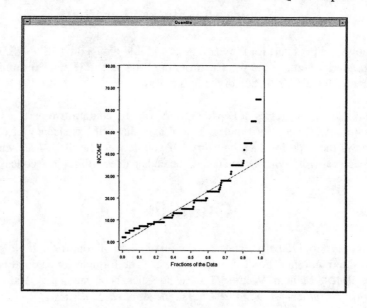

Figure 5.16 Quantile Plot Display

Quantile-Quantile Plot

Quantile-Quantile plots are sometimes called QQ plots. A QQ plot will plot the quantiles of one variable against the quantiles of another variable. Thus, it sorts two variables, both in ascending order, plotting one variable on the Y axis, the other variable on the X axis. The QQ plot allows you to compare two observed variables. You can also plot one observed variable against a known distribution to verify the distribution of the observed variable. To illustrate this plot, again we use a dataset called **exercise.ess**.

Specifying Variables

To call the Quantile-Quantile plot, click on the **QQ** icon shown above. A dialog box will appear, allowing you to specify variables (Figure 5.17).

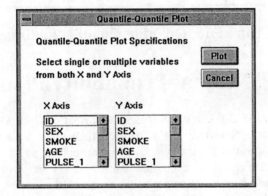

Figure 5.17 Quantile-Quantile Plot Dialog Box

Unlike the frequency plots (i.e. histogram, pie chart, etc.), you can specify up to 12 variables on each axis. In this illustration we are interested in the **PULSE_1** and **PULSE _2** variables. After selecting **PULSE _1** for the X axis and **PULSE _2** for the Y axis, click the **PLOT** button to activate the plot.

Display QQ Plots

The resulting QQ plot is shown in Figure 5.18. The dot pattern of the QQ plot shows that the distributions of these two variables are quite different. If the distributions of the two variables were identical, they would form a straight line along the diagonal line of the plot. The current dot pattern appears to be close to a straight line with the exception of one case. The offset from the diagonal suggests that the two variables may have a similar distribution pattern, but with different means. The case in the upper right corner may be an outlier.

More discussions on the shape of the dot pattern and its meaning can be found, for example, in Hamilton's text.

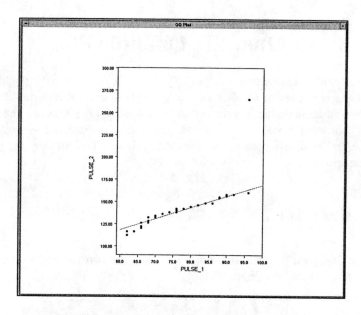

Figure 5.18 Quantile-Quantile Plot Display

Normal Probability Plots

Normal Probability plots are also known as Quantile-Normal or Normal-Quantile plots. They are a variation of the QQ plot. Note that the QQ plot graphs two sorted variables to compare the distributions. If you replace the Y axis by a known distribution, say a normal distribution, you are actually comparing the distribution of a variable against the normal distribution. To compute the Y axis, we take the expected normal value from the rank of an observed variable against the actual variable sorted in ascending order. You can find a detailed description of expected standard normal value in the BMDP manual or any standard statistical textbook.

Since we are plotting the expected standard normal value against an observed variable, a straight line lying on the 45 degree diagonal means that the distribution of the data is perfectly normal. The distribution of the observed variable is implied in the dot patterns of the plot. Hamilton's text, cited above, has an extensive discussion of the various possible patterns.

Use **exercise.ess** as the test dataset illustrating the normal probability plot. The variable is PULSE_1.

Specifying Variables

Click on the Normal Probability plot icon to get the variable specification dialog box (Figure 5.19). Then select the **PULSE _1** variable from the list box in the figure. Click on the **PLOT** button when you are ready to plot.

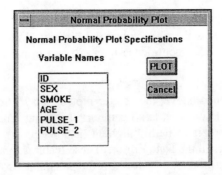

Figure 5.19 Normal Probability Plot Dialog Box

Display Normal Probability Plot

The normal probability plot is shown in Figure 5.20. The dot pattern shows that the PULSE_1 variable is not perfectly normally distributed. The observed variable does not skew, because the dot pattern crosses the Y axis at about 0.0. The dot pattern shows that both tails are long and flat.

Again, consult a standard statistical text for more details on this type of plot.

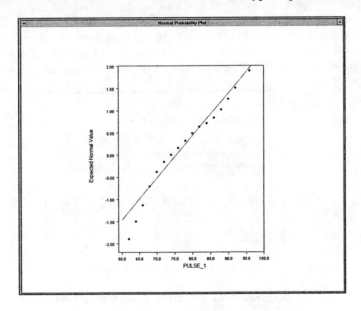

Figure 5.20 Normal Probability Plot Display

Scatter Plots

The scatter plot is one of the most widely used statistical plots. It plots two variables against each other to examine the scatter of the observations. You can select up to 12 variables for each axis. The scatter plot is a good tool for displaying the relationship between variables, evaluating their linear relation, and detecting outliers.

The beginning of this chapter has an example of the scatter plot in EQS for Windows (Figure 5.4). The scatter plot option displays the plot, draws the bivariate linear regression line, provides upper and lower boundaries of the 95% confidence interval, and prints the regression equation and its R square.

Besides the features mentioned above, the scatter plot option in EQS for Windows displays matrix plots (more than one variable on each axis), supports brushing (encircling a few data points in one plot causes the same data points to be highlighted in other plots), zooming, temporary removal of outliers, and marking outliers in the Data Editor. These features dynamically link your data and your plot. You can use the scatter plot not only to show the plots, but also use the plot to diagnose outliers.

To demonstrate the scatter plot, we use **fisher.ess** from the *BMDP Statistical Software Manual*. The dataset contains sepal length and width and petal length and width for three species of iris. Since we showed the single scatter plot earlier, this example will demonstrate a matrix plot with three variables on both X and Y axis.

Specifying Variables

Click on the Scatter Plot icon to get the Scatter Plot specification dialog box. The dialog box gives you the choice of displaying the plot with or without a grouping variable. The default is **Without grouping variable**, so make no change now.

Note that there are two list boxes in the dialog box. The list box on the left side represents the **Y Axis**, while the list box on the right side is used by the **X Axis**. Select the first three variables from each list box, and click on the **PLOT** button. The scatter plot will appear.

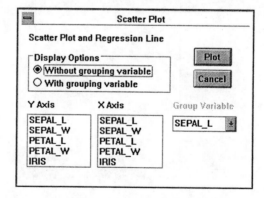

Figure 5.21 Scatter Plot Dialog Box

Note: To select multiple noncontiguous variables from the list, hold down the <Ctrl> key while clicking on each variable. To select multiple contiguous variables from the list, you can simply drag the cursor over each variable, or hold down the <Shift> key while clicking on each variable.

Display Scatter Plots

Figure 5.22 shows the 3 by 3 matrix plot. Note that you have selected the same variables on the X and Y axes. Thus, the diagonal plots in the matrix would be scatter plots of one variable against itself, resulting in a straight line. Rather than display the straight line, EQS for Windows displays the histogram of the variable.

Note: Any variable with more than 15 score levels will be subjected to automatic grouping (see the Histogram section for a detailed description).

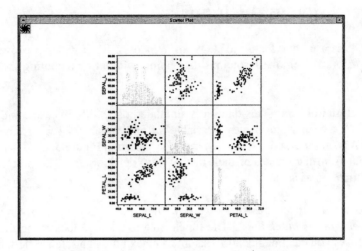

Figure 5.22 A Matrix of Scatter Plots

Notice that several of the scatter plots show points that are grouped together, with some blank spaces. Evidently, the scores cluster to form groups.

Brushing

Brushing is a technique that has been frequently used in recent years. Brushing is generally applied in the matrix plot, but is also useful in a single scatter plot. In a matrix plot, you might be interested in certain data points in one cell and want to know where those cases are in another cell of the matrix plot. The brushing technique allows you to encircle a group of points in one cell by creating a rectangle defined by a broken line. The color of the enclosed data points will change, and that color will be picked up by the same cases in the other cells. Moreover, you can drag the designated rectangle to another position in the cell, highlighting any data points that are enclosed. This is a useful feature to identify a few data points that are unique and require more attention.

To create a brushing effect in EQS for Windows, place your mouse pointer in one cell and *drag a rectangle from the upper left to the lower right*. After you release the mouse button, the rectangle will stay and all data points within the rectangle will turn yellow.

We call the rectangle a **brush**. The brush must enclose one or more data points, or it will disappear. Once you have created the brush, you can drag the brush anywhere in the cell. To remove the brush, click once outside the brush (within the same cell), and the brush will disappear.

Zooming

When you have a matrix on the screen, you may want to investigate one cell more closely, or determine the R square for a particular cell. EQS for Windows provides a solution. You can blow up any cell in a matrix plot by zooming.

To zoom a cell, double click anywhere within the boundary of the cell that you want to zoom. The matrix plot will be replaced by a single scatter plot with the regression line, the 95% confidence interval, and the R square. To return to the matrix plot, just double click on the plot again.

Outlier Detection and Diagnosis

Outlier detection is a unique feature of EQS for Windows. It provides a convenient way to display outliers and temporarily remove suspicious data points without recomputing the plot or changing the data file.

Open the dataset **manul7.ess**. This dataset is simulated data with 50 cases, and case 50 is an outlier case. Let's create a scatter plot between variable V1 and variable V4 where the V1 is on the Y axis and variable V4 is on the X axis. The scatter plot is shown in Figure 5.23. Note the dot on the upper right corner, far from the cluster of data in the lower left corner. The plot provides the bivariate regression information as usual.

If you want to see the R square without this outlier, you can temporarily remove that outlier by *dumping the point in the black hole*. The **black hole** is the icon located on the upper left corner of the scatter plot. As you can imagine, it looks like a black hole in a science fiction movie. It is a place for temporary storage of undesirable data points.

To use the black hole storage, create a brush to mark those undesirable data points. Once they are marked, you can drag the entire brush into the black hole. The size of the brush does not matter, as long as the mouse pointer lies directly over the black hole when you release the mouse button. After you release your mouse button, a dot appears in the center of the black hole. That dot is a reminder that you have something in the black hole.

After you dump one or more data points into the black hole, the plot information will be recalculated. Therefore, you can see the slope of the regression line, the confidence interval lines, and the R square change (see Figure 5.24). You can repeatedly put data points in the black hole. To recover the data points from the black hole, just double click on the black hole.

Note: Do not put all data points into the black hole, because that may generate unpredictable results.

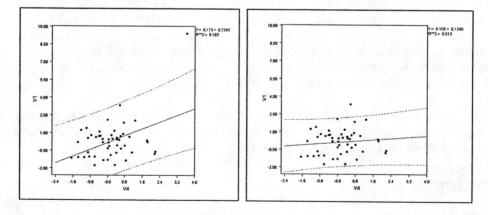

Figure 5.23 & 5.24 Scatter Plot with Outlier (left) and without Outlier (right)

Mark Selected Data Points in Data Editor

Since you can examine the potential outliers from the scatter plot by dumping cases in and out of the black hole, it would be nice to mark those outlying cases in the Data Editor so that you can exclude them from further analysis. EQS for Windows allows you to mark cases in the Data Editor. To do so, follow these steps:

Step 1: Put outlying cases in the black hole

The black hole is the bridge between the scatter plot and the Data Editor. Therefore, move cases to be marked into the black hole. If you followed the scatter plot example above, you already have one case in the black hole.

Step 2: Mark points to data sheet

To mark the data point(s) deposited in the black hole, press the <Shift> key on your keyboard while clicking your mouse in the black hole once. The data point(s) in the black hole will be marked in the Data Editor.

Notes: You must press and click simultaneously.

Step 3. Verify the marked cases or reverse selection

After you have marked a case in the Data Editor, you can verify your action by clicking **Data** and selecting **Information**. An informational dialog box will appear, indicating the number of cases marked. If you then perform an analysis, that analysis will be performed on the marked cases.

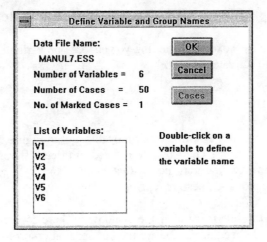

Figure 5.25 Data File Information after Marking

You may find it necessary to reverse the marking selection! In Figure 5.25, for example, you may be interested in the 49 cases that are not marked. In such a situation, you can go to the main menu, select **Data** and **Use Data**. Then you get the **Case Selection Specification** dialog box, where you check **Reverse Selection/Unselection of Cases**. This marks the 49 nonoutlier cases.

If you are creative in applying these dynamic features, along with the data handling capabilities, you can fully explore your data. EQS for Windows can take you to a new level of data analysis.

3D Spin Plot

A 3D Spin Plot is a useful tool for viewing your data. It takes three variables and plots them against each other. It then displays the variables on three-dimensional axes, where the axes can rotate continuously so that you can see the relative position of your data from different angles. This is a good way to locate clusters or gaps in data.

The data in this example is **manul7.ess** with six variables and 50 cases. We pick variables 1, 2, and 3 to demonstrate the 3D spin plot.

Specifying Variables

Click the 3D Spin Plot icon to start the plot. The 3D Spin Plot dialog box appears.

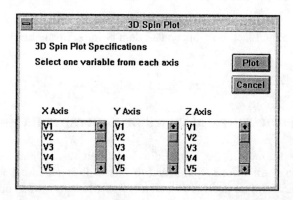

Figure 5.26 3D Spin Plot Dialog Box

The dialog box has three list boxes, each letting you choose one variable. Select one variable in each list and click on **PLOT** to activate the plot.

Display Spin Plot

You can see a static display of the continuously movable plot in Figure 5.27. The plot has three axes, each 90 degrees from the others. The axes are marked in three different colors. The data points in the plot are white. However, you may notice that there is one cyan dot in the plot. That dot is actually the center of the plot and does not represent a data point.

There are six icons in the left margin of the window. There is one icon for each direction for **Horizontal, Vertical,** and **Circular**. These are the buttons that control the rotation directions. Click once on a button for an incremental move; click and hold for continued movement. You can try clicking these buttons to get a feel for the controls.

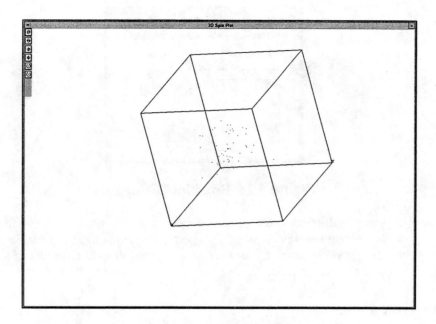

Figure 5.27 3D Spin Plot Display

Box Plot

The box plot is widely used for viewing the distribution of data and the possible outliers. This is in contrast to Quantile and QQ plots which show the raw scores.

The box plot only plots summarized information. It consists of three parts: the body, the tail, and the outlier. The body part is actually the box itself. The top of the box is the third quartile or Q3 (75% of the cases will fall below this line and 25% of the cases will fall above this line). The bottom of the box is the first quartile, or Q1. The range between the top and the bottom of the box is called the inter-quartile range or IQR. The mean and median are also shown.

There is an upper tail above the box at the position of Q3+1.5IQR, or the maximum of the data, whichever is smaller. There is also a lower tail at the position of Q1-1.5IQR, or the minimum of the data, whichever is larger. The data points which fall beyond the upper or lower tails will be plotted in their real position.

We use **manul7.ess** to illustrate the box plot.

Specifying Variables

Click the box plot icon as shown above to get the Box Plot dialog box. You can select up to 12 variables from the list box. When selecting multiple variables, be sure to choose variables with similar ranges. Otherwise, the extreme ranges may make the plot unreadable, because EQS for Windows uses the range of values for the first variable to define the axis. Choose the first three variables and click **PLOT** to display the box plot.

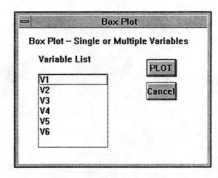

Figure 5.28 Box Plot Dialog Box

Note: To select multiple noncontiguous variables from the list, hold down the <Ctrl> key while clicking on each variable. To select multiple contiguous variables from the list, you can simply drag the cursor over each variable, or hold down the <Shift> key while clicking on each variable.

Display Box Plot

The box plot display is shown in Figure 5.29. It plots three variables side by side. You can see that there are outliers in the plot; they appear in a contrasting color on a color monitor. Near the center of each box, there are two horizontal lines which may sometimes overlap. These two lines represent the mean and the median of the variable. The broken line is the mean and the straight line is the median.

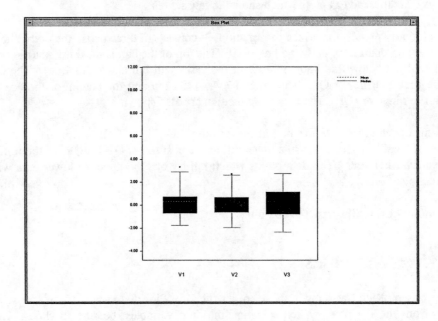

Figure 5.29 Box Plot Display

142

Error Bar Chart

The error bar chart plots summarized information for several variables. It consists of the mean and the error bars for each variable. The means are connected by a line.

We use **manul7.ess** to illustrate the error bar chart.

Specifying Variables

Click the Error Bar chart icon as shown above to get the **Error Bar Chart** dialog box. You can select up to four variables from the list box. When selecting multiple variables, be sure to choose variables with similar ranges. Otherwise, an extreme range may make the plot unreadable by making one standard error too narrow to be visible. Select the first three variables now and click **PLOT** to display the error bar chart.

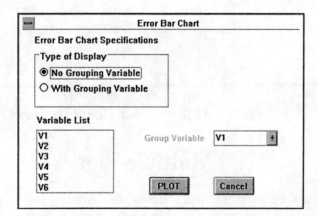

Figure 5.30 Error Bar Chart Dialog Box

> *Note*: To select multiple noncontiguous variables from the list, hold down the <Ctrl> key while clicking on each variable. To select multiple contiguous variables from the list, you can simply drag the cursor over each variable, or hold down the <Shift> key while clicking on each variable.

Display Error Bar Chart

Figure 5.31 shows an error bar chart. It plots three variables side by side with a line connecting the means of the variables. It also displays one standard error around each mean.

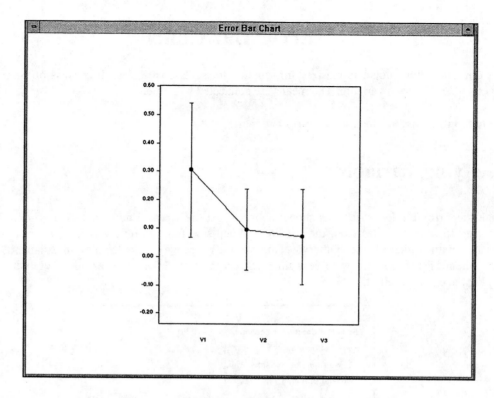

Figure 5.31 Error Bar Chart Display

Multiple Plot

When presenting your data, sometimes it is useful to show different plots of the same variable in the same screen. For example, you might want to show the distribution of a variable using histogram, normal probability plot, quantile plot, and univariate scatter plot simultaneously. Alternatively, you may want to compare different variables in their respective plots. EQS for Windows permits you to show several plots within the same window. These multiple plots, or Multi Plots, can then be printed on the same piece of paper.

Specifying Variables

To activate a Multi Plot, you must have at least two plot windows opened. After you activate the Multi Plot function from the plot tool bar, the plots contained in the opened plot windows will move to the Multi Plot window. All single plot windows will disappear.

Display Multiple Plot

The plots within the Multi Plot are arranged from left to right, in the order in which you opened them.

> *Note:* We recommend that that you use no more than six plots per Multi Plot, because Multi Plot uses a lot of memory.

Do not try to include a 3-D spin plot in your Multi Plot. Those plots are so complicated that they cannot combine well with other plots in a Multi Plot.

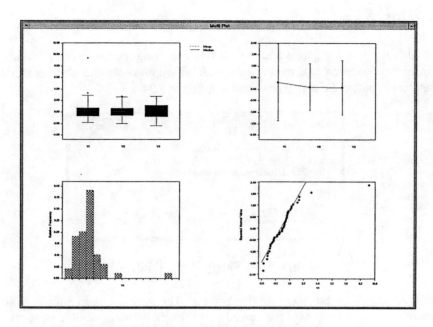

Figure 5.32 Multi Plot Display

Missing Data Plot

The missing data plot and missing data imputation were discussed in Chapter 3. Please consult that chapter for detailed descriptions. The material will not be reiterated here.

Customize Your Plot

EQS for Windows not only lets you perform analyses, but also will produce a publication quality plot. Best of all, there is no need to take the plots to a different graphics program for enhancement. EQS for Windows includes features that let you tailor your plots. To customize or modify your plot, you can pull down the **Custom** menu from the plot window. The **Custom** menu, shown in Figure 5.33, contains options that allow you to modify the label of the axis, range and tick increment of the axis. It also allows you to add labels and comments to the plot, change the size, color and shape of the plot symbol, change the width and color of a line and plot frame, and change the color of the background window.

Figure 5.33 Custom Plot Menu Options

Modify Plot Axes

You can modify the variable names and axis tick values using the **Setup Axis** option. Let's use the line plot in Figure 5.6 as an example for modifications. Pull down the **Custom** menu and click on **Setup Axis** item to obtain the dialog box shown in Figure 5.34.

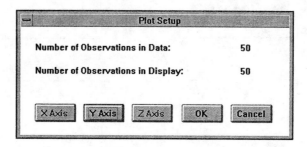

Figure 5.34 Setup Axis Dialog Box

On the bottom of the dialog box there are five buttons. The three left-most buttons indicate X, Y, and Z axes, where the X and the Z axes are grayed out. This is because the plot we are working on is a line plot and line plot data come from one variable. If your plot needs two variables (i.e. scatter plot), the **X Axis** and **Y Axis** buttons will be effective. To modify the information displayed on the Y axis of the plot, click the button indicating **Y Axis**.

Figure 5.35 shows the dialog box that appears after you click the **Y Axis** button. It shows the **Axis Label** in the top edit box. The label is actually the variable name of the data or the label of the Y axis. You can modify this label, using up to 64 characters. The modification will appear on the Y axis later.

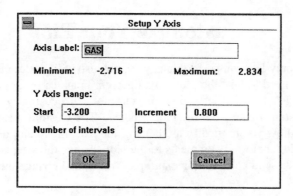

Figure 5.35 Y Axis Dialog Box

The dialog box shows the minimum and maximum score of the variable as well as the starting value of the axis, number of intervals in the axis, and increment on each interval. You can modify the starting score, number of intervals, and the value between two tick marks. When changing an **Axis Range**, the program will not allow you to omit data by changing the starting value of the axis range.

When you have defined the modifications, click on the **OK** button. You will go back to the dialog box in Figure 5.34. Click the **OK** button to make the change effective.

Adding a Title or Comments to a Plot Window

Sometimes, a plot window needs a title, comments, or labels to improve its effectiveness as a communication. The plot window in EQS for Windows permits you to add as many comments as you want. To add comments, pull down the **Custom** menu and select the **Text** option. When the menu disappears, move the mouse pointer to the plot window.

As soon as your mouse pointer enters the client area of the plot window, the mouse pointer will become an I beam cursor. You can click once anywhere in the plot window and start typing your title or comments. Press the <Enter> key after you finish typing. The title or comment will stay on the plot window until you delete it. You can repeatedly add comments as you wish.

To move the position of the comments, click the comment once. The bounding rectangle of the comment will appear on the screen. You can drag the rectangle to any position on the plot window.

Changing Text Font

To change the font of the comment, you should click the comment once to highlight it. Then use the **Font** menu to change the font size and font type. You can use the Font menu to change the font type, as well as font characteristics such as point size, bold, italic, underline.

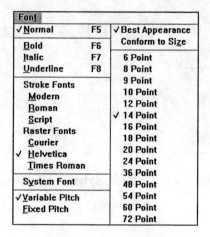

Figure 5.36 Font Menu

Changing Text Orientation

To change text orientation, double click on the text. The **Text Orientation** dialog box will appear.

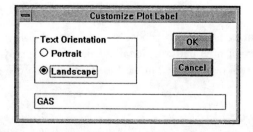

Figure 5.37 Text Orientation Dialog Box

Click on the **Landscape** radio button to change to landscape, or sideways, orientation. You can also edit the text in the text box. Click on **OK** when finished.

Deleting Text

To delete any comment, click the comment once to highlight it. Then pull down the **Edit** menu and select **Cut** to delete the text.

Modify Size, Shape, and Color of a Plot Symbol

To customize a plot symbol, pull down **Custom** from the plot window and select **Plot Symbol**. On a non-frequency plot (e.g. line, scatter, NP, Q, and QQ plots), the Plot Symbols window consists of various plot symbols in a matrix. You can use this dialog box to change the size, shape, and color of the symbol.

The Plot Symbols specification dialog box will appear as shown in Figure 5.38. Surrounding **Preview** in the plot symbol dialog box, there are symbol tables, a symbol size scroll bar, a variable list box, a **Symbol Color** button, and an **OK** button.

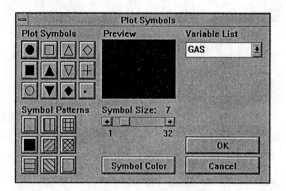

Figure 5.38 Plot Symbols Dialog Box

Select Plot Symbol

Click on the **Plot Symbols** table to choose a new shape for your plot symbol. The **Plot Symbols** table is a matrix of 12 symbols, located on the upper left corner of the **Plot Symbols** dialog box. When you pick a new symbol, your choice will be displayed in the **Preview** box located in the center of the **Plot Symbols** dialog box.

Select Patterns

Click on the **Symbol Patterns** table to choose a new pattern for your plot symbol. The **Symbol Patterns** table is a matrix of nine patterns, located below the **Plot Symbols** table. When you pick a new pattern, your choice will be displayed in the **Plot Symbols** matrix and in the **Preview** box.

Change Symbol Size

You can change the plot symbol size by scrolling the **Symbol Size** scroll bar left and right. The scroll bar is located in the lower section of the **Plot Symbols** dialog box (Figure 5.38). The current symbol size is shown on top of the scroll bar. By moving the thumb of the scroll bar, or pressing the left or right arrow on the scroll bar, you can change the symbol size. The changes will be displayed with your symbol choice in the **Preview** box.

Change Symbol Color

You can change the color of a symbol by clicking the **Symbol Color** button in the **Plot Symbols** dialog box. When you push the **Symbol Color** button, a color palette shown in the left side of Figure 5.39 will appear.

You can click on one of the **Basic Colors**, then on **OK** to change a symbol color. If you prefer a custom color, click on the **Define Custom Colors...** button to bring up the right side of Figure 5.39. Note that the right side has a large square of varying colors.

You can move the arrow on the far right vertically to change the proportions of white and black in the colors. Then you can click in the **Color Palette** to choose a custom color for the plot symbol. The new color will appear in the **Color|Solid** field for evaluation, along with the characteristics of the color in the **Hue**, **Sat** and **Lum**.

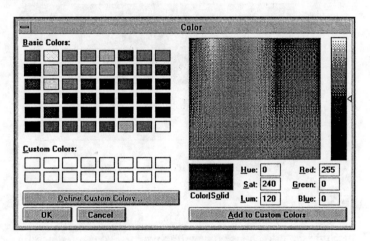

Figure 5.39 Color Palette Dialog Box

When you are pleased with your chosen custom color, click on the **Add to Custom Colors** button. Your custom color will appear in a box under **Custom Colors** on the left of the screen. You can use that custom color as a symbol color at any time.

After choosing a color, click on the **OK** button to go back to the **Plot Symbols** dialog box. The newly changed color will be displayed in the **Preview** box of the **Plot Symbols** dialog box. Click on **OK** to accept and change the color of the plot symbol. If you do not see a wide range of colors on your color monitor, you should increase your monitor settings using the Windows controls or the controls on your monitor.

Select Variable to Modify

Each variable plotted has its own plot symbol. Therefore, any changes you make apply only to the variable shown in the **Variable List** located on the upper right corner of the Plot Symbols dialog box (Figure 5.38).

If you have more than one variable plotted within the same window, you can modify those other variables too. To change the variable in the Plot Symbols dialog box, click on the list box and select the variable which you want to modify. After selecting the variable, repeat the procedures described in this section to change the plot symbol.

Modify Width, Style, and Color of a Plot Reference Line

To customize a reference line, pull down **Custom** from the plot main menu and select **Lines**. On a non-frequency plot (e.g. line, scatter, NP, Q, and QQ plots), the **Plot Lines** dialog box (Figure 5.40) provides a choice of three plot lines. You can use this dialog box to change the type, width, and color of the line.

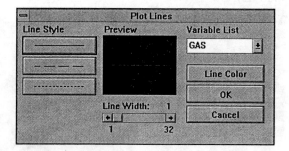

Figure 5.40 Plot Lines Dialog Box

Select Line Style

Click on the **Line Style** table to choose a new line type for your reference line. The plot **Line Style** table provides three line styles, located in the upper left corner of the dialog box. When you pick a new line style, your choice will be displayed in the **Preview** box located in the center of the dialog box.

Change Line Width

You can change the plot reference line width by scrolling the **Line Width** scroll bar left and right. The scroll bar is located in the lower section of the dialog box. The default line width is shown on top of the scroll bar.

By moving the thumb of the scroll bar, or pressing the left or right arrow on the scroll bar, you can change the line width. The changes will be displayed with your line type choice in the **Preview** box.

Change Line Color

You can change the color of a line by clicking the **COLOR** button in the Plot Lines dialog box (Figure 5.40). When you push the **Line Color** button, a color palette like Figure 5.39 will appear, and you can choose or adjust the color as described there.

Modify Size, Shape, and Color of a Marked Plot Symbol

To customize a *marked* plot symbol, pull down **Custom** from the plot window and select **Marked Symbols**. On a non-frequency plot (e.g. line, scatter, NP, Q, and QQ plots), the Marked Symbols dialog box is identical to the Plot Symbols dialog box. It consists of various plot symbols in a matrix. You can use this dialog box to change the size, shape, and color of the marked symbol. Please read **Modify Size, Shape, and Color of a Plot Symbol** above for details on using this dialog box.

Modify Plot Frame

You can change the color of the plot frame by clicking the **Frame Color** button in the **Plot Frame** dialog box (Figure 5.41). When you push the **Frame Color** button, a color palette like Figure 5.39 will appear. You can click in the color wheel to choose a color from the basic color table for the plot frame, or you can make adjustments in various ways. Please read the **Color Palette** text above for details on using this **Frame Color** button.

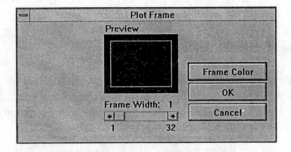

Figure 5.41 Plot Frame Dialog Box

Customizing Text and Background Color

To change the color of the plot text or background, use the **Custom** menu **Color** option in the **Plot Frame** dialog box (Figure 5.41). When you choose the Color option, you will be prompted to choose between **Text** and **Window**.

> *Note*: If you want to change the color of *text* in the plot, you must first select the text with the mouse.

When you choose the **Color** option and **Window**, the **Window Color Options** dialog box will appear. It provides a choice of **Single Color** or **Graded Color,** while the **Preview box** displays the current window color.

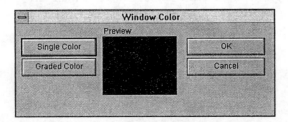

Figure 5.42 Window Color Options Dialog Box

First click on the radio button to choose **Single Color** or **Graded Color**. If you choose **Single Color**, you will go the the **Color Palette** dialog box shown in Figure 5.39. Select your color as described earlier and click **OK** on the **Color Selection** box. When you return to the **Window Color Options** box, you can see your color choice in the Preview box. When you are satisfied with the color, click **OK**.

If you choose **Graded Color**, you will also go the the **Color Selection** dialog box shown in Figure 5.39. Select your base color for the color gradation and click **OK** on the **Color Selection** box. When you return to the **Window Color Options** box, the Preview box displays the gradation, from lightest to darkest, for your chosen color. When you are satisfied with the color gradation, click **OK**.

Predefined Plot Screen

The **Custom** menu provided in EQS for Windows allows you to customize your plots in many ways. We have noticed that it takes some artistic ability and effort to customize into a desirable format. To help you to produce a good color data plot for your presentation, we provide some predefined screens for you to use. These screens differ in background color, axis color, text color, and plot symbol color. Note that some of the background colors are custom colors, displaying a gradation from one color to another. We call these eight predefined screens the **Gallery.**

To bring up the gallery template, click on the **Custom** menu from a plot window and select the **Gallery** option. The template is shown in Figure 5.43. You can click one of the eight gallery buttons to automatically change the screen display of your current plot to your chosen color combination.

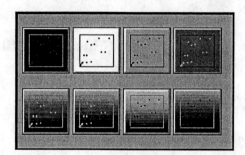

Figure 5.43 Plot Window Gallery

Customizing Bars in the Histogram and Bar Chart

When your current plot is a bar chart or histogram, the **Custom** menu displays the option **Customize Bar** in place of the **Plot Symbol** option. To use the option, first click on a bar to select that bar and all similar bars. After you choose the **Customize Bar** option, the **Customize Bar** dialog box appears.

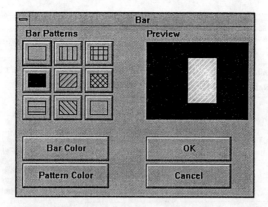

Figure 5.44 Customize Bar Dialog Box

Click on **Bar Color** to bring up the **Color Selection** dialog box and choose a new color for the bars. Then apply a pattern by clicking on a **Bar Patterns** button. After you have chosen a pattern, you can click on the **Pattern Color** button to bring up the **Color Selection** dialog box to choose a color for the pattern.

> *Notes*: 1. The empty **Bar Patterns** square is the *no pattern* choice. It will apply the *bar color* completely to the bars, omitting the pattern.
> 2. The black **Bar Patterns** square is the *fill pattern* choice. It will apply the *pattern color* to the bars, omitting the pattern and any previously-chosen bar color.

> *Note*: When you are customizing the bars in a grouped bar chart, click on one bar in the desired group to select the entire group for customization.

Save your Plot in a Picture File

You can save a plot created by EQS for Windows. Start with your open plot window. Select the **File** menu to get Figure 5.45.

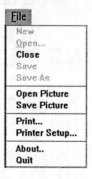

Figure 5.45 File Menu in Plot Window

Click on **Save Picture** and you will see a dialog box similar to that in Figure 5.46.

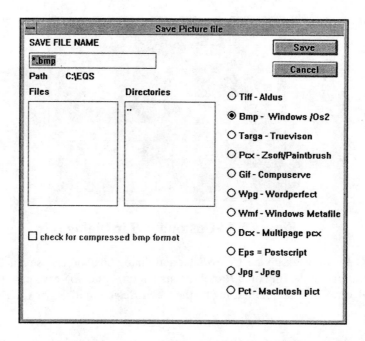

Figure 5.46 Save Picture File Dialog Box

Click on the appropriate radio button to select a graphic format. The program will fill in a pathname for your file, based on the pathname of the data sheet. You can change the name and path of the file as you like. After you have entered the correct name, click on **Save**.

Note: Saving a graphics file is display card and display driver dependent. Depending on your display driver and resolution, you may not be able to save in some formats, while you can save in others. However, you can always save in ***.bmp** or ***.tif** formats.

Open Picture Files

When you have EQS open, you can open a graphics file saved by EQS for Windows. Select the **File** menu to get Figure 5.47.

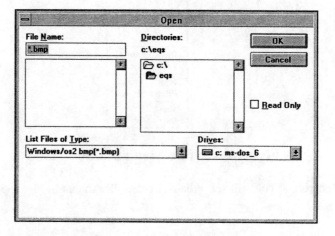

Figure 5.47 Open Picture File Dialog Box

Use the List Files of Type field to select a graphics file type. When you see the list of files, click on the file that you want to open. Click **OK**, and your plot will appear.

Move Plot from EQS for Windows to Other Applications

You can move plots from EQS for Windows to a form available for use in other programs. You might do this transfer because you want to include an EQS for Windows plot in a publication created with another Windows application. Or, you might want to further customize your plot.

Copy To Clipboard

You can use the Clipboard to put the plot in a common format where all Windows applications can access it. The Clipboard is a temporary storage facility where the format of the plot is available to all Windows applications.

To put the plot window into the Clipboard, click the **Edit** menu from the main menu and select **Copy**. This action places a color plot window in the clipboard. You can then access that plot from any Windows application.

Print your Plots

To print the plots produced by EQS for Windows, confirm that the plot window is active. Click on the **File** menu from the main menu and select the **Print** option. Each plot will be printed as it appears on the screen, although plots displaying the back hole will print without that tool. Each plot will print in the center of the paper. This version of EQS for Windows does not support color printing.

The default orientation of the printout is portrait mode. To print landscape mode (sideways on the paper), change the printer setup by using **File** menu **Printer Setup** option. Select a target printer, and then choose the **Landscape** orientation. Click **OK**.

After setting the printer to landscape mode, use **File** menu from the main menu and select the **Print** option. Your plot will print out in the desired orientation. These instructions also apply to printing a diagram or a text window in landscape mode.

6. ANALYSIS: BASIC STATISTICS

This chapter discusses some of the basic statistical tools that are available to you in the EQS for Windows environment. These include descriptive statistics, tables of frequency distributions, *t*-tests, cross-tab tests, analysis of variance, factor analysis, and correlation and regression analysis. You will find these tools under the **Analysis** choice on the main menu.

As usual, we shall use small datasets to illustrate what we are saying. We invite you to use your EQS for Windows program to work with us on these topics.

Descriptive Statistics

A small data file called **chatter.ess** gives the scores of 24 patients on four variables. This file is included with the EQS for Windows package. Also, you can find the data in Table 1 of the source: Chatterjee, S. & Yilmaz, M. (1992). A review of regression diagnostics for behavioral research. *Applied Psychological Measurement*, **16**, 209-227. The data represent:

V1 Patient's age in years
V2 Severity of illness
V3 Level of anxiety
V4 Satisfaction level

Except for V1, the variables are imprecise rating variables.

Descriptive statistics can answer questions on these data. Just how old are the patients? What is the range of scores on anxiety? These are the types of questions that are answered by descriptive statistics.

Open the file **chatter.ess**. Then, in the main menu, select **Analysis.** Click on **Descriptive**. You will see the following dialog box.

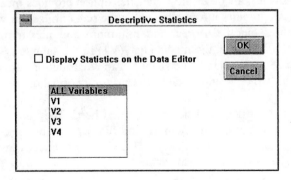

Figure 6.1 Descriptive Statistics Dialog Box

You can choose descriptive statistics on some or all of the variables, since the descriptive statistics are univariate statistics. They describe the characteristics of one variable at a time. Click **OK** with the default **ALL Variables** selected, and you will immediately get an informational message that the descriptive stats are done.

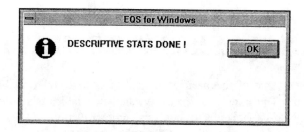

Figure 6.2 Descriptive Statistics Completion Message

At the prompt, click the mouse button, and you will find yourself in the file **output.log**. This file will show the following information.

```
DESCRIPTIVE STATISTICS


4  Variables are selected from file CHATTER.ESS

  Number of cases in data file are ..........    24

   Variable                                               SUM of
     ID      NAME    CASES      MEAN          SUM          SQUARE
      1       V1       24      40.583       974.000       2101.833
      2       V2       24      51.375      1233.000        627.625
      3       V3       24       2.283        54.800          2.293
      4       V4       24      60.583      1454.000       6467.833

            Standard                One        Three
     ID    Deviation    Median    Quartile   Quartile   Minimum    Maximum
      1      9.560      40.500     33.000     47.000     28.000     63.000
      2      5.224      50.500     48.000     54.000     43.000     65.000
      3      0.316       2.300      2.150      2.400      1.700      2.900
      4     16.769      58.500     48.500     73.500     26.000     89.000

     ID     Range    SKEWNESS   KURTOSIS
      1     35.000     0.525      -0.349
      2     22.000     0.918       1.105
      3      1.200     0.339       0.460
      4     63.000     0.104      -0.457
```

For each of the four variables, the descriptive statistics option provides mean and median information about central tendency. It provides information about the scatter of scores with the standard deviation as well as first and third quartile scores, and minimum and maximum scores along with their difference, the range. For example, the median age (V1) in the sample is 40.5, and the age range of the sample varies from 28 to 63 years. The shapes of the distributions are described by the measures of skewness and kurtosis, which would be close to zero for a normal distribution.

The definitions of these statistics need not be repeated here. They are given in standard statistics books and are consistent with usage in the SAS and SPSS program packages. We will not discuss how to interpret these basic descriptive statistics. Hopefully, you already know this. If you do not, you should consult a basic statistics book for information.

Statistics Displayed on the Data Editor

If, in the dialog box of Figure 6.1, you had marked the check box to **Display Statistics on the Data Editor**, you would have created the window **describ.ess** automatically. This window is shown in Figure 6.3, and is available to you via the Window menu.

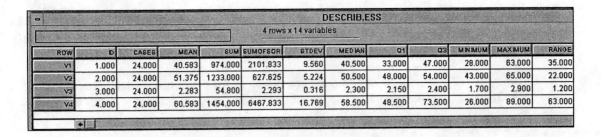

ROW	ID	CASES	MEAN	SUM	SUMOFSQR	STDEV	MEDIAN	Q1	Q3	MINIMUM	MAXIMUM	RANGE
V1	1.000	24.000	40.583	974.000	2101.833	9.560	40.500	33.000	47.000	28.000	63.000	35.000
V2	2.000	24.000	51.375	1233.000	627.625	5.224	50.500	48.000	54.000	43.000	65.000	22.000
V3	3.000	24.000	2.283	54.800	2.293	0.316	2.300	2.150	2.400	1.700	2.900	1.200
V4	4.000	24.000	60.583	1454.000	6467.833	16.769	58.500	48.500	73.500	26.000	89.000	63.000

DESCRIB.ESS — 4 rows x 14 variables

Figure 6.3 Descriptive Statistics in the Data Editor

The information is identical to that given in the earlier printout, but the information is in a different format. There is an important advantage to this Data Editor format in some applications.

This seemingly minor feature, the ability to place statistics in the Data Editor, has important implications for your ability to understand your data. **Once statistics are in the Data Editor, you can apply to these numbers any of the plotting and analysis procedures available within EQS for Windows**. After all, this is just a data matrix.

For example, you could run a descriptive statistics analysis on the columns of this new data. The result would be similar in format to that shown above, but computed on the statistics given for the different variables.

More specifically, you could plot or correlate the columns labeled MEAN and STDEV to see if means and standard deviations are systematically related. With these data, this might not be an interesting question, but there are some datasets in which it is. For example, if V1-V4 represented four different samples from a single normally distributed population, then the sample means and variances would be uncorrelated. Would means and standard deviations also be uncorrelated?

Frequency Tables

You can display frequency distributions on variables in table form. For example, click on **Window** and **chatter.ess** to make the file **chatter.ess** active again. Click on **Analysis** and then **Frequency**, to bring up the dialog box shown in Figure 6.4. It asks you to select one or more variables, and gives you the option to also display descriptive statistics.

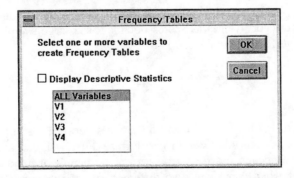

Figure 6.4 Frequency Tables Dialog Box

A frequency table gives the ordered distribution of scores on a single variable. The default is **ALL Variables**, but we choose only V3. If you place an **x** into the checkbox to **Display Descriptive Statistics**, the simple descriptive statistics mentioned above are also printed in the output.

When you click **OK**, you will be told that the computations for the frequency tables are done. When you click **OK** again, you will go to the file that contains the results, **output.log**. In this case, you will see the following.

```
FREQUENCY TABLES
1  Variables are selected from file CHATTER.ESS
   Number of cases in data file are ..........    24

   **************
   *    V3    *
   **************

        MEAN:      2.283        MEDIAN:      2.300
         SUM:     54.800   ONE QUARTILE:    2.150
  SUM OF SQR:      2.293  THREE QUARTILE:    2.400
   STND dEV.:      0.316      SKEWNESS:      0.339
     MINIMUM:      1.700      KURTOSIS:      0.460
     MAXIMUM:      2.900
       RANGE:      1.200

     CATEGORY                     P E R  C  E  N  T
      VALUE         COUNT       CELL      CUMULATIVE
      1.70            1         4.17          4.17
      1.80            2         8.33         12.50
      1.90            1         4.17         16.67
      2.10            2         8.33         25.00
      2.20            4        16.67         41.67
      2.30            6        25.00         66.67
      2.40            4        16.67         83.33
      2.50            1         4.17         87.50
      2.90            3        12.50        100.00
  --------------------------------------------------------
      TOTAL COUNTS    24    TOTAL PERCENT  100.00
```

The output tells you the variable chosen for analysis, the file used, the number of cases used in the computations, and provides counts of the number of cases having each particular score. The scores are arranged from small to large. In this case, scores range from 1.7 to 2.9 (as you could tell from the descriptive statistics computed above). In this example, although V3 is supposedly a continuous variable, it has only nine different values due to the coding of the variable. The score **2.20** occurred four times, which represents 16.67% of the sample of 24 cases. The final column gives the cumulative percent.

Note that a frequency table becomes unwieldy if you have a truly continuous variable that has hundreds of different category values as scores obtained in a large sample. The frequency table is most meaningful for categorical variables.

t-Test

The *t*-test is a standard way to evaluate mean differences between variables. Virtually all statistics books describe this test, which takes one of two forms. First, you can use the test to evaluate one mean, or to compare two means, based on scores from one sample of subjects. Secondly, you can use it for similar purposes when comparing two different sets of subjects. We shall discuss the one-sample and two-sample cases separately.

One-Sample *t*-Test

We shall use some data given in Table 7.1 of the following standard text to illustrate the one-sample test: Moore, D. S., & McCabe, G. P. (1993). ***Introduction to the Practice of Statistics, 2nd Ed.*** New York: W. H. Freeman. This is the file **mm508.ess**, which you should **Open** at this time.

Data File Organization

The data consist of the listening ability scores of 20 French teachers before and after an immersion program. Each teacher has one score before the program, and one score afterwards. These data are organized in a 20 by 2 data matrix. Since there are 20 subjects, there are 20 rows to the matrix. The two before/after variables are the columns in the data matrix. In general, one-sample data will be organized in this way. You will specify which one variable, or which two variables, you want to analyze in this matrix.

Test of a Single Mean

We can ask two different questions about these data. The first is whether these particular teachers are representative of French teachers in general. That question is addressed in this section. We could also ask whether the training program improved the teachers' scores from pretest to posttest. That will be addressed subsequently.

Press **Analysis** on the main menu, and then click on **t-Test**. You will see the dialog box shown in Figure 6.5. There are two main parts to this box, the one-sample *t*-test, and the two-sample *t*-test.

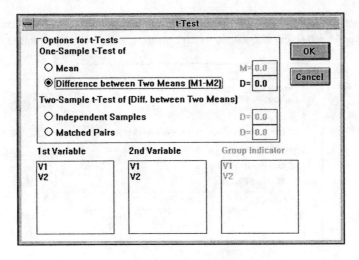

Figure 6.5 *t*-Test Dialog Box

Since we have a single sample of 20 subjects, we are interested in the top half which deals with the **One-Sample t Test**. We have two choices. For this discussion, we shall discuss the first, a test on one **Mean**. The default, shown marked in the figure, the **Difference between Two Means (M1-M2),** would tell us whether two means are significantly different. We will want to investigate the difference between means as our second question, and that option will be discussed below. The two list boxes in the bottom of the figure show that there are two variables, **V1** and **V2**, in the data file. The variables contain Pretest and Posttest scores, respectively.

As you see in the first line, you can perform a test on the **Mean** of a single variable, and you can specify whether your hypothesis is **M=0.0** or some other value. When you select the radio button for **Mean**, the list box **1st Variable** also remains active, while the list box **2nd Variable** becomes inactive.

Use the **1st Variable** list box to specify the variable you want to analyze. The remaining information in the dialog box is irrelevant in this example. For example, the inactive list boxes for **2nd Variable** and **Group** are not important in this analysis.

The *t*-test on a single mean is rarely used, since it is typically difficult to specify an appropriate null hypothesis. In some circumstances, however, this test can be very informative. Suppose in the example that the listening test of spoken French were a well standardized test, for which the norming population distribution is essentially known. That is, we might know that the norming population of French teachers has a mean on the test of, say, 22.1. Under appropriate conditions, we then also will know the distribution of sample means. In general, samples from this population would have means that are not too far from 22.1. (There is a precise formula; check your statistics text!)

On the other hand, the current sample comes from some population. Assuming that we have a simple random sample from this population, we may want to evaluate whether its population mean at PRETEST could be 22.1. If we cannot reject this null hypothesis, this population may well be the same as the population of the standardized test. In practice, we would conclude that the sample can be considered to be a random sample from the norming population. But if we reject the null hypothesis, the sample PRETEST mean would be very different from the hypothesized value. Then we cannot consider the mean of the population from which these particular teachers come to be the mean of the norming population. We would conclude that they are a sample from some other population.

To perform such a one-sample test, click on the **Mean** radio button. To its right the *default null hypothesis value* **M = 0.0** will become active, permitting you to enter any value.

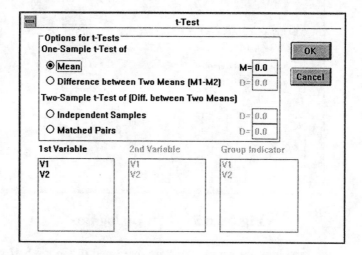

Figure 6.6 One-Sample Mean *t*-Test Dialog Box

The population value we are considering is 22.1, and so we enter **M = 22.1**. Since the **1st Variable** list box is active, you can select the variable that you want to test. Select **V1** as shown in Figure 6.7.

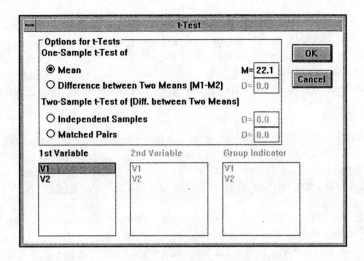

Figure 6.7 One-Sample *t*-Test Dialog Box

Click **OK**, and the one-sample, single mean *t*-test is computed. As usual, the program will inform you when the *t*-test is done, so click **OK**. The results are found in **output.log**:

```
t-TEST

Variables are selected from file C:\EQS\MM508.ESS

Variable V1  N=    20
          MEAN:        25.800       MEDIAN:        27.000
           SUM:       516.000       SKEWNESS:      -0.952
   SUM OF SQR:        755.200       KURTOSIS:       0.492
   STND. DEV.:          6.305
      MINIMUM:         10.000
      MAXIMUM:         33.000
        RANGE:         23.000


             STD. ERR   t-STATISTIC      DF    P-VALUE
      ---------------------------------------------------
      DIFFERENCE   1.4097        2.6246      19    0.0167
      25.80 -22.10
```

The output shows the data file and variable being used, along with some descriptive statistics. In the last line, the output shows the specific difference being tested, its standard error, the *t*-statistic, degrees of freedom, and the probability level for the two-tailed test.

In this example, we can reject the null hypothesis. That is, the mean of the population from which these teachers come is unlikely to be 22.1 (which is not surprising, since we picked 22.1 arbitrarily to make a point). In fact, the sample mean is 25.8, indicating that these teachers perform substantially better, even before any immersion training, than one would expect if one had a random sample of French teachers from our imaginary norming population.

Difference Between Two Means

The main interest in a study such as this is, of course, the second question. Did the training program have any impact? Some teachers may have improved, and others not, so this second question must be phrased more precisely. Did the mean scores improve significantly, when we consider them relative to the variability in those scores i.e., given that some individuals may have changed substantially while others changed very little? Or, phrased somewhat more neutrally, can we reject the null hypothesis that there was no change, on the average, between pretest and posttest?

This question addresses a standard application of the one-sample *t*-test. That standard application is the program's default, as is shown in Figure 6.5. The radio button **Difference between Two Means**

(M1-M2) is marked. The test of difference between two means also gives the *default null hypothesis value* of **D = 0.0**. That is, under the null hypothesis that M1 = M2, the difference D = M1 - M2 would be zero. The *t*-test provides a statistical evaluation of this hypothesis. If we had a hypothesis that the difference in means is a specific value, say 3 points, we could type **3** in the text box. However, since such a null hypothesis can be only rarely justified, this example retains the default value of **0**.

Of course we need to specify the two variables whose means are to be compared. At the bottom of the figure you will see listings for the **1st Variable** and **2nd Variable**. These list boxes contain the names of the variables in the current file. Here, we have Pretest and Posttest scores, in variables V1 and V2. Thus, we take the **1st Variable** to be **V2** and the **2nd Variable** to be **V1**.

The hypothesis on M1 - M2 is, in this example, a hypothesis on **V2 - V1**. So, if the teachers improved, the scores should have become larger, and the mean difference should be positive. You could, of course, select the V1 as the 1st Variable, and the V2 as the 2nd Variable; in that case the mean difference should be negative if the teachers improved. When you click **OK**, the statistic is computed, and the results go to **output.log**:

```
t-TEST

Variables are selected from file C:\EQS\MM508.ESS
Compare V2 and V1  D=  0.000

Variable V2  N=    20
        MEAN:           28.300        MEDIAN:          27.500
         SUM:          566.000        SKEWNESS:        -0.739
 SUM OF SQR:          672.200        KURTOSIS:        -0.324
 STND. DEV.:            5.948
    MINIMUM:           15.000
    MAXIMUM:           36.000
      RANGE:           21.000

Variable V1  N=    20
        MEAN:           25.800        MEDIAN:          27.000
         SUM:          516.000        SKEWNESS:        -0.952
 SUM OF SQR:          755.200        KURTOSIS:        -0.492
 STND. DEV.:            6.305
    MINIMUM:           10.000
    MAXIMUM:           33.000
      RANGE:           23.000

DIFFERENCE
        MEAN:            2.500        MEDIAN:           3.000
         SUM:           50.000        SKEWNESS:        -1.094
 SUM OF SQR:          159.000        KURTOSIS:         2.751
 STND. DEV.:            2.893
    MINIMUM:           -6.000
    MAXIMUM:            6.000
      RANGE:           12.000

               STD. ERR   t STATISTIC      DF    P-VALUE
----------------------------------------------------------
DIFFERENCE       0.6469       3.8649        19    0.0010
2.50 - 0.00
```

The results include basic statistics for each of the two variables, and then statistics for the difference variable which is the actual basis of the *t*-test. The mean of the difference variable is 2.5, which is tested against the null value of 0.0. The standard error of the difference is about .65, leading to a *t*-statistic of 3.86. The null hypothesis of no change can be rejected.

Moore and McCabe (1993) discuss this example further, with regard to violation of assumptions such as independence of observations, ceiling effects on the scores, and the assumption of normality of the difference scores. EQS for Windows provides many ways that you can explore violation of assumptions. For example, you could use **Transformation** to compute the difference scores, and then plot them to see if you can locate an outlier point that might lead one to question normality. Or, you could use the scatter plot of the two variables to see if you can spot some outliers from the regression line. Similarly, you could see if the correlation between Pretest and Posttest changes substantially by omitting an outlier. (Hint: it does.)

Two-Sample t-Test

The dialog box in Figure 6.5 also shows a **Two-Sample t-Test of (Diff. between Two Means)**. This is reproduced for a different example in Figure 6.8, below. In the two-sample case, there are two sets of subjects, possibly drawn from different populations. The procedures differ slightly when the scores of these sets of subjects are independent, or if the scores are functionally related. The typical example of a functional relation occurs when the subjects have been matched in some way. We shall discuss these two cases in turn.

Data File Organization

Data for two-sample *t*-tests require an organization in the Data Editor that is different from the one-sample test. In two-sample data, data for one sample is given in the top part of a data matrix, and the corresponding data for the second sample is given in the bottom part of the same matrix. The rows, as usual, correspond to subjects, and the columns, to variables. The potential dependent variable whose mean is of interest will be a column of this matrix. You will specify which column to use. This is called the **1st Variable**.

In addition, the two-sample tests require the existence of a special variable in the matrix whose entries code group membership. This variable is called the **Group** variable. A typical coding might be **1** for each subject in group 1, and **2** for each subject in group 2. Thus, the variable must be dichotomous. You will specify the grouping variable.

Independent Samples

The file **werner.ess** can be used to illustrate the independent samples *t*-test. Please **Open** this file now. You will see that it contains nine variables and 188 cases. There are some missing data values in this file, but the variables we shall work with, V5 and V6, contain no missing data. V6 gives the cholesterol level scores for all 188 subjects and will be the dependent variable.

V5 is the group indicator variable containing the coding for two groups. Some of these subjects, all females, use birth control pills (code=2), while other subjects do not use these pills (code=1). Our question is: Do the women who use birth control pills differ on cholesterol level when compared to the women who do not use such pills?

Go to **Analysis** and select **t-Test**. A dialog box similar to Figure 6.5 will appear.

Click on the radio button beside **Independent Samples**. The screen will resemble Figure 6.8. As usual, the statistical null hypothesis is framed in the reverse fashion, namely, that the means of the two populations are equal, and hence that the difference between these means is zero. The *default null hypothesis value* is shown in the dialog box as **D = 0.0**. If the null hypothesis you are interested in testing were a different one, for example, D = 5.4, you would move your pointer into the text box and type in the appropriate value. As noted above, null hypotheses other than D = 0.0 are often difficult to justify.

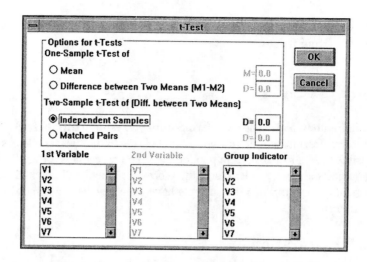

Figure 6.8 Two-Sample *t*-Test Dialog Box

You will see that the list boxes for **1st Variable** and **Group Indicator** are highlighted. The **2nd Variable** list box is not highlighted, indicating that it is not active and cannot be used. As noted above, it is assumed for the independent samples *t*-test that the dependent variable data for the two groups are in different rows of the data matrix in the Data Editor.

The **1st Variable** is the dependent variable whose means are to be compared. In this example, we want to analyze the cholesterol scores, so click on **V6**. The **Group Indicator** is the binary or dichotomous variable that serves to show whether a subject belongs to one group or the other. The grouping variable is V5, so select **V5** under **Group Indicator**.

Click **OK**, then click **OK** again when you see the prompt telling you that the computations have finished. When the *t*-test is done, the following results are shown in **output.log:**

```
t TEST

Variables are selected from file C:\EQS\WERNER.ESS

V6 is grouped by        V5 D=  0.000

V6 on V5(  1.00)  N=    94
            MEAN:        232.968        MEDIAN:       230.000
             SUM:      21899.000        SKEWNESS:       0.301
     SUM OF SQR:     175910.904        KURTOSIS:      -0.602
     STND. DEV.:         43.492
        MINIMUM:        155.000
        MAXIMUM:        335.000
          RANGE:        180.000

V6 on V5(  2.00)  N=    94
            MEAN:        241.223        MEDIAN:       236.000
             SUM:      22675.000        SKEWNESS:       2.306
     SUM OF SQR:     322786.309        KURTOSIS:      14.922
     STND. DEV.:         58.914
        MINIMUM:         50.000
        MAXIMUM:        600.000
          RANGE:        550.000

METHOD       TEST STATISTICS     DF      P-VALUE
POOLED    t          -1.0930   186.0      0.2758
SEPARATE  t          -1.0930   171.2      0.2759
```

Some descriptive statistics are shown for each group. You can see that the means of the two groups are 232.968 and 241.223, respectively.

The *t*-statistics are given at the bottom of the printout, computed in two standard ways. These are called the **pooled** and **separate** *t*-tests. They use the same mean difference, but estimate the standard error and degrees of freedom differently. The pooled test uses formulas given by Moore and McCabe (1993), eqs. (7.5)-(7.6), while the separate test uses formulas (7.3)-(7.4). Most statistics textbooks discuss these formulas, both computationally and conceptually. You can also see the *BMDP Statistical Software Manual* for more information. In this example, both test statistics are small, and we cannot reject the null hypothesis that **D=0.0**.

Matched Pairs

If the data come from two samples, but the dependent variable scores are functionally related somehow, then it is not appropriate to use the independent samples *t*-test. The standard violation of independence occurs when subjects in two samples have been matched, or paired. That is, the pairs of scores are specifically linked in some way.

In the **werner.ess** data there is, in fact, such a dependency. The 188 cases are age-matched, and the matching creates data that are paired. Each pair is a given age, and one member of each pair uses birth-control pills while the other member does not use such pills. Hence, it was inappropriate to do an independent samples *t*-test with these data! We should have used the **matched pairs** *t*-test.

In the matched pairs procedure, it is assumed that *pairs are matched by their sequence on the* **Group** *variable*. In practice this means that the scores on the **Group** variable will exist in one of two standard formats. These are the **alternating** and **sequential** formats.

> **Alternating format**. The group variable alternates the two possible scores, and each pair of scores is matched. In the **werner.ess** file, if you look at V5, you will see that the scores in sequence are 1,2,1,2,1,2, and so on. Furthermore, each (1,2) pair is matched. That is, cases 1 and 2 are matched, so are cases 3 and 4, and so on.

> **Sequential format**. The group variable is organized so that all cases with a given code come first, then all cases with the other code follow. In addition, pairs are matched case by case across the two sequences. Suppose we had reorganized the **werner.ess** file so that all the **1** scores on V5 came first, and all the **2** scores were below that, but that the ordering of cases within the **1** category was not changed, and the ordering of cases within the **2** category also was not changed. Then the first cases in each set are paired, so are the second, and so on. Stated differently, if the group indicator variable is such that the scores are 1,1,1,1,...,2,2,2,2,... in sequence, it is assumed that the case having the first **1** is paired with the case having the first **2**, the second **1** is paired with the second **2**, and so on.

> *Note:* If your file is not organized in one of these two ways, you will obtain misleading results.

Let us rerun the **werner.ess** *t*-test procedure as a matched-pairs test. Choose **Window** and **werner.ess**, then **Analysis** and *t*-**Test**.

Click on the **Matched Pairs** radio button. Click on **V6** in the list box **1st Variable**, **V5** in the **Group** list box. The resulting *t*-statistic takes on the value of -1.07, virtually the same as before. It yields the same conclusion as that yielded by the incorrect analysis. There is no evidence against the hypothesis that population cholesterol means are the same among birth control pill users and nonusers.

One Sample Data As Matched Pairs

Although we have pointed out that one-sample and two-sample data are differently organized, you may find that some data files are organized in an unexpected way. In particular, you may find one-sample data organized in the format of two-sample data.

You will remember that the file **mm508.ess** represented before/after data (in two columns) for 20 subjects (in 20 rows). Another way to organize the same data is given in the file **mm508grp.ess**, which you should **Open** now.

You will see that this file contains 40 rows and two columns. The first variable contains the before/after data, end to end, instead of side-by-side, as in the original file. As a result, the rows of the data matrix no longer represent data from independent cases; the data are paired using the **sequential** format described above. The second variable contains the group indicator variable. It is dummy coded as 1 or 2, depending on whether the row represents data from before treatment, or from after treatment.

It is indeed all right to analyze data such as this by the **Matched Pairs** *t*-test, since the results will be exactly the same as the **One Sample t-Test of Differences Between Two Means**. Go ahead and click on **Analysis**, **t-Test**, and use the **Matched Pairs** with **V1** as the **1st Variable** and **V2** as the **Group Indicator**.

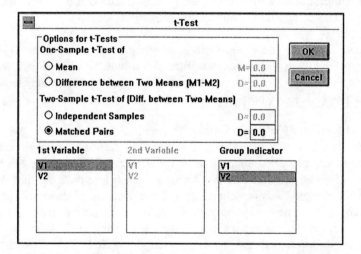

Figure 6.9 Matched Pairs *t*-Test Dialog Box

Click **OK**. Click **OK** again when prompted at the end of the calculation, and you will see that the resulting *t* = -3.865. This is the same value as before, except for sign. The sign is reversed due to our choice of coding V2 and the way we organized the pretest and posttest data sequentially in the data matrix.

Crosstab: Two-Way Tables

EQS for Windows provides a test of independence of two categorical variables with its **Crosstab** option in the **Analysis** menu. The procedure is straightforward. We shall use the **survey.ess** data from the *BMDP Statistical Software Manual*. The file represents the responses of 294 subjects to a survey on depression and related mental and physical health variables.

Let us determine the relation between two depression items. V10 indicates how frequently a subject felt depressed, and V23 how often the subject slept badly. It seems likely that subjects who are more frequently depressed would also have sleeping difficulties. Responses are coded 0-3 for each variable. We shall evaluate the null hypothesis that depression and sleeping difficulties are independent.

Open the **survey.ess** file now. When this file is active, go to the main menu and select the **Analysis** option, then scroll down to **Crosstab** and select it. You will see the following dialog box.

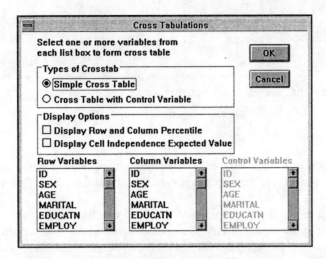

Figure 6.10 Cross Tabulations Dialog Box

When you first see the box, the radio button **Simple Cross Table** will be marked as a default. We want to keep that choice. The two check boxes, **Display Row and Column Percentile** and **Display Cell Independence Expected Value** are not marked by default, but you should click on these to make them active. Also, you should select **V10** from the list box **Row Variables** and **V23** from the list of **Column Variables.**

Click **OK** to start the computations. When the computations are completed, the program will tell you **CROSSTAB DONE.** Click on **OK** to move to the **output.log.** You will see the following result.

```
CROSS TABULATIONS

Variables are selected from file C:\EQS\SURVEY.ESS

  Number of cases in data file are ...........   294
  Number of cases used in this analysis are ..   294

CROSS TABLES for V10 AND V23 ...


            Column Variable is V23
```

V10	0.000	1.000	2.000	3.000	TOTAL
0.000	123	42	7	2	174
CELL %	41.84	14.29	2.38	0.68	59.18
ROW %	70.69	24.14	4.02	1.15	100.00
COLUMN %	75.46	51.85	21.21	11.76	
EXPECTED	96.47	47.94	19.53	10.06	
1.000	33	30	18	3	84
CELL %	11.22	10.20	6.12	1.02	28.57
ROW %	39.29	35.71	21.43	3.57	100.00
COLUMN %	20.25	37.04	54.55	17.65	
EXPECTED	46.57	23.14	9.43	4.86	

2.000	6	7	5	6	24
CELL %	2.04	2.38	1.70	2.04	8.16
ROW %	25.00	29.17	20.83	25.00	100.00
COLUMN %	3.68	8.64	15.15	35.29	
EXPECTED	13.31	6.61	2.69	1.39	
3.000	1	2	3	6	12
CELL %	0.34	0.68	1.02	2.04	4.08
ROW %	8.33	16.67	25.00	50.00	100.00
COLUMN %	0.61	2.47	9.09	35.29	
EXPECTED	6.65	3.31	1.35	0.69	
TOTAL	163	81	33	17	294
TOTAL %	55.44	27.55	11.22	5.78	100.00
ROW %					
COLUMN %	100.00	100.00	100.00	100.00	

```
MINIMUM ESTIMATED EXPECTED VALUE IS     0.694 IN ( 4,  4)

STATISTICS            VALUE      D.F.    P-VALUE
Pearson Chi-Square   106.2811      9     0.0000
Likelihood Ratio      80.9381      9     0.0000
```

The first entry in each cell of the table is the frequency count with which a particular combination of responses was observed. These frequencies sum to 294 across the cells. That is the sample size.

An actual cell count needs to be compared to the bottom entry for the cell, the expected number of cases in that cell under the model of independence of row and column variables. If the variables are independent, the observed frequencies will be close to the expected values. A substantial discrepancy implies a lack of independence. The table also computes percentages for each cell count when considered in relation to its row, and separately, when considered in relation to its column totals.

When you compare the observed and expected cell counts in the 0,0 cell, the 3,3 cell, and in related cells, it is apparent that these cells have larger observed counts than expected under the model of independence. For example, people who score the maximum value of **3** on both V10 and V23 occur more frequently than expected under the null hypothesis of independence (6 observed cases versus .69 expected). The null hypothesis can be rejected by both **Pearson** and **Likelihood Ratio** chi-square statistics, since the statistics are large compared to degrees of freedom. Evidently, depression and sleeping badly are associated.

As noted in the line **MINIMUM ESTIMATED EXPECTED VALUE**, however, there is a cell in which the expected value is sufficiently small that there may be a question of the adequacy of the probability, or *p*-value, of the chi-square statistic. Also, six cells of the table have expected cell counts of less than 5, confirming caution in accepting the *p*-value of the statistic too precisely. It might be desirable to combine adjacent categories in these variables, and then to redo the analysis. If you wanted to do this, you could do the recoding with the **Group** option from the **Data** main menu item.

The independence test can be done after controlling on a third variable. This is the option **Cross Table with Control Variable**. It is not illustrated, since the procedure is basically the same as the example provided above. Cross tables are generated for each level of the control variable, and the simultaneous independence in each of these separate tables is assessed.

As illustrated in the example, input data to the **CROSSTAB** analysis is the usual file of scores of cases on variables, as visualized in the Data Editor. At present, there is no capability for reading table information in a condensed format.

170

ANOVA

The analysis of variance (ANOVA) is one of the most widely used statistical methods in behavioral and social sciences. It is used to study the effect of experimental manipulations on an outcome variable measured on subjects who were randomly assigned to experimental conditions. You can also use ANOVA, with caution, in non-experimental contexts.

In EQS for Windows, you can do simple one-way and two-way anovas with the **ANOVA** option in the **Analysis** menu. It is assumed that your model is balanced, that is, that you have an equal number of observations per cell.

One-Way Analysis of Variance

We shall use the **mm725.ess** dataset to illustrate this method. These data were taken from page 725 of Moore and McCabe's (1993) text, cited previously. They describe the pretest reading comprehension scores of three groups of children who were later assigned to different methods of instruction. **Open** this file now.

You will see that there are three columns of data, labeled **GROUP**, **ID**, and **READING**. The ID variable is a case index number and is not of interest in this example. The question is whether mean reading scores differ by group. That is, we want to test the null hypothesis that the population means for these three groups are equal.

From the main menu, select **Analysis**, and then **ANOVA**. You will see the dialog box shown in Figure 6.11.

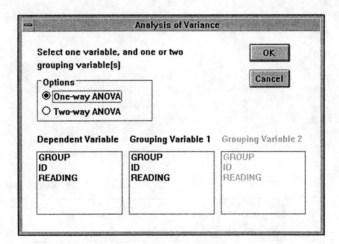

Figure 6.11 Analysis of Variance Dialog Box

The default option is the **One-way ANOVA**, and its radio button is preselected. We need to choose only the **Dependent** and **Grouping** variables, namely **READING** and **GROUP**. Since this is a one-way ANOVA, there is only one grouping variable. A grouping variable must be a categorical variable. In this example, the grouping variable, **GROUP**, has three categories coded as **1**, **2**, and **3**. Choose **READING** as the **Dependent Variable** and GROUP as the **Grouping Variable 1**. Click **OK**, and the analysis will proceed.

When it is finished, you will see the message **ANOVA IS DONE**. Click **OK**, and the results will appear in the **output.log**. As usual, the first part of the results provide information on the method and data used. Then, basic statistics are provided for the total set of subjects, and then similar statistics are given for each of the three groups. The breakdown of variance is given at the end.

```
One Way ANOVA
Variables are selected from file C:\EQS\MM725.ESS

* * * * * * * * * * * * * *
*    READING    *
* * * * * * * * * * * * * *

Variable    READING
Number of cases in data file are ........... 66
Number of cases used in this analysis are .. 66

        MEAN:        9.788        MEDIAN:         9.000
         SUM:      646.000  ONE QUARTILE:         8.000
 SUM OF SQR:      593.030 THREE QUARTILE:        12.000
 STND. DEV.:        3.021      SKEWNESS:         0.078
    MINIMUM:        4.000      KURTOSIS:        -0.760
    MAXIMUM:       16.000
      RANGE:       12.000

READING is grouped by      GROUP

GROUP(  1.00)  N=    22
        MEAN:       10.500        MEDIAN:        11.500
         SUM:      231.000      SKEWNESS:        -0.251
 SUM OF SQR:      185.500      KURTOSIS:        -0.209
 STND. DEV.:        2.972
    MINIMUM:        4.000
    MAXIMUM:       16.000
      RANGE:       12.000

GROUP(  2.00)  N=    22
        MEAN:        9.727        MEDIAN:         9.000
         SUM:      214.000      SKEWNESS:         0.930
 SUM OF SQR:      152.364      KURTOSIS:         0.142
 STND. DEV.:        2.694
    MINIMUM:        6.000
    MAXIMUM:       16.000
      RANGE:       10.000

GROUP(  3.00)  N=    22
        MEAN:        9.136        MEDIAN:         8.500
         SUM:      201.000      SKEWNESS:         0.004
 SUM OF SQR:      234.591      KURTOSIS:        -1.450
 STND. DEV.:        3.342
    MINIMUM:        4.000
    MAXIMUM:       14.000
      RANGE:       10.000

                ANALYSIS OF VARIANCE
                =====================
```

	SUM OF SQUARES	DF	MEAN SQUARES	F-RATIO	P-VALUE
GROUP	20.5758	2	10.2879	1.132	0.329
ERROR	572.4545	63	9.0866		
TOTAL	593.0303	65			

```
         P VALUE    =    0.3288
```

The analysis of variance table gives the usual breakdown of the sum of squares into between-means and error, along with the associated degrees of freedom. The corresponding mean squares provide the basis for the F test. In this case the $F(2,63) = 1.132$, with a probability value of .329, indicating that the null hypothesis of equal means cannot be rejected. Since this is a pretest, it shows that the groups are equal before the intervention takes place.

Two-Way Analysis of Variance

In two way analysis of variance, there are two coded categorical variables that represent group membership and one dependent variable. Thus, three variables are analyzed. The analysis aims to determine the effect of the categorical variables and their interaction on the dependent variable. In addition to partitioning the variance, statistical tests evaluate the null hypotheses that the main effects and the interaction on the dependent variable are zero.

> *Note*: This version of ANOVA handles only balanced cells. That is, the sample sizes in all cells must be equal. You cannot have a missing cell.

The file **pancake.ess** shows 24 case scores on three variables, **QUALITY**, **SUPPLMNT**, and **WHEY**, taken from: Ryan, B. F., Joiner, B. L., & Ryan Jr., T. A. (1992). *MINITAB Handbook*, **2nd Ed. Rev.**. Boston: PWS-Kent, p. 206. The data represent the effects of two factors, a food supplement and whey, on the rated quality of pancakes that were baked using various levels of these factors. There were four levels of whey and two levels of the supplement, so there are eight treatment combinations or cells. With three ratings in each cell, there are $8 \times 3 = 24$ overall quality ratings. The task is to determine the effects of the independent variables, and their interaction, on the rated quality of pancakes.

As before, click on **Analysis** on the main menu, and then choose **ANOVA** to get the ANOVA dialog box. This time, click on the button **Two-way ANOVA** so that the dialog box looks like Figure 6.12.

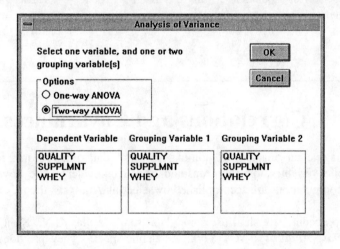

Figure 6.12 Two-Way ANOVA Dialog Box

In the bottom of the dialog box, select the variable **QUALITY** as the **Dependent Variable**, **SUPPLMNT** as the **Grouping Variable 1**, and **WHEY** as the **Grouping Variable 2**. Then click **OK**.

The results of the anova are, as usual, shown in the **output.log** file. The format is very similar to that of the one-way analysis shown above. The summary statistics for the entire set of subjects are given first, then statistics are given for each combination of independent variables. As just noted, **SUPPLMNT** has two levels and **WHEY** has four levels, so there are eight possible combinations of groups, and the output provides statistics for each such combination. To save space, only the first group's summary is presented here.

```
Two Way ANOVA
Variables are selected from file C:\EQS\PANCAKE.ESS

**************     **************     **************
*   QUALITY   *  on  *   SUPPLMNT  * and *      WHEY  *
**************     **************     **************

Variable   QUALITY
Number of cases in data file are ........... 24
Number of cases used in this analysis are .. 24

          MEAN:          4.487         MEDIAN:         4.600
           SUM:        107.700  ONE QUARTILE:         4.050
   SUM OF SQR:         11.406 THREE QUARTILE:         4.900
   STND. DEV.:          0.704       SKEWNESS:        -0.583
      MINIMUM:          3.100       KURTOSIS:        -0.446
      MAXIMUM:          5.600
        RANGE:          2.500

QUALITY is grouped by  SUPPLMNT and       WHEY
SUPPLMNT(  1.00) and WHEY(  1.00)  N=      3
          MEAN:          4.400         MEDIAN:         4.500
           SUM:         13.200       SKEWNESS:         0.000
   SUM OF SQR:          0.020       KURTOSIS:        -2.333
   STND. DEV.:          0.100
      MINIMUM:          4.300
      MAXIMUM:          4.500
        RANGE:          0.200

            - some output omitted -

              ANALYSIS OF VARIANCE
              ====================
```

	SUM OF SQUARES	DF	MEAN SQUARES	F-RATIO	P-VALUE
SUPPLMNT	0.5104	1	0.5104	17.014	0.001
WHEY	6.6912	3	2.2304	74.347	0.000
INTERACTION	3.7246	3	1.2415	41.384	0.000
ERROR	0.4800	16	0.0300		
TOTAL	11.4063	23			

Correlations and Covariances

It is hard to imagine an analysis of non-experimental data that doesn't require evaluating the correlations among variables, or, their unstandardized equivalents, the covariances. In EQS for Windows, these computations are accomplished by selecting **Analysis**, then **Correlations**.

To illustrate the procedure, we shall use some data from Mardia, K. V., Kent, J. T., & Bibby, J. M. (1979). *Multivariate Analysis*. New York: Academic, p. 3. They provided exam grades for 88 students in five technical topics. The topics were mechanics, vectors, algebra, analysis, and statistics. One might expect that students who do relatively well in one of those quantitative areas would also do relatively well in the others. That is, we expect the variables to be substantially correlated.

Open the **mardia3.ess** file now. You should see the 88 by 5 matrix in the Data Editor. Click on **Analysis** and then **Correlations**. You will see the dialog box shown in Figure 6.13.

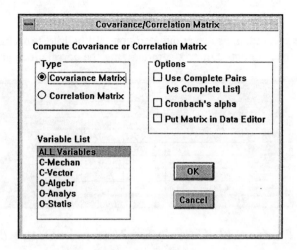

Figure 6.13 Covariance/Correlation Matrix Dialog Box

As you can see, you are instructed to select the variables that you want to include in the analysis. These are given in the bottom list box. The default, **ALL Variables**, is preselected, and is an appropriate choice for now. If you wanted to analyze only selected variables, you would click on the ones that you want.

If you simply want to evaluate the interrelations among variables, you should mark the radio button for **Correlation Matrix**. Do this now. It is not the default, since, for structural equation modeling, the covariance matrix is generally the more appropriate choice.

Missing Data in Covariance/Correlation

There is also an option to deal with missing data, which is activated automatically. By default, the computations will be done on those subjects in your data file that contain no missing data, i.e., the complete cases. If you do not like this default, you could click on the check box **Use Complete Pairs.** When you choose that option, your correlations or covariances are computed for all subjects that had data for a given pair of variables.

Cronbach's Alpha

To get a summary statistic on the reliability of the unit-weighted simple sum score which you could compute across the variables being correlated, click on the **Cronbach's alpha** option. The result will give Cronbach's measure of internal consistency. In general, alphas based on correlation and covariance matrices will differ. The alphas based on the covariance matrix is a lower bound to the internal consistency of the raw-score sum. A sum based on standardized scores would require the use of the correlation matrix.

Putting the Matrix in the Data Editor

A valuable option is: **Put Matrix in Data Editor**. Please click on this option now. With this option, not only do you receive the standard output in the **output.log**, but the matrix is also placed into the Data Editor under the name **matrix.ess**. The correlation or covariance matrix could be retrieved from this window when you do a factor analysis, or when you do structural modeling. Or, you can simply save your matrix.

Click **OK**. When the computations are completed you will be told **MATRIX DONE**. Click **OK** to see Figure 6.14. It gives the symmetric matrix summarizing the correlations among all variables.

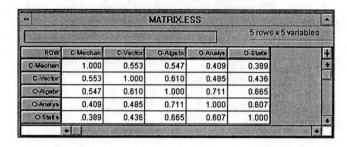

ROW	C-Mechan	C-Vector	O-Algebr	O-Analys	O-Statis
C-Mechan	1.000	0.553	0.547	0.409	0.389
C-Vector	0.553	1.000	0.610	0.485	0.436
O-Algebr	0.547	0.610	1.000	0.711	0.665
O-Analys	0.409	0.485	0.711	1.000	0.607
O-Statis	0.389	0.436	0.665	0.607	1.000

Figure 6.14 Correlation Matrix in Data Editor

The **output.log** provides the same information as the **matrix.ess** file, but in a slightly different format. Only the lower triangle of correlations is printed.

```
CORRELATION MATRIX
5  Variables are selected from file C:\EQS\MARDIA3.ESS

          C-Mechan C-Vector O-Algebr O-Analys O-Statis
C-Mechan    1.000
C-Vector    0.553    1.000
O-Algebr    0.547    0.610    1.000
O-Analys    0.409    0.485    0.711    1.000
O-Statis    0.389    0.436    0.665    0.607    1.000


Number of cases in data file are ..........   88
Number of cases used in this analysis are ..   88
```

As you can see, this output provides information about possible selection of variables, the particular file used in the analysis, and the number of cases in the data file, as well as the number of cases used in the analysis. In this example, there are no missing data, and the numbers match.

It is apparent that the students' scores on these various tests are all positively correlated. The highest correlation is between the algebra and analysis tests. Don't forget that these correlations could be affected substantially by a few cases that are outliers. To see if there are any outliers, and to determine the effect on the correlations, you can use, for example, the scatter plot icon. (Yes, there are some questionable cases here.)

The procedures and output related to the computation of a covariance matrix are essentially the same. The **output.log** will be titled appropriately, and you will see variances in the diagonal of the matrix, with covariances in the off-diagonal positions.

Regression

Linear regression is used to predict the scores on a dependent variable from one or more independent variables. The procedure estimates the weight for each of the independent variables that would yield a predicted score for each case that is as close as possible to the actual dependent variable score as possible, using a least-squares criterion. We shall illustrate this method with some data on 24 subjects and four variables from Chatterjee, S. & Yilmaz, M. (1992). A review of regression diagnostics for behavioral research. *Applied Psychological Measurement*, **16**, 209-227.

Please **Open** the file **chatter.ess** now. It is a small dataset, but it was used effectively by the authors to show potential problems with the blind use of linear regression. Nonetheless, let us blindly use the data now, and only later provide some words of warning.

Click on **Analysis** on the main menu, and then select **Regression**. You will see the dialog box shown in Figure 6.15, which instructs you to select the dependent variable from the left list box, and its predictors from the right list box. To do this example, select **V4** on the left, and **V1-V3** on the right.

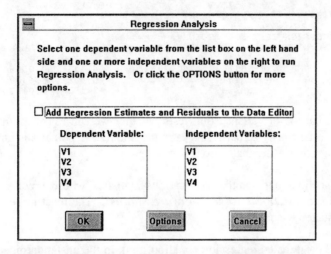

Figure 6.15 Regression Analysis Dialog Box

Note: To select multiple noncontiguous variables from the list, hold down the <Ctrl> key while clicking on each variable. To select multiple contiguous variables from the list, you can simply drag the cursor over each variable, or hold down the <Shift> key while clicking on each variable.

In addition, you see the check box **Add Regression Estimates and Residuals to the Data Editor**. Please click on it. This choice will add two columns to your starting data matrix. The columns will be: the predicted scores (for **V4** in this example) and the residuals (**V4** minus optimally predicted **V4**). This option makes these new scores available for plotting and, indeed, for any other purpose for which data scores might be used.

There are also some **Options**, but we shall ignore these for now. When you click **OK**, the computations begin. Almost immediately, you will see the message, **MULTIPLE REGRESSION DONE** . When you click **OK**, you will be in the **output.log**, and will see the following results.

```
MULTIPLE REGRESSIONS
4  Variables are selected from file C:\EQS\CHATTER.ESS

Number of cases in data file are.......... 24
Number of cases used in this analysis are.. 24

                    ANALYSIS OF VARIANCE
                    ====================

             SUM OF SQUARES    DF    MEAN SQUARES  F-RATIO  P-VALUE

REGRESSION     4433.1663        3      1477.7221   14.525    0.000
RESIDUAL       2034.6671       20       101.7334
TOTAL          6467.8333       23


Dependent Variable  =        V4
Number of obs.      =        24
Multiple R          =    0.8279
R-square            =    0.6854
```

```
Adjusted R-square  =    0.6382
F( 3,    20)       =   14.5254
Prob > F           =    0.0000
Std. Error of Est. =   10.0863
Durbin-Watson Stat.=    1.5764


=======MULTIPLE REGRESSION EQUATION=======
     V4 =        156.622 +        -1.153*V1        +        -0.265*V2
     +     -15.594*V3         + ERROR;

=====STANDARDIZED REGRESSION EQUATION=====
     V4 =    +        -0.657*V1        +        -0.083*V2
     +        -0.294*V3         + ERROR;

=======REGRESSION TEST STATISTICS=======
VARIABLES          COEFFICIENTS  STD. ERROR        t   P-VALUE
Intercept          156.62244
       V1            -1.15310      0.2792      -4.131    0.0005
       V2            -0.26544      0.5440      -0.488    0.6309
       V3           -15.59366      7.2430      -2.153    0.0437
```

First, you get the analysis of variance that tests whether we can reject the null hypothesis that the coefficients are simultaneously zero. In this example, the null hypothesis is unlikely. The population R-square is significantly greater than zero.

Next, there is a section that summarizes various statistics whose precise definition is given in standard texts and the ***BMDP Statistical Software Manual***. The most important of these are the R-square and the Adjusted R-square.

Next you will see the estimated regression equation, first, in the unstandardized form, and then in the standardized form. The sign of each of the regression weights is negative (in the original report, one was given as positive). Two-tailed significance tests on the regression coefficients are given in the final section. V2 has no significant effect on V4 in the context of the other predictors.

Estimates and Residuals in Data Editor

As stated above, the option to **Add Regression Estimates and Residuals to the Data Editor** modifies the input data file in the Data Editor by adding two columns of numbers. You will see this if you go back to **Window**, and select the window **chatter.ess**.

An illustration is provided in Figure 6.16, which shows the new data variables **YEST01** and **RESID01**, the default names used in the program for the estimated and residual variables from the regression. If you were to do other regression analyses (or any other analyses) with the **chatter.ess** file, you could use these variables just like any other variables. If you were to do another regression, again requesting estimates and residuals to be added to the Data Editor, those new variables would be added to the previously existing variables. Of course, you can eliminate any column in the Data Editor with the usual **Edit** and **Delete** commands, after highlighting the column by clicking on the appropriate variable name.

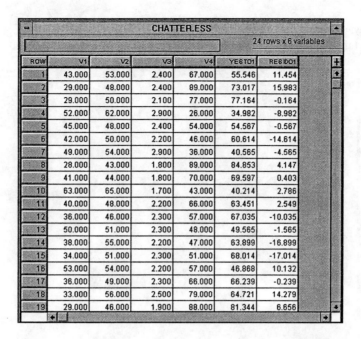

Figure 6.16 Estimates and Residuals in the Data Editor

As you see in Figure 6.16, the estimates and residuals add to the observed variable scores. For case 1, the estimate is 55.55, the residual is 11.45. Their sum equals 67 (within rounding error). Of course, the smaller the residuals, the better the regression equation can predict the dependent variable.

Plotting Residuals and Predictors

You may remember that predicted and residual scores in regression are uncorrelated. You can check this yourself by choosing the scatter plot icon, and plotting these two variables against each other. You will find that the correlation between the variables is indeed zero, and the regression line is completely flat. If you do not remember this type of fact from regression, a plotting procedure will quickly remind you about it.

Chatterjee and Yilmaz present a variety of other plots and diagnostics that are valuable for evaluating whether regression assumptions are met. For example, they present other residuals besides the standard ones we compute, and discuss measures of distance and volume that are sometimes valuable. They point out that the standard results, such as EQS for Windows reports, can be quite sensitive to various characteristics of the data.

Not all of their diagnostics are immediately available in EQS for Windows, but creative use of the program will give you a lot of useful information. For example, even though the predicted and residual scores are uncorrelated, they may be nonlinearly related. You could create a new variable that is the square of the residual, and check whether the squared residual is linearly related to the size of the predicted scores.

The variety of diagnostics for regression is remarkable (there are more than 25 diagnostic indexes in the literature). However, in our opinion, you can use carefully the plotting and transformation procedures in EQS for Windows to get quite a good idea of potential problems with your data.

To illustrate, we note that Chatterjee and Yilmaz used several specialized plots to illustrate that case #10 in this data file is an influential observation. We will take a simpler plotting approach and look at one of the bivariate regressions in this data file. Figure 6.17 displays the regression of V2 on V3. You can obtain this picture by clicking on the scatter plot icon, and selecting variables V2 and V3.

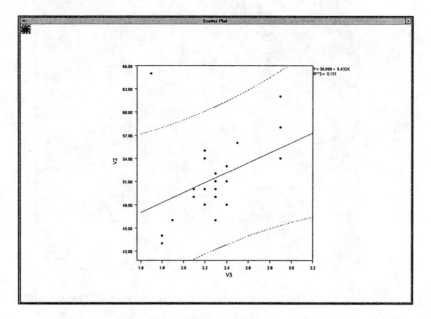

Figure 6.17 Scatter Plot for V2-V3 in chatter.ess

The regression line is in the center. The two lines that demark the 95% confidence interval around the regression are given above and below the center line. It is apparent that there is an unusual case in this data file. It is outside the confidence interval lines by a substantial amount. We can find out immediately what effect this case has on the results by encasing the dot in the upper left corner with a square and dragging it into the black hole.

Try this now. Note that EQS recomputes R-square immediately; R-square changes from .151 to .631.

Marking Points in the Data Editor

If you want to mark the selected point in the data editor, you can do so. To mark the data points in the black hole, first press the <Shift> key on your keyboard while clicking your mouse in the black hole once. The data points that are stored in the black hole will be marked in the Data Editor.

> *Notes:* You must press the <Shift> key and click the mouse **simultaneously**.
> When you mark one or more cases, you are selecting those cases.

There certainly is no need for highly specialized diagnostic statistics to discover a major problem with the original model for the entire data file. The importance of plotting your data to discover such anomalies cannot be overemphasized.

Regression Options

In addition to doing standard simultaneous estimation of the beta weights in multiple regression, you can control the regression substantially. Click on **Window** and **chatter.ess** to bring up the **chatter.ess** file again. Click on **Analysis** and **Regression**. You will see a figure similar to Figure 6.15 with TEST01 and Resid 01 added.

Select to predict V4 from V1-V3 as before. This time, before clicking on **OK**, click on **Options**. When you do so, you will see the dialog box shown in Figure 6.18.

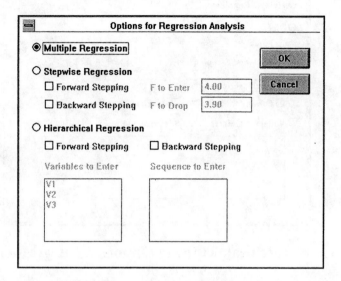

Figure 6.18 Options for Regression Analysis Dialog Box

The top radio button, **Multiple Regression**, is active by default. It corresponds to what you have already done.

The next alternative, **Stepwise Regression**, permits you to specify the type of stepping. In **Forward Stepping**, variables are added to the prediction in turn. In **Backward Stepping**, all predictors are used initially, but then some are dropped if they are not significant. In stepwise regression, you can control the **F-to-Enter** and **F-to-Drop** values, which are defaulted at commonly-used values.

You can try the hierarchical option. You will see in the **output.log** that the results are a series of regression results of the form previously presented, each dealing with the set of variables active at that particular time. **F-to-Enter** or **F-to-Drop** statistics appear, depending on your method.

Alternatively, you can do the regression purposefully, which is what you should do if you know something about these variables. When you press on **Hierarchical Regression,** the option **Forward Stepping** becomes available to you, as shown in Figure 6.19. (**Backward Stepping** comes in a later release.)

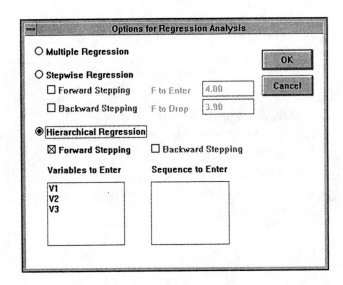

Figure 6.19 Hierarchical Setting in Options for Regression Dialog Box

In contrast to **Stepwise Regression**, here you need to specify the precise order in which variables are entered or dropped. Each time you select one of the **Variables to Enter** by clicking on it, its name gets added to the list box **Sequence to Enter**. Click on **V1**, **V3**, and **V2** in turn to get Figure 6.20.

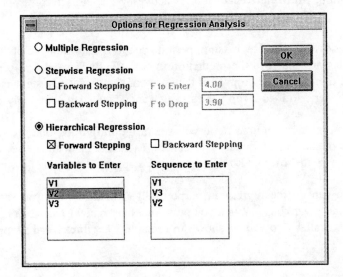

Figure 6.20 Options for Regression Analysis Dialog Box

When you click **OK**, the analysis will be done, and you will see three sets of regression outputs of the type shown above. This output is not especially new. We will not allocate space for it here, but you can try it if you like.

Closing up After Regression

We are not going to use the **chatter.ess** data any more. So, you can use the **Window** choice on the main menu to bring up all Data Editor windows systematically. As each window appears, close it. Also, you may as well check the **output.log** and clean it up by highlighting any written material and clicking on the <Delete> key to eliminate everything that you highlighted. If you prefer, you can quit the EQS for Windows program, and then bring it up again by clicking on its icon.

Factor Analysis

In this section we shall review the basic concepts of factor analysis. Then we will show how to use the **Factor Analysis** option from the **Analysis** choice from the main menu.

A model that relates measured variables to latent factors is called a *measurement model*. Most measurement models are just factor analysis models, but it is standard to distinguish between confirmatory and exploratory factor analysis.

Confirmatory Models Created with Build_EQS Option

Measurement models used in structural modeling are *confirmatory* factor analysis models. In confirmatory factor analysis, the researcher presumably knows—or at least, has a strong hypothesis about—the number of factors necessary to explain the intercorrelations among variables. In addition, one knows which measured variables are supposedly good indicators of each of the factors, and which variables are unrelated to a factor.

In *confirmatory* models, variables are often presumed to be factorially simple. That is, a given variable is usually expected to be influenced by very few factors, typically only one. Path diagram representations of factor analysis usually imply confirmatory factor models, since they are very specific about these details. Of course, a researcher's hypotheses may be incorrect. The structural modeling evaluation will provide evidence on the adequacy of the hypotheses. To perform a confirmatory factor analysis, use the structural modeling part of EQS for Windows, **Build_EQS** on the main menu.

Exploratory Models Created with Factor Analysis Option

On the other hand, factor analysis is most frequently done in an exploratory mode. In an *exploratory* factor analysis, one suspects that variables correlate because there are one or several underlying latent factors that generate the observed data. We may have a vague but not precise idea about this, however. We may suspect that there are one or several factors, but we may not know precisely how many factors are needed to explain the intercorrelations among variables. Perhaps there is one factor, perhaps there are five factors. In addition, even if we are pretty sure about the existence of a particular factor, we may not know which variables are the best indicators of the factor. The **Factor Analysis** option of **Analysis** does an exploratory factor analysis.

The Basics of Factor Analysis

Before we go into operational details, we review some of the basic ideas of factor analysis to be sure that you know what is reasonable to expect from a factor analysis, and what is not. This is not the place to provide a discourse on factor analysis, but you must know certain basic facts about the methodology to use latent variables effectively. Those of you who are knowledgeable can, of course, skip these sections.

What Factors Imply About Variables

It is often said that factors explain the correlations among variables. Let us expand on this idea, without becoming mathematical, using path diagram notation. In general, you have a path diagram containing a latent factor, called an F variable in EQS. Arrows emanate from that latent factor and aim at several V variables, or measured variables in EQS. When you have such a diagram, you are making the strong claim that these particular V variables are highly intercorrelated (the sign, + or -, of a correlation is irrelevant here).

For example, in the diagram V1←F→V2, the factor F generates the two measured variables V1 and V2. The reason for their intercorrelation is that these Vs are generated by the same F. Or, stated differently, if the F variable were controlled, or eliminated statistically, the V variables would no longer correlate. This is the meaning of the first factor ever hypothesized, the IQ or general intelligence factor. According to the general intelligence hypothesis, the IQ factor generates the correlation among various indicators of intellectual performance.

In the typical case, there will be many variables and more than one factor. In addition to claiming that V1 and V2 are correlated because they share the same factor, you also are making the claim that these V variables are relatively lowly correlated with other V variables that are not directly influenced by this same factor.

When studying intelligence, if V3 and V4 are nonintellectual variables, such as attitudes toward school and studying, then V3 and V4 would be expected to be less highly correlated with the intellectual variables V1 and V2 than the intellectual variables would correlate among themselves. When you have several factors, such as F1, F2, and F3, and have different indicators for each factor (e.g., V1, V2, V3 are indicators of F1; V4, V5, V6 are indicators of F2; and V7, V8, and V9 are indicators of F3), a substantial number of such predictions are implied by the factor analysis model.

Choosing Between Exploratory and Confirmatory Models

When you do an exploratory factor analysis, you may be uncertain about the types of claims you can make about the correlations among your variables. The factor analysis will give you results: the number of factors, the factor loadings, and possibly the factor correlations. These will permit you to make statements such as those above, illustrating how the variables are, in fact, generated from your data.

If you know enough about your data to anticipate these results, you should skip the exploratory step and do a confirmatory factor analysis. That is, if you have a good idea about the expected number of factors to be found, and the variables that you expect to be highly influenced by a particular factor, you need not bother with an exploratory analysis.

The Naming Fallacy

There are two aspects to what we call a naming fallacy.

1. After giving a particular name to a set of variables, we conclude that these variables must share a factor.
2. After finding a factor analysis result, we know which variables are highly correlated with the factor, so we think we know what the factor is.

We must be careful to avoid these fallacies. Both of these naming fallacies can interfere with our understanding of the data.

First, before you do an analysis, you may expect a factor to appear because of some shared feature of your data. This may be a naive expectation. You need to be sure that you have worked through the various implications of what factors imply about variables, as we summarized above.

For example, suppose that you have given a similar name to a particular set of variables (e.g., V1 through V5 are all "demographics"; or V6-V9 represent "attitude"). Does this mean that you should expect to see a "demographic" factor and an "attitude" factor? Perhaps, if your subjects happen to respond in such a way as to create high correlations among the variables within each set, and lower correlations between the sets.

On the other hand, the names may simply mislead you. For example, the demographics of subjects' height and number of children in the family are likely to be uncorrelated. No matter that they are both "demographic" variables, sharing a name, these variables most likely will not form a factor. It does not seem probable that taller children come from families with more (or fewer) children.

Factor Indeterminacy

After an analysis in which you see that several Vs are good indicators of a factor, you may become convinced that you understand the factor. It is, after all, whatever the variables share in common. But there is an extensive technical literature on the topic called *factor indeterminacy*. The literature implies that you can become certain about what a factor is only when the number of variables that have high factor loadings on that factor increases without limit. In practice, you will have only a few good indicators of a given factor. So, don't claim too much knowledge about your own factors, when the nature of the first, and most famous of all factors, general intelligence, is still being debated today.

Exploratory vs. Confirmatory Factor Analysis

We can now expand on the earlier discussion of exploratory and confirmatory factor analysis. A structural modeling analysis that tests a completely *a priori* theory does not need to rely on an exploratory factor analysis. The model can simply be specified, e.g., with **Build_EQS**, and tested using **Factor Analysis**. In fact, an exploratory factor analysis may not be able to capture the structure implied by some measurement designs. In contrast, a confirmatory factor analysis could represent the relations of variables to factors. Whether exploratory or confirmatory factor analysis is appropriate for your situation will depend on your objectives and your state of knowledge about your data.

Highly Structured Measurement Models

In general, models that are more appropriate to confirmatory than exploratory methods are highly specialized structural measurement models. Such models contain many factors relative to number of variables, or have a highly complex loading pattern on the basis of the design of the variables.

The multitrait-multimethod model is an example of a highly specialized structural measurement model. In such a model, V variables are generated under a systematic design in which certain methods of measurement (e.g., self-report, behavioral observation, physiological scores) are fully crossed with the trait variables intended to be measured (e.g., anxiety, aggression, depression). That is, each trait is measured by each of several methods. When this design applies, factors can be hypothesized to separate the various sources of variance, especially, into trait and method factors. Interest is usually on the trait factors, while the method factors are usually of little substantive interest. However, the method factors are needed in the analysis, since they provide an important basis for correlations among variables.

> *Note: An exploratory factor analysis generally cannot find or verify such a specialized loading pattern.* You must do a confirmatory factor analysis.

A confirmatory factor analysis can help you to clarify the measurement structure of your variables, whether in the context of a measurement model or a general model that also contains some factors.

But be careful about claiming too much from a measurement model. As noted with regard to the naming fallacy, the nature of a factor may remain obscure until further research is done. In a multitrait-multimethod model, for example, you may find a "physiological" factor. But what does it mean? The body's physiology is quite complex.

The Factor Model within a General Model

When working with a general structural model, you may be interested in determining whether the measurement part of your model is correct. This could be done by exploratory or confirmatory methods, depending on the structure you hypothesize. If you know little about your variables, or your measurement structure is very simple, an exploratory factor analysis should be fine. But if your measurement hypothesis is complicated, you may not get evidence about your hypotheses without doing a confirmatory analysis.

Even if you do not have a specialized, complex factor loading pattern in mind, you may be able to specify precisely the pattern of fixed and free-to-be-estimated factor loadings to be expected in your measurement model, as part of some larger structural model. Then you can transform any latent variable structural model into a confirmatory factor model by eliminating the regressions among factors, and changing all dependent F variables into independent F variables.

Generally, you should let all of these factors covary. Such a measurement model without equations for Fs is a confirmatory factor analysis model. If you can specify it, don't waste your time with exploratory factor analysis. The results of a modeling run should be good enough to provide evidence on the empirical validity of your measurement hypotheses.

On Modifying a Bad Measurement Model

When running a confirmatory factor analysis, or any other specific *a priori* structural model, the model either will fit the data well from a statistical point of view, or it will not fit the data well. Of course, if the model does not fit, it could be due to one of three causes:
1. The measurement model is in some way flawed.
2. The hypothesized relations among factors are not consistent with the data.
3. Other paths and covariances are misspecified.

If you have no theoretical way to modify your *a priori* model, it may be necessary to rely on model modification procedures such as Lagrange Multiplier (LM) or Wald (W) tests. If you have minor problems in your model, these tests will help you to modify the model so that it is more consistent with your data. See the *EQS Structural Equations Program Manual* for more information.

Often, however, LM and W tests are not as good as an exploratory factor analysis in finding flaws in a measurement model. For example, you might have a model that specifies three factors, but there really are four or five factors in your data. Then an exploratory factor analysis will inform you about this situation much more effectively than any confirmatory factor analysis, or even the most creative use of the LM test.

In conclusion, an exploratory factor analysis may be a useful precursor to further modeling work when:
1. You do not know much about the number of factors of a given set of variables.
2. You do not know which variables provide especially good indicators of your various factors.

Factor Analysis in EQS for Windows

Background

There are many methods of factor analysis, and EQS for Windows does not provide a menu of choices for the initial unrotated and subsequently rotated solutions available in general packages such as the BMDP 4M factor analysis program. EQS for Windows provides a single method that is very fast and reliable. It typically yields a very good approximation to more complex methods.

When you click on **Analysis** on the main menu, and then **Factor Analysis**, you obtain an exploratory factor analysis. This factor analysis consists of three solutions in sequence, an initial unrotated factor solution, an orthogonally rotated factor solution, and an oblique or correlated factor solution.

Initial Unrotated Factor Solution

The initial unrotated factor solution is based on a method in which the unique variances are initially taken as equal, permitting the computations to be done explicitly and quickly. In an unpublished report, Kaiser proposed using this method for its ability to be untroubled by linear dependencies among variables, by improper solutions with negative variance estimates, or from failure to converge. Kaiser named this method *EPIC*, for Equal Prior Instant Communalities.

He reported that "EPIC solutions are very close to that which experts consider subjectively to be optimum..." Kaiser, H. F. (1990). Outline of (a) EPIC, a new method for factoring a reduced correlation matrix.... *Paper presented at Society of Multivariate Experimental Psychology*, Providence, RI, October, 1990. The method was discussed previously by others, especially Anderson, T. W. (1984). Estimating linear statistical relationships. *Annals of Statistics*, **12**, 1-45. The mathematical rationale for the computations done in EQS for Windows can be found in Anderson (p. 21).

The method used to obtain the solution is not widely known. It is used in EQS for Windows as a compromise between two methods:
1. The principal components method, which is computationally simple, but often misleading as a method of factor analysis.
2. The full maximum likelihood factor analysis, which is computationally complex, and frequently leads to problems such as negative variance estimates.

Our method gains freedom from computational difficulties at a price: the unique variances of the correlation matrix are presumed to be equal under the model. There are three reasons why this assumption is not as restrictive as it seems:
1. The unique variances for the covariance matrix, not used in the computations, are not presumed to be equal under the model. Rather, the ratio of common factor variance to unique variance is hypothesized as equal for all variables under the model.
2. The estimated communalities for the correlation matrix, obtained from the solution, can vary substantially in practice.
3. For a small number of factors, the distortion induced by the restricted hypothesis becomes trivial as the number of variables gets large.

Rotated Factor Solution

The rotated solutions are: the orthosim solution for orthogonal rotation, and the direct oblimin solution for oblique rotation. The orthosim rotation produces results that are very similar to those produced by varimax, the standard in the field (Bentler, P. M. 1977. Factor simplicity index and transformations. *Psychometrika*, **42**, 277-295).

Oblique Factor Solution

In spite of its age, the direct oblimin oblique solution remains one of the best available (Jennrich, R. I., & Sampson, P. F. 1966. Rotation to simple loadings. *Psychometrika*, **31**, 313-323).

Factor Analysis Dialog Box

You run Factor analysis from the main menu. As always, you must activate a data file before we specify the method of analysis. Please bring up the **mardia3.ess** file at this time. As you saw when we introduced this file in the section on correlations, above, it has the scores of 88 cases on five variables.

Select **Analysis** and click on the option **Factor Analysis**. You will see the dialog box shown in Figure 6.21.

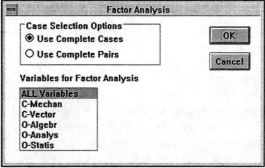

Figure 6.21 Factor Analysis Dialog Box

The top part of the figure gives you two options to use if you have missing data. By default, the radio button **Use Complete Cases** is marked. However, you could also select the option to **Use Complete Pairs**. It is up to you to consider whether listwise or pairwise computations of correlations are more appropriate in your situation.

Other options are available via the missing data icon. In our example, there are no missing data. The only other choice involves the selection of **Variables for Factor Analysis**. By default, the option to use **ALL Variables** is preselected, but you could select from the Variables for Factor Analysis list box. In this example, then, you need only click **OK**. The computations will proceed.

The speed of computation depends on the number of variables and the speed of your computer. When the calculations have finished, you will see Figure 6.22, which gives the eigenvalue size against the eigenvalue or **Component Number**.

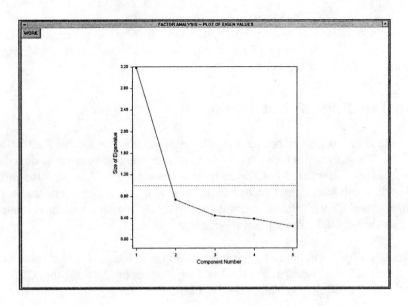

Figure 6.22 Factor Analysis — Plot of Eigenvalues

Selecting Number of Factors

This plot shows the relative size of the eigenvalues of the correlation matrix. A horizontal line (white on the screen) shows the Guttman-Kaiser eigenvalue **1** line. By that criterion, it seems that only one factor is called for. To get more information, and to proceed, you should click on **WORK** in the upper left corner. When you do so, you will see the following dialog box.

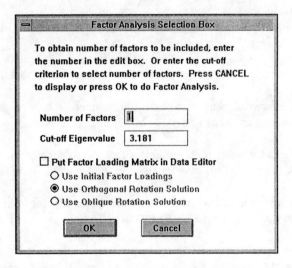

Figure 6.23 Factor Analysis Selection Box

Initially, the **Number of Factors** is marked at **1**, and the **Cut-off Eigenvalue** is defaulted to 1.0. This shows that there was one eigenvalue greater than 1.0.

If you enter **2** in the edit box **Number of Factors**, the **Cut-off Eigenvalue** automatically shows at the value 0.740, or whatever the actual number is for the second eigenvalue in your data. As you choose a different number of factors, the corresponding eigenvalues are shown.

Alternatively, you can place some arbitrary number in the **Cut-off Eigenvalue** edit box, and the number of factors that equal or exceed that value will be shown. In this way, you can dynamically adjust the number of factors to your satisfaction.

Factor Loadings in Data Editor

Also shown in Figure 6.23 is an option that you will often find useful, **Put Factor Loading Matrix in Data Editor**. The effect is to create a new window that you can later input directly into a structural modeling setup, as is discussed in Chapter 6 on **Running EQS**. Although the program will always compute initial, orthogonal, and oblique solutions, and place these into the **output.log**, you can choose among them for the solution you want to use for setting up a structural model. By default, the choice is **Use Orthogonal Rotation Solution**.

If you click **OK** with **2** entered in the **Number of Factors** box, a 2-factor solution will be obtained. Click on the checkbox beside **Put Factor Loading Matrix in Data Editor**. Click **OK**, and you will immediately see the following result in the Data Editor.

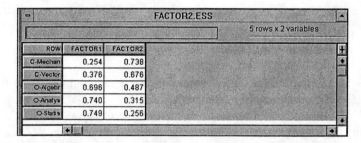

Figure 6.24 Factor Loading Matrix in Data Editor

Note the name **factor2.ess**. The name **factor?.ess** is used by default for factor loading matrices placed in the Data Editor, with **?** being replaced with the number of factors, which is **2** here.

> *Note:* If you do several runs with the same number of factors, and keep all the windows in memory, this name will be used several times. Be careful.

More typically, you will try a different number of factors, so each of the window names will be kept distinct. You can, of course, always save any data in the Data Editor, using the usual procedures.

As far as content is concerned, you will see that the factor loadings show the first two variables to load more heavily on **FACTOR2** than on **FACTOR1**. In contrast, the last three variables load more heavily on **FACTOR1**.

Now look at the **C** and **O** prefixes to the variable names. In their description of the data, Mardia, Kent, and Bibby note that the three test scores differed in their presentation format. The C variables represented exams given in closed book format, while the **O** variables represent exams given in open book format. Evidently, student exam performance depends to some extent on the exam format.

A structural modeling setup can be created automatically when a **factor?.ess** file is in memory. According to your criterion of what a "large" factor loading is, a variable will serve as an indicator of a factor if its loading is greater than your criterion in absolute value. As you will see in Chapter 7, you can set up a confirmatory factor model from the exploratory factor analysis results almost instantaneously.

As stated above, the complete results are given in the **output.log**, some of which is presented below.

```
FACTOR ANALYSIS

5  Variables are selected from file C:\EQS\MARDIA3.ESS

   Number of cases in data file are ...........    88
   Number of cases used in this analysis are ..    88


             C-Mechan C-Vector O-Algebr O-Analys O-Statis
   C-Mechan   1.000
   C-Vector   0.553    1.000
   O-Algebr   0.547    0.610    1.000
   O-Analys   0.409    0.485    0.711    1.000
   O-Statis   0.389    0.436    0.665    0.607    1.000

     Eigen Values

       1      3.181
       2      0.740
       3      0.445
       4      0.388
       5      0.247

   Numbers of Factor selected are 2
   Constant for non-selected eigenvalues=    0.360

   INITIAL FACTOR LOADINGS (PRINCIPAL COMPONENTS)
                      FACTOR 1    FACTOR2
        C-Mechan      0.7127     -0.5551
        C-Vector      0.7694     -0.3797
        O-Algebr      0.8976      0.1110
        O-Analys      0.8151      0.3336
        O-Statis      0.7816      0.4046

   INITIAL FACTOR LOADINGS
                      FACTOR 1    FACTOR2
        C-Mechan      0.6712     -0.3978
        C-Vector      0.7246     -0.2721
        O-Algebr      0.8453      0.0795
        O-Analys      0.7676      0.2390
        O-Statis      0.7361      0.2899

   FACTOR LOADINGS (ORTHOSIM SOLUTION)
                      FACTOR 1    FACTOR2
        C-Mechan      0.2541      0.7377
        C-Vector      0.3762      0.6765
        O-Algebr      0.6958      0.4866
        O-Analys      0.7398      0.3147
        O-Statis      0.7487      0.2555

   FACTOR LOADINGS (DIRECT OBLIMIN SOLUTION)
   Converge after 6 iterations
                      FACTOR 1    FACTOR2
        C-Mechan     -0.0512      0.8148
        C-Vector      0.1378      0.6720
        O-Algebr      0.6478      0.2600
        O-Analys      0.7929      0.0159
        O-Statis      0.8348     -0.0649

   FACTOR CORRELATION MATRIX

             FACTOR1   FACTOR2
     FACTOR1   1.000
     FACTOR2   0.694     1.000
```

In general, the output is self-explanatory. It contains information on the input data being used, the correlation matrix, its eigenvalues, the number of factors requested, and the constant that is the mean of the rejected eigenvalues (here, #3 - #5), used in computing the initial loading matrix. Finally, initial, orthogonal, and oblique solutions are presented. These are standard matrices interpreted in the usual way.

Using Correlation/Covariance Matrix Input

There is no particular reason to use the raw score data matrix for input into factor analysis. You also have the choice of using the derived correlation or covariance matrix. If you are going to be doing many factor analyses of a very large dataset, it is certainly better to use the correlation or covariance matrix. When you do that, you omit the recomputation of the correlation matrix each time. With smaller datasets, and a good computer, using the raw data file does not really have any speed penalty worth worrying about.

We can illustrate the procedure by starting from scratch with the **mardia3.ess** data. Choose **Window** to activate and close each window associated with the recent factor analysis. Choose **Window** and **mardia3.ess** to bring up the data file again. Select **Analysis**, then **Correlations**, and choose the **Correlation Matrix** and **Put Matrix in Data Editor** options. Click on **OK**, and you will get the 5-variable correlation matrix called **matrix.ess**. This is the default name for a correlation matrix that can be put into the factor analysis procedure, though, in fact, you could rename this file with any other *.ess designation.

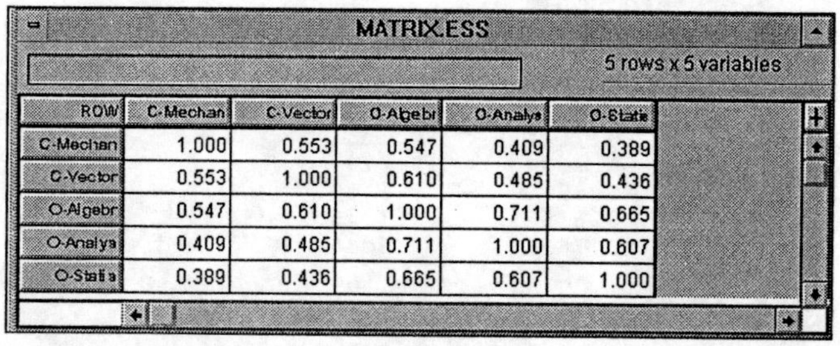

MATRIX.ESS					5 rows x 5 variables
ROW	C-Mechan	C-Vector	O-Algebr	O-Analys	O-Statis
C-Mechan	1.000	0.553	0.547	0.409	0.389
C-Vector	0.553	1.000	0.610	0.485	0.436
O-Algebr	0.547	0.610	1.000	0.711	0.665
O-Analys	0.409	0.485	0.711	1.000	0.607
O-Statis	0.389	0.436	0.665	0.607	1.000

Figure 6.25 Matrix.ess

With **matrix.ess** as the active window, click on **Analysis**, and then **Factor Analysis**. The entire set of options and results in factor analysis, as described above, now are available to you. It is not necessary to repeat their description.

You can also compute the covariance matrix rather than the correlation matrix and save it as **matrix.ess** or with any other relevant file name. EQS for Windows knows whether the data file being analyzed is a raw score data file, a correlation matrix, or a covariance matrix, and acts accordingly. Thus covariance matrix input will yield the same results that we have already described.

7. EQS MODELS AND ANALYSES

If you are an experienced EQS user with a small set of data, or a covariance or correlation matrix, you should find that the short example in Chapter 2 will be sufficient to get you started using EQS for Windows. However, both relatively new and experienced structural modelers will benefit from this discussion of various practical features of EQS for Windows. It includes tips such as how to move from exploratory to confirmatory factor analyses in a highly integrated fashion. If you will take a bit of time to learn a few basics now, you will save substantial time and effort later.

Though EQS is easy to run, you still should know something about structural modeling. For example, you should know the basics of path diagrams, confirmatory factor analysis, and latent variable structural models. If your experience is minimal, you should make an effort to do background reading in sources outside this user's guide. Your best single source is, of course, the EQS manual (Bentler, P. M. *EQS Structural Equations Program Manual*. Encino, CA: Multivariate Software, Inc. 1995). The manual not only presents the theory of modeling, but also describes the EQS program which underlies the EQS for Windows integrated package.

In this user's guide, we do not review such topics as general concepts involved in structural modeling, theory and implementation of specific statistical tests, or various details on EQS program output. However, we will give suggestions for making your modeling practice more fun and rewarding, as well as scientifically meaningful.

EQS Basics: A Review

In this section, we remind you about some basic features of EQS for Windows. Even if you have had some experience with other structural modeling texts and computer programs, you may still want to review the concepts used in the EQS program. Approaches used by other programs are sometimes quite obscure and are often not very enlightening about basic principles. You can skip this section if you are an experienced EQS user.

An EQS Run: Model File, Computation, Output File

While EQS for Windows does virtually all operations and computations immediately and interactively when you click on some option, a complete structural modeling run requires more preparation. A full modeling run consists of a sequence of four procedures:

1. Open a *.ess file
2. Create a Model (*.eqs) File with **Build_EQS** from main menu
3. Choose the **Run EQS/386** option on **Build_EQS** menu
4. Review the output file

The model file, called here a *.eqs file, gives the model specifications, statistics desired, and data file information to be used in the structural modeling run. As you will see below, **Build_EQS** on the main menu will help you to create this file easily and accurately in EQS for Windows. In Chapter 8, you will see how EQS for Windows creates this file automatically from the path diagram that you can create with **Diagrammer**. However, even if you use **Diagrammer**, you should be aware of the basic principles that we summarize in this chapter.

When the model file is completed, click on the **Run EQS/386** option in the **Build_EQS** menu.

When the EQS program has completed its estimation and model testing procedures, the program's Output File dialog box automatically comes to the screen. Click on OK to bring the name of your output file into the list of files. Double click on the file name to bring up the file. This file name is ***.out**, where * represents the name you used in the input file. Then you can review the output which describes the results of the modeling run.

Record-Keeping Suggestions

Unless you have a very simple theory and no competing alternatives, it is likely that you will make more than just one "run" (estimation and testing of a given model) on a single problem. In fact, so much material (e.g., output files) will be generated that you can easily get confused about what was done when, and why you did it. A good way to avoid difficulties is to keep an organized record of your work.

Of course, you should have a path diagram to represent your model. If you do not use **Diagrammer** on each run, you will help yourself by making several photocopies or printouts of your base diagram, clearly showing all of the variables that you might use in any run. Then you can specialize the diagram on any given page so that the diagram corresponds exactly to a specific run, and put the name of the ***.eqs** model file on the diagram page.

When the run is completed, you can also put selected results on the page, such as the chi-square, degrees of freedom, *p*-value, and comparative fit index. Use the next base diagram photocopy in a similar way for the next model. You might use a different color (such as red) to highlight any changes made to the previous model to yield the current model. Such a practice will give you a clear record of what you were doing each time. Otherwise, after many runs, it is often difficult to remember just exactly what was done when.

Even if you do not make a new diagram for every model, you will find it helpful to keep a log of every run. You should include such information as the model file name, output file name (if not logically tied to the model file name), key statistical results from the run, and any changes in model made as a result of evaluating the output. Such a record also will help you to honestly report on your work when you write up the results.

You should try to adopt a coherent naming and sequencing convention for models and runs. For example, if all of your models deal with IQ, your model files in sequence could be IQ1.eqs, IQ2.eqs, and so on. The default output files from these runs would be IQ1.out, IQ2.out, etc.

Some EQS Conventions

Upper/Lower Case and Abbreviations

The ***.eqs** model file will contain title, specification, equation, variance, covariance, and other information as summarized below. Different paragraphs begin with a slash (/).

You can use either upper or lower case for paragraph headings and other letters in the ***.eqs** model file, as you like. Thus, /title or /TITLE, and v4 or V4 are equally appropriate in the model file. On the other hand, parts of the EQS for Windows interface require capital letters, so you might as well use capital letters consistently.

A variety of information is needed in a ***.eqs** file to run the program correctly. Different program setup sections contain key words that you can abbreviate. While you can spell out these words, such as /SPECIFICATIONS or /METHOD, in general, two or three letters will do. For example, /LMT is fine, though /LMTEST is more complete.

V, F, E, D Variables

The EQS program uses four types of variable names, *V*, *F*, *E*, and *D*. Use those abbreviations, which stand for variable, factor, error, and disturbance, to specify models. The **Build_EQS** procedure uses these names automatically, but you should know the conventions. They help you to label your path diagram appropriately and follow what EQS is doing.

V Variables

Measured variables, i.e., observed data that are in your input file, are called V1, V2, and so on, in sequence. The numbering of the variables refers to the specific data file being analyzed. This means that any model setup that you had for one data file is unlikely to be appropriate for any other data file. If you write an equation involving V20, the equation refers to V20 in the particular file being analyzed. The numbering is not arbitrary.

E Variables

Every V variable that is predicted by other variables via a regression equation has associated with it an E, or error, variable. The numbering of E variables is arbitrary, but by convention the E number is matched to the V number. Thus, E7 will go with V7.

F Variables

The numbers assigned to factors, e.g., F1 or F6, are arbitrary. A latent variable is called an F-type variable, or factor, when that variable is hypothesized to account for the intercorrelations among a set of measured variables that are influenced by the factor.

A path diagram having arrows that go from an F variable to several V variables makes the statement that the V variables are highly related. The reason for the high correlations is that the variables are generated by a factor.

D Variables

Every factor that is predicted by other variables or factors has associated with it a D, or disturbance, variable. The numbering of D variables is arbitrary, but by convention the number of F and D variables match. That is, D3 goes with F3.

You may provide mnemonic labels for V- and F-types of variables, e.g., V1=INCOME. Such labels will help to clarify your results in the program output. You cannot provide separate labels for E or D variables.

One of the helpful features of EQS is that when you increase the size of a model by including new V variables, you can maintain in the larger model the designations for factors that you had in your smaller model. For example, if there is an F4 in the small model, you can feel free to add an F7 without changing F4 unless you want to. Or, you can drop F3 from the model but keep F4 intact. The numbers are arbitrary and can be maintained. The same idea holds as you drop variables, but don't expect to maintain a factor when all its indicators are removed from the run! This continuity makes it easy to remember changes across models when you review your results many months after the runs were made.

Path Diagram

You should have a model in mind when you start using EQS. It's a good idea to draw a diagram with the V, F, E, and D variable names and numbers explicitly included. Then when you start building your model, you will know which variables go where and with what. You can use Diagrammer, or simply draw the model by hand.

Here are two rules of thumb for drawing the diagram by hand:
1. The rectangles in your diagram will be the V variables.
2. The EQS for Windows program will ask you for the number of latent factors, which you should draw in circles or ovals if you follow typical practice. You must know how many F variables you are planning to use, and you should number them unambiguously.

If you number these variables correctly, it will be a simple matter to read off the model equations and variance-covariance specifications from the diagram. You will find that you can make the diagram correspond perfectly to the model setup if you denote each free parameter with an *. (Parameters are described below).

You will want to avoid confusion about what V1 or F3 actually represents. Thus, you should use label names (like gender, iqscore, income) along with the EQS designation.

Structural Equation Models

A structural equation model consists of one or more equations with variance and covariance specifications.

Dependent Variables

Variables on the left side of equations are called *dependent* variables. In a path diagram, dependent variables have at least one one-way arrow aiming at them. There are as many equations as there are dependent variables in the model.

Independent Variables

Variables that are never on the left side of any equation, but are part of the model, are called *independent* variables. In a path diagram, independent variables do not have any one-way arrows aiming at them. Independent variables have variances, and, possibly, covariances.

Equations

As just noted, every variable in a path diagram that has one or more one-way arrows aiming at it is a dependent variable. There are three rules:
1. Each dependent variable must have an equation in the model specification.
2. Only V and F variables can have equations.
3. A model will have as many equations as there are V and F variables with one-way arrows aiming at them.

Predictor variables are terms on the right side of the equation. The number of predictor variables in a specific equation is equal to the number of one-way arrows aiming at the variable.

For example, part of a model diagram might be:

$$V12 \rightarrow V20 \leftarrow F1$$
$$\uparrow$$
$$E20$$

Then V20 is a dependent variable and needs an equation. V12, E20, and F1 are three predictor variables in the equation.

Equations in EQS are written in the form V20 = .8*F1 + .6*V12 + E20;

1. Various equations and other EQS specifications are separated by a semicolon (;).
2. Each arrow in a model diagram corresponds to a partial regression coefficient.
3. Numbers to the left of the asterisk (here, .8 and .6) are start values or initial guesses for the regression coefficients. Start values are not needed in the EQS program, so you could write V20 = *F1 + *V12 + E20;
4. The asterisk, *, indicates that a parameter is a free parameter to be estimated. The absence of *, as before E20, indicates that the number (here, implicitly 1.0) is intended to be a fixed value. It is good practice to mark your diagram with * where needed so that you are clear about every free and fixed parameter.

Note: You can mix V's and F's arbitrarily as predictors in equations; the specification you use will depend on your theory.

Measurement Equations

Equations that express V variables in terms of F variables, e.g., V2= *F1 +E2;, are called *measurement equations*, and the set of such equations is called the *measurement model*. The regression coefficients representing F→V paths are often called factor loadings. Since the scale of a latent variable is arbitrary, for model identification you must fix either a path (usually at 1.0) from the F variable to one V variable, or you must fix the variance of the F variable (usually at 1.0) if it is an independent variable.

Construct Equations

Equations for dependent F variables, such as F2 = *F3 + *V1 + D2;, are called *construct* equations in EQS. This is due to the fact that factors are sometimes referred to as latent constructs.

Residuals in Regression Equations

E- and D-types of variables are residuals in regression equations. Whenever you write an equation for a dependent variable, you must be sure that it contains a residual as a predictor of that variable. You could arbitrarily assign E and D variables. However, generally, E-type or error residuals are attached to V variables in equations using the same numbers, e.g., V7 = *F2 + E7;. The D-type or disturbance residuals are attached to equations in factors, e.g., F3 = .5*F2 + D3;. The variance of a residual variable is the unexplained variance in the dependent variable.

Bentler-Weeks Model

Internally, EQS uses the matrix equations of the Bentler-Weeks structural equation system to represent models and their mean and covariance structures; see Bentler, P. M. & Weeks, D. G. (1980). Linear structural equations with latent variables. *Psychometrika*, **45**, 289-308. You will not deal with these matrix equations directly. However, since model specification is done in such a way that the program can set up the Bentler-Weeks model internally, you should know a few basic facts about the Bentler-Weeks approach. Any model setup will consist of equations, variances, and possibly covariances because of the following basic idea.

Parameters

The parameters of any linear structural equation model are the regression coefficients in equations and the variances and covariances of independent variables.

Equations were already illustrated above. Every dependent variable will have an equation, and the * in each equation is a free parameter, a regression coefficient, to be estimated. Equations are collected in a section titled, appropriately enough, /EQUATIONS.

Every independent variable must have a variance as a parameter. These variance parameters are often not explicitly shown in the path diagram, but they should be included in the model specification. Variances are given in the /VARIANCES section of the program, and are stated in a form as V1 = .5*; where, again, the number to the left of the * is the start value (which need not be given) and * indicates that the variance is a free parameter. If a variance parameter is to be fixed, as in F3 = 1.0;, then no * is given; sometimes variances of factors are fixed for identification purposes. Residual variables are almost always independent variables, so their variances will also need to be stated. V, F, E, and D variables all can be independent variables, depending on the model.

Dependent variables can not have variances as parameters of the model. As in regression, the variance of a dependent variable is explained by the behavior of its predictors (which in turn, depending on the model, may be a function of other variables via additional equations) and the residual.

Covariances of independent variables also are parameters if there are two-way arrows connecting independent variables in the path diagram. Note: A dependent variable cannot have a covariance with another variable as a parameter! But a dependent variable will have an associated residual, which is an independent variable, that can carry such covariance information if needed. Covariances are specified in the program in the /COVARIANCES section, using a "double-label" designation, e.g., the V1-V3 covariance has the designation V1,V3 as if it is the off-diagonal element of a matrix (which it is, internally). Here are some examples: V1,V3 = .5*; F3,F5 = *; V6, E3 = *;. Any pair of independent variables may covary, as long as the model is identified.

This basic approach to the specification of models via equations, variances, and covariances, covers all linear structural models, including regression, path analysis, simultaneous equations, confirmatory factor analysis, LISREL-type models, and so on. This simplicity and generality is a fundamental advantage of EQS.

Structured Means

When you specify a model that contains structured means, your path diagram will contain a constant "variable" with arrows emanating from that constant to other variables in the model. For example, in the equation $y = \alpha + \beta x + \varepsilon$, α is the intercept. The constant 1 is implicit, because we can rewrite the equation as $y = \alpha 1 + \beta x + \varepsilon$, thinking of the constant as a variable. This equation can be diagrammed as

$$1 \rightarrow y \leftarrow x$$
$$\uparrow$$
$$\varepsilon$$

where the path $1 \rightarrow y$ is the coefficient α, and the path $y \leftarrow x$ is the coefficient β. As usual, the diagram will be translated into equations, variances, and covariances, but interpretation of some parameters will be different. You should know a few additional concepts.

1. The parameters of the model include not only regression coefficients and variances and covariances of independent variables, but also *the intercepts of the dependent variables and the means of independent variables*. Thus in the example, α and μ_x (the mean of x) are also parameters.

2. An independent variable with a mean is treated as a dependent variable in EQS. In the example, x is an independent variable. But the model is modified to

$$1 \rightarrow y \leftarrow x \leftarrow x_d$$

since the equation $x = \mu_x 1 + x_d$ is added. The path $1 \rightarrow x$ represents μ_x, and x_d is the deviation-from-mean variable. Thus x is now a dependent variable. The constant 1 is called V999 in EQS, and equations with it are in the form V1 = 8*V999 + E1;.

3. The coefficient for regression on a constant is an intercept. Thus, in the equation F1 = *V999 + D1; the * regression coefficient is an intercept for factor 1.

4. The constant V999 is always taken as an independent variable that has no variance and no covariances with other variables in a model.

All of the ideas summarized above, plus additional modeling concepts, are spelled out in greater detail in the *EQS Structural Equation Program Manual*.

Data File Preparation

You should not immediately start modeling your data unless you have given some preliminary thought to the sequence of models that you might consider beyond your first model. The easiest and most efficient way to use EQS for Windows is to have a manageable dataset in which you plan to use all or nearly all of the variables.

If you have a large, cumbersome dataset from which you will just be selecting a small subset of variables for analyses, you would be forcing the program to search the larger file with each run, thus wasting a lot of your own time. Surveys can have hundreds of variables, and working with such large files is a bad idea if you are going to be using 20 or fewer variables. Thus, we *strongly* suggest that you create for yourself a nice tidy little subset of the variables that will contain all of the variables that you are likely to be using in the entire sequence of models. The rest of the data should be set aside.

If you decide to add some more variables from your big dataset later on, that's not a problem. You can use the **Join** feature of EQS for Windows and add some more variables to your smaller dataset.

Variable Selection

If you have a file with a large number of variables and want to cut this file down to manageable size, you can use what you know about the data to do logical, *a priori* variable reduction, eliminating redundant variables or those not relevant to your specific model. Alternatively, you may reduce your data by creating new composite variables that are sums of previously separate variables. Even after you create composite variables, however, you may have too many variables to use in a model. Then a procedure such as factor analysis may help you to select variables. We will discuss these various approaches to variable selection, but also will describe a situation in which you may want to create more, rather than fewer, variables.

A Priori Selection of Variables

The selection of variables was described in Chapter 3, but we repeat some of the essential details here. We assume that you have imported your data into EQS, so that the file has the **ess** extension.

Open your large ***.ess** file now, so that it becomes the active window. Click on **Save As** in the **File** option list.

> *Very Important Note:* When the **Save As** dialog box appears, give a *NEW* name to the new, smaller file you will be saving. Otherwise, you will be irrevocably cutting down your large file.

After you enter the new file name in the **Save As** dialog box, confirm that the **Save File as Type** lfield shows EQS **System File**. Click on **OK** to save this new file. You will see the **Save Selected Cases or Variables** dialog box.

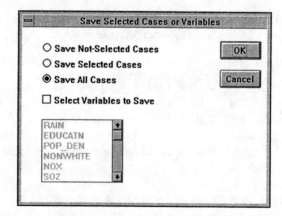

Figure 7.1 Save Selected Cases or Variables Dialog Box

Click on the check box to choose the option to **Select Variables to Save**. When you do so, the variables in the list will change color from gray to black. At that point, you can click on the specific variables that you want to maintain in your data file.

> *Note*: To select multiple noncontiguous variables from the list, hold down the <Ctrl> key while clicking on each variable. To select multiple contiguous variables from the list, you can simply drag the cursor over each variable, or hold down the <Shift> key while clicking on each variable.

When you are finished choosing variables, click **OK**. EQS for Windows will save your new, smaller file.

When you are ready to start using the new file, close the original data file. Then use the **File** menu **Open** option to open the smaller file.

Remember that, when you create your model, the measured variable names V1, V2, and so on, must correspond to the sequence of variables in your new file, that is, in the file you are actually using when you run EQS. If you are using a cut-down set as described above, you should make a record of the corresponding new numbers. For instance, you may have saved only variables V2, V4, V6, V8 and V10 from a larger file. In the cut-down file, they will be numbered V1, V2, V3, V4, V5, respectively.

You should also update the labels. Updating the labels will not be a problem if you do all your work within EQS for Windows. Since the labels are attached to variables in your EQS ***.ess** files, this updating will occur automatically; the labels will follow your variables. But if you work without ***.ess** files, you will have to do this updating yourself.

Creating New Composite Variables

There are times when it is difficult to decide which of several variables to eliminate, yet you know that you cannot use all of the variables. For example, you may have a dozen attitude variables. However, because of the overall size of the model, you may want to use only three of these variables as indicators of a factor. Which variables should you keep, and which ones should you eliminate?

You can use factor analysis to help you decide, as we note below. However, another approach is to keep all of the variables, and to combine them in new ways to produce a composite variable. A composite variable is a weighted sum of other variables. There are two major ways to create a composite variable: matched composites, and homogeneous composites.

Matched Composites

Without taking a stand on whether your variables are unidimensional or multidimensional, you can create matched composites that should behave similarly. Such composites would have similar means and correlate similarly with other variables. You would assign variables to groups that are logically equivalent in terms of your knowledge of the total set of variables. If your 12 variables deal with two content domains, you could create two composite scores in which each composite contains items from both content domains. If the variables deal with four content domains, you would assign items so that each composite covers the four content domains.

In the absence of content domain knowledge, you could assign variables to composites systematically. Here are two examples:
1. To create three indicator variables from 12 in a file, take V1, V4, V7, and V10 and add the raw scores on these variables to create one new variable. Then add the scores on V2, V5, V8, and V11 to create a second composite variable. Finally, add V3, V6, V9, and V12 to create the third composite variable.
2. You can create your new variables by randomly assigning variables to one of the several new composites.

In the matched composite approach, there is no reason to expect any one of the composites you create to be different from another. Each new composite should measure the same construct, or combination of constructs, as measured by a single composite of all original scores. The only exception would be for content variation among variables that you did not anticipate, and the lower reliability of composites based on fewer variables.

Homogeneous Composites

If there is some systematic variation in content among the variables, you could also create the composite variables by combining variables having similar content. So if your 12 variables represent facets of intelligence, and some of the variables stress verbal ability, while others stress quantitative ability, and still others stress spatial visualization, you could add up the verbal scores to create a new verbal composite. Similarly, you can create quantitative and spatial visualization composites.

In contrast to the previous approach, the new composites may correlate quite differently with other variables. For example, the quantitative score may correlate more highly than the verbal score with success in engineering. When you take these new composites as indicators of a single construct, you can consider the latent variable to be a second-order factor that is based on the first-order factors of verbal, quantitative, and spatial intelligence. Of course, when you actually run a model based on only the three composite indicators, the factor would appear as a first-order factor. However, because of the content variation among indicators, you may want to consider whether nonstandard paths are appropriate (see the EQS manual, p. 102, for information on nonstandard models).

Direction of Scoring and Weighting

However you decide to create new composite variables, you should remember that, when you combine variables, you must take the direction of scoring into account before you add scores. For example, a high score may indicate a positive attitude on one variable, but a high score on another variable may indicate a negative attitude. If you were simply to add two such variables, a person with a positive attitude would wind up in the middle of the continuum.

There are several ways to deal with this problem:

1. You can rescore one of the variables. For example, you could use the **Data** menu **Reverse** option to reverse the scoring of a 7-point V2 so that 1→7, 2 →6, 3 →5, and so on.

2. You can change the sign of one of the variables before adding them. For example, use **Data**, **Transformation**, and choose **Sign** as the **Function** to transform the variable.

3. Instead of rekeying, you could simply use the **Data** menu **Transformation** option to create V1 - V2. This is, of course, the same as adding V1 + (-V2), i.e., changing the sign on the variable that needs rekeying. But this has the same effect as rekeying as far as variances and correlations are concerned.

Variable Transformations

In general, you must use **Data** from the main menu, and **Transformation**, to create new variables based on linear or nonlinear transformations of existing variables. When you create such variables, you must decide whether you want to weight variables differently when creating your composite.

In general, in the absence of knowledge about optimal scoring based on a previous use of a formal methodology, we suggest that you use equal weights with an appropriate sign, i.e., ±1 weights. However, if you want unequal weights, the EQS for Windows transformation procedure permits you to create an unequally weighted composite variable such as V1 + .5*V2 - .3*V3. You should be sure that such a weighting is well-justified.

Avoiding Linear Dependencies

When you create a new composite variable, you should be sure that your final data file does not include both the original variables and a composite made up of a weighted sum of the original variables. To illustrate, you should not use a new file that contains V1 and V4, where V4 = V1 + V2 + V3. There will be an artificial dependency among such variables, and your correlation and covariance matrix will not be usable in structural modeling.

Using Factor Analysis to Select Variables

When the variables in a data file are items on a questionnaire, it is usually desirable to add several items together to create a composite variable as described above. The new variables are more reliable and cover a wider range of substantive content than any single item could cover. But there may be times when the variables in your file have an intrinsic meaning.

For example, a particular variable might be the Stanford-Binet Intelligence Test, a well-known standardized test. Then you may want to keep this particular variable in your model, if it is a good indicator of an IQ factor that you are studying.

If you did a factor analysis of a lot of variables, including many that were reputedly alternative indicators of IQ, you might want to select those variables for your final model that are the best indicators of IQ. That is, you would select variables based on their factor loadings on an IQ factor which you obtained from an exploratory factor analysis.

The procedures for doing an exploratory factor analysis have been discussed in Chapter 6. When you have a large number of variables whose factorial structure you need to discover, you will want to do several factor analyses prior to getting ready for any structural modeling. But when you need only minor adjustments to your choice of indicators, you can use exploratory factor analysis to select variables for direct incorporation into a model setup. A method of doing this in practice is discussed below.

Disaggregating Variables

Although there is not necessarily an EQS for Windows procedure for accomplishing this, there may be times when you should do the very opposite of creating new composite variables. Rather, you should consider taking an existing variable in your data file and *disaggregating* it, taking it apart into its components.

Consider, for example, that you want to create a latent variable model for the predictors and consequences of depression. Unfortunately, you have only one depression score in your data file. It would seem that you are relegated to doing a measured variable path model for this part of your model. Not true!

It is possible that your depression variable actually is a composite of a set of items. For example, it might be a total score computed across 20 or 60 specific item responses of your subjects. Then you can create multiple indicators of a depression factor by going back to your original study and disaggregating the total score. Instead of creating one total score, you can create, say, two, three, or four.

To create two composites, you could use the matched or homogenous approaches described above, depending on your purpose. For example, you could add the odd items (properly scored positive or negative, depending on the content direction) to get one new score, and add the even items to create another score.

It may be necessary to do this disaggregation by hand, for example, by rescoring items using another scoring template. It cannot be accomplished within EQS for Windows, unless you happen to have a data matrix that contains the item responses. Then, of course, you can use the data transformation procedure discussed previously to create your new composites.

Case Selection

In any modeling situation, you must be sure that the model is relevant to the sample of subjects at hand. For example, a model may be appropriate for males, but not for females. Using case selection to accomplish separation of your file into meaningful constituent files was discussed in Chapter 3. We do not want to repeat that discussion, but it is important to recognize applications for splitting a file, and for deleting an outlier case from the data file prior to using the **Build_EQS** procedure.

One of the perennial problems in structural modeling is that one's *a priori* model is liable to be inadequate to explain all variation and covariation in the data. Hence you may be enticed to do *post hoc* model modification with Lagrange Multiplier and Wald tests. A serious problem with this procedure is that it leads you to capitalize on chance associations in your data, making your model look better than it actually is.

If your data file contains enough subjects, why not randomly split your sample into two separate samples? You can build the model using as much *ad hoc* model modification as you like. Then, use the second sample to cross-validate the results. The statistical tests you will get in sample 2 will not be biased by the model modification you did in sample 1.

To select cases, bring up your current data file to the active window. Go to **Data** in the main menu, and click on the option **Use Data**. You will see the dialog box called **Case Selection Specifications**.

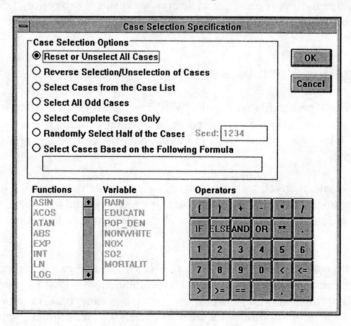

Figure 7.2 Case Selection Specifications Dialog Box

There are several options, but for modeling you should consider two useful options, namely, **Select All Odd Cases** and **Randomly Select Half of the Cases**.

Select All Odd Cases

If your subjects' data is placed sequentially in the file in a totally random manner, then a convenient way to select a random sample is to select the odd cases. Selecting odd cases will choose cases #1, 3, 5, and so on.

If the case sequence is systematic on a variable that you want to control on, selecting odd cases may make sense. For example, if subjects are arranged by time of finishing a test, then by selecting odd cases you would select subjects who finished early, middle, and late.

To implement this option, click on the **Select All Odd Cases** option and click **OK**. When you return to the data file, the odd cases will be highlighted.

Randomly Select Half of the Cases

If you are not certain about the sequencing of subjects, you may want to choose the option to randomly select half of the cases. This is done by clicking on **Randomly Select Half of the Cases**, giving a seed number, and then clicking **OK**. You will see the data file become active again, with some cases highlighted. These are the cases that were selected by the random number procedure.

Saving Selected and Nonselected Cases

In the usual application of case selection, one tends to be interested in only the selected cases. But when randomly or systematically selecting cases for cross-validation purposes, you should save data from the selected cases and also data from the unselected cases. Of course, these data should be saved into separate files, so that you can do separate analyses on these files.

Now that some of the cases are highlighted, go to the **File** menu, and select **Save As**. Enter the new file name for the selected cases and make it an **EQS System File**. Click **OK**.

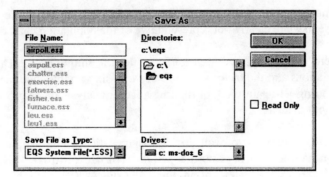

Figure 7.3 Save As Dialog Box

The **Save Selected Cases or Variables** dialog box will become active. Mark the option **Save Selected Cases** and click **OK**.

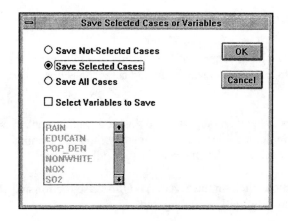

Figure 7.4 Save As Case Selection Dialog Box

You have now created the new file for the selected cases, and the option box will disappear.

The original file with the highlighted cases will be shown again on your screen. Repeat the saving process, but this time you should save the *unselected* cases in their own file. Go to **File** again, and click on **Save As**. Give the new file name for these unselected cases, choose **EQS System File** and click **OK**. This time, mark the option **Save Not-Selected Cases** and click **OK**.

You will now see the original file with the selected cases still highlighted on your screen. You can close this file. For safety's sake, you may want to bring up the two newly created files to verify that they contain the data that you expect to see there. Remember that you can use **Data** from the main menu, and then **Information** to get a quick summary of the number of cases in the new file. Between them, the new files should contain all cases from the original file.

Creating the File Manul7a.ess: Deleting an Outlier Case

The file at hand must contain the logically relevant subjects. Also, it may be necessary to eliminate some cases because they are clearly not representative of the population characterized by the sample.

We know that there is a problem with case #50 in the file **manul7.ess**. This outlier case creates havoc in the correlations and the factor structure of these six variable, two factor data. You can see the problem by plotting V1 against V3, or running a factor analysis on data containing case #50, and again on data without that case.

One way to handle outliers is to wait for the diagnostic in the output regarding the case's contribution to Mardia's coefficient of normalized multivariate kurtosis. Then, if the contribution is serious, use the DELETE=50; statement in the /SPECIFICATION section of the model setup to eliminate the case.

On the other hand, if you will be doing a variety of analyses with a file, and some of these methods do not have easy ways of dealing with outliers, you should probably create a file that has been purged of the offending cases. We shall create a new file without the outlier case, in preparation for an exploratory factor analysis. The factor analysis procedure available under **Analysis** does not have a simple method for deleting cases.

We shall create a new file, **manul7a.ess**, that does not contain case #50. You can do it yourself, based on what you learned in Chapter 3. Or, you can follow one of the methods below.

1.   Open the **manul7.ess file**. Double click on the missing data icon ▨ . The **Missing Data Specifications** dialog box will appear. Click the check box **Display Univariate Outlier** and click **OK**.

The **Missing Data Pattern** diagram of the data matrix will appear. The diagram will show no missing data but will show that one case is an outlier on several variables. Click on the case to see that it is case 50. Choose **Compute** on the main menu, and select **Mark Outliers**. Click **OK** when you see **Selected cases are marked in data sheet**.

You will be taken back to the **Missing Data Pattern** plot. Close the plot and you will see the **manul7.ess** file. If you use the vertical scroll bar to get to the end of the file, you will see that case #50 has been highlighted in blue. Now you can go to **File**, click on **Save As**. In the **Save As** dialog box, give the name manul7a.**ess**, click on **EQS System File** and click **OK**.

The **Save Selected Cases or Variables** dialog box will appear, and you should click on the button to **Save Not-Selected Cases**. Then click **OK**. Your new file has now been created. You can close **manul7.ess** and bring up **manul7a.ess** to check, if you like.

2.   Use the **Edit** procedures. Select **File** and **Open** to select the **manul7.ess** file. Use the vertical scroll bar to go to the end of the file. Click on case number 50. Case number 50 will be highlighted. Click on **Edit** from the main menu, and then **Delete**. The case will disappear from the file.

Now you can go to **File**, click on **Save As**. In the **Save As** dialog box, give the name manul7a.**ess**, click on **EQS System File** and click **OK**. In the **Save Selected Cases or Variables** dialog box, **Save All Cases** will be marked. Click **OK**. You have now created the new file. You can close the original **manul7.ess** file and bring up the **manul7a.ess** file.

3.   Use the **Select Cases** procedure. There are several alternatives, outlined in Chapter 3. We discuss the one based on Figure 3.32. In short, you invoke **Data**, then **Use Data**, to **Select Cases Based on the Following Formula**. The formula you use is V1 < 9. That will select and highlight all cases except #50. Use **Save As** to give the new file name, **manul7a.ess**, and **Save Selected Cases**. The new file will have 49 cases and six variables. Bring up this file so that we can work on it.

Data Plotting and Missing Values

Before you embark on modeling, you should have explored your data using various plot and basic statistics features to assure yourself that the data are ready to be modeled. There is no point to modeling a dataset that contains missing values, outlier cases, or other anomalies.

You should be sure that your data file contains no missing values. EQS will not run with missing values. Worse yet, the program may treat missing data codes as real scores of subjects on variables. However, as you saw in Chapter 3, there is a utility in EQS for Windows that allows you to impute missing values and to clean up your data. Alternatively, you can compute correlations and covariances based on available data for reading into the EQS model file. If for some reason you have not already dealt with this issue, do it now before you go on to do your modeling. Any raw score data file that you use for modeling should be a full file, with no missing entries.

Factor Analysis as a Precursor to *Build_EQS*

If you know your model and your data very well, you can skip this section and go to the next section on **Building an EQS Model File**. Similarly, if you are doing a model in which there are no latent variables, you also can skip this section. But if you have specified latent variables in your model, and have some doubt about whether these factors provide a good representation of the intercorrelations among your indicators, you could do a preliminary exploratory factor analysis. Not only will this verify your measurement model, but, as we will demonstrate, the results will be used in EQS for Windows to help set up your model even more efficiently with the **Build_EQS** procedure.

Before we continue, you should be informed that there are varying opinions about the appropriateness of doing a preliminary factor analysis, and then following this up with a model such as a confirmatory factor analysis. Our feeling is that, when you know enough about your model to be able to specify it quite well, especially when you have a good idea of the underlying measurement model, then there is indeed no reason to do a preliminary factor analysis. On the other hand, if there is little knowledge about the measurement structure of the variables, such an analysis may be necessary before a modeling run would even converge. In any case, honesty is the best policy: be sure to report what you did, and why.

In this section we will not cover in detail the material presented on factor analysis in Chapter 6. We want to concentrate on how to integrate exploratory factor analysis into an EQS model file when using the **Build_EQS** procedure. We discuss this matter here, rather than in the section on **Build_EQS** below, because *you must run the factor analysis before you invoke* **Build_EQS**. The results of the factor analysis must be available in a window that can be accessed during the **Build_EQS** procedure.

Open the six variable, 49 case **manul7a.ess** data file. (If you do not have the file, see the section above where we described how to create this file). In the main menu, click on **Analysis**. Then from the list box, select **Factor Analysis**. You will be shown the following dialog box.

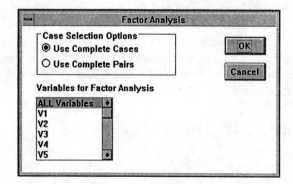

Figure 7.5 Factor Analysis Dialog Box

By default, the appropriate selections will already be made, namely, that you want to **Use Complete Cases**, and to do the analysis on **ALL Variables**. Click **OK** and the analysis will begin.

Almost immediately, you will get a plot of the eigenvalues of the correlation matrix (Y Axis) against the eigenvalue number (X Axis).

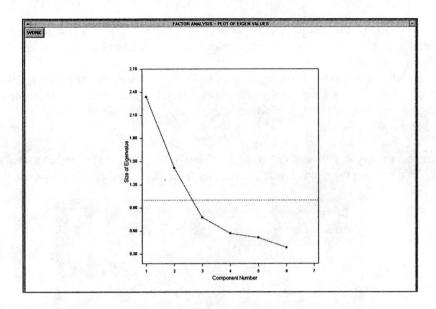

Figure 7.6 Plot of Eigenvalues

You will see that the white horizontal line for the cutoff for number of factors is defaulted at the value 1.0 on the Y Axis. There are two eigenvalues greater than 1, the default cutoff for the number of factors in EQS. The eigenvalues are 2.339, 1.415, and .775 in sequence, as you would see if you went to **Window** and selected the **output.log** for the numbers.

The choice of two factors as indicated by the number of eigenvalues above the white line seems to be appropriate, since there is a good-sized gap between the 2nd and 3rd eigenvalues. Also, the remaining eigenvalues, under the line, form an approximately straight line. This line is often called the "scree" line. Some researchers urge selection of the number of factors by the scree test, keeping the next largest eigenvalue above the scree line. In any case, since there should be at least 3 good univocal indicators per factor, when we have 6 variables, we should be satisfied with 2 factors.

To start the factor analysis, click on **WORK** in the upper left-hand corner. The **Factor Analysis Selection Box** shown in Figure 7.7 will appear.

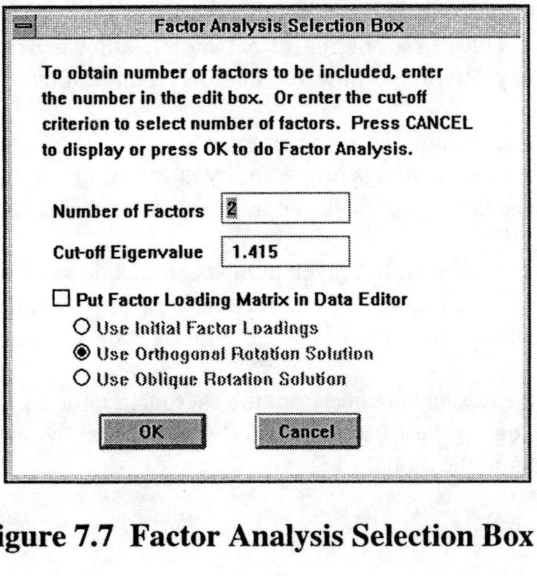

Figure 7.7 Factor Analysis Selection Box

This box allows you to change the number of factors, or modify the cutoff eigenvalue criterion for determining the number of factors. But we are not interested in changing the number of factors.

Mark the check box **Put Factor Loading Matrix in Data Editor** so that the **Build_EQS** options can use the information. Since we generally recommend selecting the orthogonally rotated solution for determining the loading pattern in a modeling run, accept the default by clicking **OK**. The program will do the factor analysis.

Almost immediately, you will see an information box telling you that the factor analysis is done. Click **OK**. You will see the newly created file called **factor2.ess** as the active window.

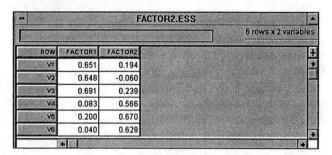

Figure 7.8 Factor Loading Matrix in Data Editor

This file name is picked by default; whenever a factor analysis is sent to the data editor, a **factor?.ess** file will be created, and **?** will be replaced by the number of factors in the run (here, **2**). This file, shown in Figure 7.8, gives the factor loading matrix resulting from an orthogonal rotation of the initial factor analysis solution. If you preferred a different solution, you would have marked the relevant button shown in the bottom of Figure 7.7.

The information that will be taken from the factor loading matrix shown in Figure 7.8 to go into the **Build_EQS** procedure below, involves a decision on which variables are good indicators of each factor. Here, variables V1-V3 are good marker variables for factor 1, while variables V4-V6 provide good marker variables for factor 2.

That same conclusion can be obtained automatically, as it will be done in **Build_EQS**, if you consider a good indicator as one that has a loading greater than .5 in absolute value. (Remember that the signs of *all* variables in a column of a factor loading matrix are arbitrary. They can be reversed, since a sign only determines how you interpret the meaning of a high score on the factor.)

In this analysis, it is quite certain that we want exactly two factors. In your own analyses, you may not be sure whether you have the best solution until you try factor solutions with a varying number of factors. Each of these can be sent to the data editor, in a **factor?.ess** file.

> *Note:* If you repeat a run with a given number of factors, say two, that file will be duplicated and there will be two sets of **factor2.ess** files. In general, you should not use the name **factor?.ess** for your own files because factor runs always will use these file names.

You can keep track of the results obtained from the **factor2.ess** file by yourself, perhaps with written notes, to use when setting up the EQS model file. But we shall show below how to automatically import this information into the model file setup.

Building an EQS Model File

Since EQS for Windows is data-driven, be sure that a dataset is ready to go before you use **Build_EQS**. In our example, we want to use the data **manul7a.ess**, so please **Open** this file *and make it the active window*. Then, in the main menu, click on **Build_EQS** and choose the **Title/Specifications** option.

Build_EQS presents you with a series of dialog boxes for specifying your model. After you complete each dialog box, its information is transferred to a new file, temporarily called **work.eqs**. This file will be in the background for you to scan, and, if you desire, to edit in case you change your mind about any options. After the model is completely specified using the usual EQS conventions, this file is sent to the EQS for Windows program to estimate parameters and yield model test results. The results from the modeling run are then placed into the output file, which is **work.out** by default.

Title/Specifications

The **Title/Specifications** option brings up the dialog box shown in Figure 7.9.

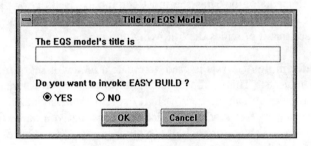

Figure 7.9 EQS Model Title Dialog Box from *Build_EQS*

Initially, the rectangular edit box is empty, and you should type in a title. Type **Two-factor model for manul7a.ess**.

Also note that you are asked **Do you want to Invoke EASY BUILD?** If you do not want EASY BUILD, only the title and specifications are created, and you can build the model file yourself, selecting only those parts of **Build_EQS** that you want to implement.

Generally, you should select the EASY BUILD feature, since it automatically generates the equations, variances, and covariances that you will need to specify for any model. This option frees you from typing every equation for each dependent variable, and provides the variances and covariances sections of the model as well. The default, **YES**, is marked, so you need only click **OK**.

The model specifications dialog box appears immediately thereafter, as shown in Figure 7.10. This contains most of the basic information in the standard /SPECIFICATIONS section of EQS input. But it does not contain all possible information. For example, the DELETE command is not shown in the box. As you will see, a text ***.eqs** file is being created, and you may find it necessary to edit this file to get features of special interest to you.

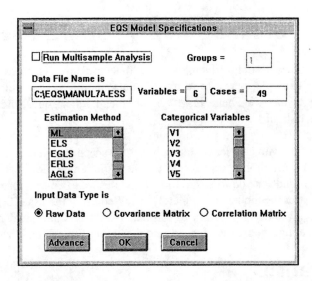

Figure 7.10 EQS Model Specifications Dialog Box

The model specifications dialog box has the most commonly used options as defaults. This entire box will probably be acceptable, and typically you can just click **OK** and proceed. However, you should look at it, to see that it provides the following options:

1. **Run Multisample Analysis** is used to create a model or set of models for more than one group of subjects. This is the appropriate procedure for comparing various parameters across two or more samples. We shall explain more about this option below. Simply stated, the sequence of model specification steps that you make for one group will, with this option, be repeated for each of the other groups. To choose this option, click on the check box, and then specify the number of groups.

2. **Data File Name** with the number of **Variables** and **Cases** comes from the file that was active when you invoked the **Easy_Build** process. Although it is not recommended for general practice, you also can invoke **Easy_Build** when no data file is active. Then you must provide the file name, as well as the number of variables and cases. In Figure 7.10 the file given is an ***.ess** file. (If the complete file name cannot be seen, make it visible by putting your pointer into the rectangle, clicking your mouse button, and then using the cursor to scroll.)

3. **Estimation Method.** You can choose several different estimation methods if you wish. Normal theory maximum likelihood (ML) estimation is the default, but another method may be more appropriate for your data. For example, nonnormal data would probably best be handled by ML, ROBUST. Click on the method or methods which you want to use. Consult the EQS manual for an explanation of the options that are available.

4. **Input Data Type** can be either raw data or a covariance or correlation matrix. When you first open a raw data file to be analyzed, as you did above, you should choose this option. If you do not want to use the raw data file, but would rather work with a correlation or covariance matrix (either within this ***.eqs** file or from another file), you should click the appropriate radio button. You must know the EQS conventions to use these other methods of input. Analysis done with any ***.ess** file will be automatic. This includes the raw data, as well as analysis with a covariance matrix that resides in a ***.ess** file.

After you are satisfied with the model specifications, click **OK**. You will proceed to the equation-building section. You will see in the background that a new file, **work.eqs**, is being created. As noted above, the information from each dialog box is translated into the standard EQS conventions and placed into this file by default. You can change this file's name later, if you want. If you were to change **work.eqs** to another file name such as **man7.eqs**, the resulting output file would be called **man7.out**.

```
/TITLE
Two-factor model for manul7a.ess
/SPECIFICATIONS
 DATA='C:\EQS\MANUL7A.ESS'; VARIABLES=  6; CASES=    49;
 METHODS=ML;
 MATRIX=RAW;
/LABELS
V1=V1; V2=V2; V3=V3; V4=V4; V5=V5;
V6=V6;
```

Figure 7.11 WORK.EQS File Created by Build_EQS

As you can see in Figure 7.11, the /TITLE, /SPECIFICATIONS, and /LABELS sections of the file are already filled out by the time you are ready to deal with **Build Equations**.

The filled out information in **work.eqs** is self-explanatory with one important exception:

You were not prompted for variable labels. Yet, the section /LABELS was created. What happens is that EQS for Windows strips the label information from the ***.ess** file, and places this information here automatically. In our example, we did not use special names such as V1 = INCOME, but if we had done so, these names would have appeared. Here, the default variable names were used instead. Whenever you have defined variable names in using the **Data** menu item with **Information**, such names will be automatically carried in the ***.ess** file and, hence, into **Build_EQS**. If no ***.ess** file is active, the program cannot automatically adopt labels since it will not know where to get labels.

Next you have to deal with the **Build Equations** dialog box. This is shown in Figure 7.12.

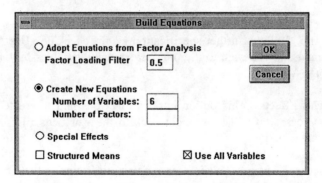

Figure 7.12 Build Equations Dialog Box

Equations

Build Equations Options

There are two steps to building equations, and the **Build Equations** dialog box is the first step. It gives you several options.

1. **Adopt Equations from Factor Analysis**. This option is not marked as the default, but we want to use it. That is because, in our example, we ran an exploratory factor analysis, whose results were saved in the **factor2.ess** file. See Figure 7.8.

    When you choose this option, the number of variables and number of factors is taken from the factor analysis results, and EQS searches this file to yield marker variables for factors. Those variables having "high" loadings on a given factor will be automatically taken as indicators of that factor. Well, what is a high loading? By default, the **Factor Loading Filter** is .5, so that any factor loading of .5 or above, in absolute value, is taken as evidence that a variable is a good indicator of a factor.

    You can, of course, change the default value to any number you like. If you use a filter of .3, more variables will be taken as indicators of a given factor. If you use a filter of .8, fewer variables will be selected as indicators of a factor. If you choose a filter too large for the given data, you may select no variables as indicators of any factor!

2. **Create New Equations**. This is the default option that you would generally use, except when you do a preliminary factor analysis. By default, the **Number of Variables** is the number in the data file. This is usually the best option. No default is given for the **Number of Factors**. You will have to put the cursor in the rectangle and type in a number. You can specify zero factors if you are going to create a model without latent variables.

    You can specify a **Number of Variables**, such as 4, that is less than the number in the data file. Without further specification via the check box **Use All Variables**, it will be assumed that you want to use the *first* so many variables in your data file, such as V1 through V4.

3. **Special Effects**. This option implies that you want to create an atypical model. In such a case you will be brought back to the **work.eqs** file so that you can give the relevant equations.

4. **Structured Means**. This is a more advanced feature in EQS in which the means of the observed variables are explained in terms of fewer parameters, such as the means of the factors. When you invoke this option, the constant variable V999 is created for you to use in your model. Consult the EQS manual for more details on models with structured means.

5. **Use All Variables**. By default, this option is checked. But if you want to use only certain Vs in your model, there are two ways to do it, depending on whether you want some Vs completely removed from the model or only removed from equations.

    (a) If your model will use all variables, but you do not want to use all of them as dependent variables, you can keep the default-checked **Use All Variables**. When you bring up the **Create New Equations** dialog box shown in Figure 7.13, you would simply not put any * for that V variable. The Vs that are not given equations then are considered to be independent Vs, so they will appear in the variance/covariance section.

(b)   If you unselect **Use All Variables**, you will subsequently be given a dialog box called **Select Variables to Build Equations**. This box lists all the variables in your file. You click on the Vs that you want to use in your model. The ones that are not selected will not appear in the equations, nor in the variance/covariance section.

In our example, we shall use all variables, and use the choice **Adopt Equations From Factor Analysis**. After clicking its radio button and then clicking **OK**, we immediately see Figure 7.13, exactly as filled out with the *s in place. If we had selected the choice **Create New Equations** by clicking its radio button, and filled in the number of factors, we would have obtained Figure 7.13, but with no *s filled out at all.

Create New Equations

When you have finished with the **Build Equations** dialog box, you will see the **Create New Equations** dialog box shown in Figure 7.13. Entries with * may or may not be visible, depending on how you handled the previous dialog box.

This dialog box contains as many rows as there possibly could be equations. The possible dependent variables are V1, ..., V6, and the two factors F1 and F2, which is all that we had specified. Thus there could be a maximum of eight equations. In a factor analysis model, only Vs are dependent variables. In more general models, Fs also would be dependent variables.

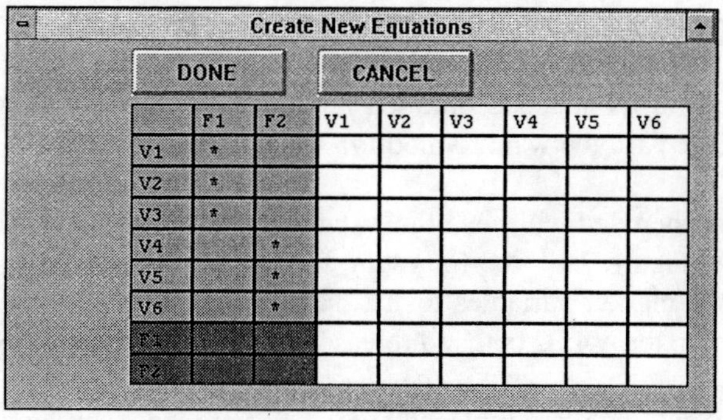

	F1	F2	V1	V2	V3	V4	V5	V6
Create New Equations								
V1	*							
V2	*							
V3	*							
V4		*						
V5		*						
V6		*						
F1								
F2								

Figure 7.13 Create New Equations Dialog Box

The columns list the possible predictors of each of the dependent variables. In the standard model setup, only Fs and Vs will be predictor variables. In a factor analysis model, only Fs are predictors of the V variables. Predictor variables may be dependent or independent variables, depending on the model. In a factor analysis, the predictor variables are all independent variables.

Some cells of the matrix in Figure 7.13 have an asterisk (*), while other cells do not have such a mark. Each * refers to a predictor variable to be used for that dependent variable. When you click on a cell in the matrix repeatedly, the * will be shown, and then removed, then shown again. Hence by clicking, you can put an * wherever you want, or remove it at will.

In our example, the setup is completed and we could click **DONE** and go on. However, we must describe the situation encountered when **Create New Equations** is completely blank. In that case, you will have to decide which dependent variables are a function of which predictor variables and click accordingly. A good way to proceed is to work by columns or by rows. If you work on one column at a time, you are specifying which variables are influenced by that column variable. In Figure 7.13, variables V1, V2, and V3 are the only variables influenced by F1.

If you work on one row at a time, you are specifying all the influences on a particular dependent variable, since each row will create one equation. The first row implies an equation for V1, i.e., V1 = ??. The right side of the equation to be generated will contain only those variables, selected from the column designations, in which you have placed an asterisk. In the example, only F1 affects V1.

EQS uses Es and Ds as residual variables. They are not shown in the dialog box. These residuals will be created automatically when the equations are created for Vs and Fs in the **work.eqs** file, so they are not listed as predictors in the columns of the matrix. If you intend that Es or Ds will have any role other than as these standard residuals, you would have to go to the **work.eqs** file and type in the relevant specification separately from this automatic equation generator.

Click, Drag, and Double-Click in Equations and Variances/Covariances

Before we continue, it is worthwhile to describe three general procedures that you can use in the **Create New Equations** and **Create Variances/Covariances** (see below) dialog boxes. We had already noted one of these: clicking and clicking again on a cell in one of these matrices makes the * visible, and then removes it.

> *Note:* Clicking in a cell with a particular mouse may be a bit delicate and it may seem that there is no response. It may be necessary to experiment to get the right feel for your hardware.

There is a simpler way to change the entries from * to no *, or the reverse. Place your pointer in the cell to the left of and above the part of the matrix you want to modify. Click on the mouse button, and drag the pointer, and its attached outlined rectangle, to the cell below and to the right of the lower right corner of the part you want to modify. Then, release the mouse button.

All the cells that were included will have their status reversed with regard to *. If you attempt this in the screen given by Figure 7.13, the following will happen. Suppose you want to unmark the *s that represent the three marker variables for F1. Place your pointer above V1 and to the left of F1 and click. Drag down to the V4,F2 cell and release. Now all of the *s will be gone.

Repeat this operation, and the * are replaced again. Experiment a bit by doing this in various parts of the matrix, and then make the results look like Figure 7.13 again.

Double-clicking on a cell in these matrices brings up a **1** instead of an *. As you know, fixed parameters are often taken with the value **1**, and double-clicking facilitates marking these fixed parameters. To remove a **1**, just do two separate single clicks in the cell. The first click adds an * to the **1**, so that you will see *1. The second click removes both of these symbols.

Back to the main topic. When you select **Adopt Equations from Factor Analysis** in the **Build Equations** dialog box (see Figure 7.12), as we did, the elements of **Create New Equations** are automatically filled with * in accord with the elements of the factor loading matrix (ours, in **factor2.ess**) that exceed the specified filter value. So, in our example, Figure 7.13 was created automatically and we can just click **DONE** to continue. If the results are not to our liking for any reason, we can edit the matrix further in the ways discussed, before we click **DONE**.

When we click **DONE**, the following set of equations appear in the **work.eqs** file:

```
/EQUATIONS
V1 = +*F1 + E1;
V2 = +*F1 + E2;
V3 = +*F1 + E3;
V4 = +*F2 + E4;
V5 = +*F2 + E5;
V6 = +*F2 + E6;
```

Evidently, these equations correspond to our specification in Figure 7.13. However, you will note that the E residuals have been added, and each equation has been completed with a ; as required by the EQS program.

Asterisks and Free Parameters: Identification Issues

In creating equations, the * refers to a variable to be included in an equation. As you see in our automatic procedure, each asterisk also is taken as a free parameter in an equation. You should think carefully about whether this is what you want to do. Remember that you must fix the scale of each factor, by fixing a path from it or possibly fixing its variance (only if it is an independent variable). You may want to fix one of the paths from an F to a V at 1.0 for identification.

In the example, you might remove the * from the equations for V1 and V4, for example. One way to do this was discussed above. Another way is to edit the equations in the work.eqs file. In either case, *identification constraints will not be added automatically for you*. You have to take care of these by yourself.

Variances/Covariances

The variances and covariances of independent variables are specified in the next dialog box, which appears automatically when you have completed the equations. The independent variables now include residual E and D variables associated with V and F variables if these are relevant to the model. Figure 7.14 shows the box **Create Variances/Covariances** for our example. The independent variables in a factor analysis model are Fs and Es.

As before, you must place an asterisk in each position that you want to represent as a free parameter. By default, as you can see, the diagonal elements of this matrix have * inserted in them. Thus by default, all of these variables have their variances taken as free parameters. This may or may not be what you want to do. And, by default, no covariances are specified. If you want some covariances, you will have to put * in the relevant positions.

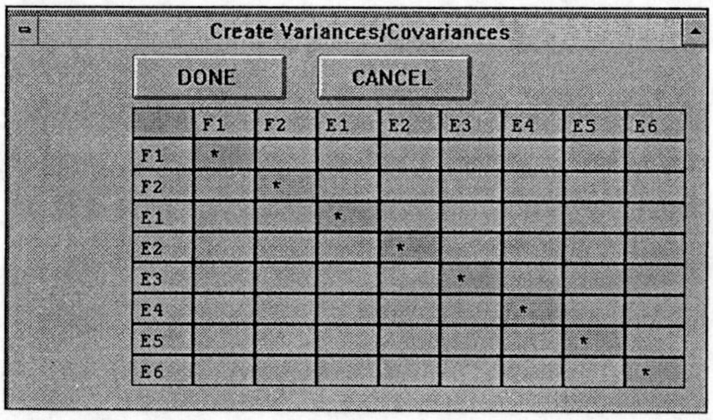

Figure 7.14 Create Variances/Covariances Dialog Box

Fixing Variances

In order to fix the scale of each factor, you either will have fixed a factor loading at 1.0, or you must fix the variance of the factor. Remember that, by default, all variances are free parameters. In our example, we did not fix any factor loadings, so we must fix the variances of the factors. This is done easily by clicking on the F1,F1 and F2,F2 diagonal cells of the matrix. The * will disappear from each cell when you click, and the corresponding variance will be fixed at 1.0. In factor analysis, this is a typical practice. It is not necessary to specify the fixed **1** in the diagonal of the matrix; this is done automatically when there is no *.

Freeing Covariances

Covariances are specified in the bottom triangle. Do not select covariances in the top triangle. Each covariance is fixed at zero unless you click on its corresponding cell. Any covariance could be a free parameter, provided the model is identified. Click on those covariances that you want to be freely estimated.

In the case of a confirmatory factor analysis model, it is typical practice to allow factors to correlate. So, in the example, click on the F2,F1 position. The * will appear, indicating a free parameter. If you wanted to allow certain correlated errors, those would be specified here as well.

Setting Variances and Covariances By Using Drag

As before, the drag method of setting parameters is easier in this example than using individual clicks. Place the pointer in the upper left corner, above and to the left of F1,F1. Then drag down past the F2,F2 cell. This reverses the previous operation. Starting from what is shown in Figure 7.14, this immediately creates the two fixed variance and one free covariance parameters. Or, it reverses that operation if it was previously done.

When you are satisfied with the variance/covariance specification, click **DONE**. The resulting specifications will be transferred to the **work.eqs** file. In our example, you would find the following:

```
/VARIANCES
F1 = 1;
F2 = 1;
E1 = *;
E2 = *;
E3 = *;
E4 = *;
E5 = *;
E6 = *;
/COVARIANCES
F2,F1 = *;
```

You see that the variances of F1 and F2 are fixed at 1.0, since they have no asterisk. All error variances are free parameters, with no start value given, since EQS will pick its own start values. The only covariance specified is that between the factors.

If this is a standard model, you could now immediately submit the job to the EQS for Windows run, as you can see below. The last part of any model file, the /END statement, will be added automatically to your file, so you don't have to write it.

Constraints

A set of linear equality constraints is set with the **Build_EQS** menu **Constraints** option. Click on it now. You will see Figure 7.15.

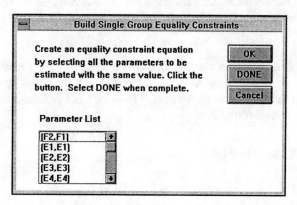

Figure 7.15 Build Single Group Equality Constraints

Figure 7.15 contains instructions in the top part of the box, and a **Parameter List** in the bottom part. In order to use constraints effectively, you must learn the EQS Double Label convention for parameters.

The dialog box shows the covariance of factors F1 and F2, and six error variances. In this convention:
1. Variances are denoted by repeating the variable name, e.g., E1,E1 as the diagonal element of a matrix.
2. Covariances are given by the similar double label name, e.g., F2,F1 for the covariance between F2 and F1.
3. Regression coefficients in equations are given by first listing the dependent variable, and then its predictor. Thus V1,F1 is the factor loading for V1 on F1.

These additional names are hidden in the list box, but are made visible when you use the scroll bar. Parentheses are used around the double-label names since this is a requirement for writing constraint equations.

For illustrative purposes, suppose you want the factor loadings for factor 1 to be equal, and also the factor loadings for factor 2 to be equal. Then, you first find each of the double-label names (V1,F1), (V2,F1), and (V3,F1) in turn, and, holding down the <Ctrl> key, click on each one to select it. Then, click **OK**.

This creates the first equality constraint. Then, you do the same thing for the factor loadings on factor 2. Finally, click on **DONE**. You will see in **work.eqs** that the model file now contains the constraints that you selected.

```
/CONSTRAINTS
(V1,F1)=(V2,F1)=(V3,F1);
(V4,F2)=(V5,F2)=(V6,F2);
```

Of course, you should have an adequate rationale for selecting such equality constraints. Remember especially that equality constraints of the sort we did are not scale invariant. Suppose that these

219

particular equalities are consistent with the data. Then they may cause model rejection if we were to rescale some of the variables.

To illustrate, if we had selected to scale some, but not all, of the variables by moving a decimal place on the scores of a variable, then this variable's variance and its covariances, and, hence, its factor loading, would change as well. So what used to be equal loadings would have to become unequal to fit the data.

Equality constraints can be placed only on free parameters, and EQS for Windows does not let you use a fixed parameter. In addition, you should remember that EQS also permits you to set up complicated general linear equality constraints. These are not facilitated with **Build_EQS**. See the program manual for more information.

Inequality Constraints

EQS automatically imposes the inequality constraint that variances of free parameters should be nonnegative, and that correlations between two variables with fixed 1.0 variances should lie in the ± 1 interval. You can override these default inequalities, and impose your own, using the **Build_EQS** menu **Inequality** option to get the dialog box shown in Figure 7.16.

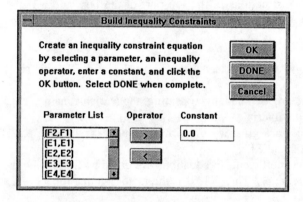

Figure 7.16 Build Inequality Constraints Dialog Box

As you can see, the instructions are very similar to equality constraints, permitting you to set up more than one constraint based on the **Parameter List** at the bottom. Only free parameters are given in this list.

For example, to force the estimated factor correlation to be nonnegative, click on **(F2,F1)**, then on > and then click **OK** and **DONE**. You will see the following lines appear in your model file.

```
/INEQUALITY
(F2,F1) > 0.0;
```

If you wanted to pick a number other than **0.0**, you would have changed the number in the edit box. Although we wanted to demonstrate this option, we don't want this constraint. So, go to your model file, highlight the two inequality lines by clicking and dragging, and then hit the <Delete> key. The lines will disappear from the file.

Lagrange Multiplier Test

The LM test, or Lagrange Multiplier test, is a test designed to evaluate the statistical necessity of one or more restrictions on a model. The restrictions that are evaluated are, typically, whether a parameter that has been fixed to a given value is appropriately fixed or might better be left free to estimate, and whether an equality restriction is appropriate, given the data. A discussion of the LM test, and how to use it in EQS, is given in Chapter 6 of the *EQS Structural Equations Program Manual*. Certain new features, especially, **Block** and **Lag** are discussed below.

Default Test

LM tests are probably the most technically demanding to implement in their full generality in EQS. That is because this is the one place where an understanding of the Bentler-Weeks matrices is really imperative. Suppose that you do not want to study this material in the EQS manual. Then we suggest that you just use the default LMtest procedure. This is implemented via the **LMtest** option from the **Build_EQS** list box. When you click on the **Build_EQS** menu **LMtest** option, you see the dialog box shown in Figure 7.17.

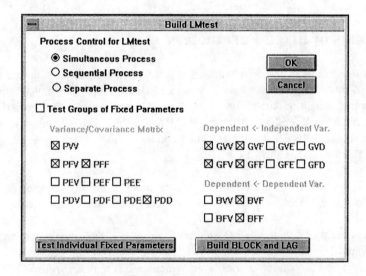

Figure 7.17 Build LMtest Dialog Box

For the default test, you would just click **OK**. (However, you should not click **OK** yet if you want to follow the examples on **Test Individual Fixed Parameters** and **Build BLOCK and LAG**.) When you click **OK**, you will get the following lines in your **work.eqs** file, which indicate that 10 parameter submatrices will be searched for fixed parameters that might better be free.

```
/LMTEST
 PROCESS=SIMULTANEOUS;
 SET=PVV,PFV,PFF,PDD,GVV,GVF,GFV,GFF,BVF,BFF;
```

If you are a beginner in modeling and EQS, just click **OK** to accept this default. Otherwise, you should study some of the additional options which we shall mention in turn. Where the EQS manual provides detailed discussion, we only provide a cursory description.

221

Process Control for LMtest

As you see in the above example, by default ten submatrices are searched for possible parameters to add to a model. You may consider some of these matrices more important than others, or you may not care. The default option, **Simultaneous Process**, suggests that you want to find the most important missing parameters, by the LMtest criterion. **Simultaneous Process** also suggests that you do not particularly care whether these parameters are factor loadings or any other type of parameter.

If you click the radio button **Sequential Process**, parameters are selected from the first listed matrix if they are liable to be important. Parameters in the next listed matrix are only searched when there are no further significant parameters in the first matrix. And so on. If you select this option, you should be sure that the list in **Set** lists the parameter matrices in order of their importance to you.

You would choose the option **Separate Process** when you want to obtain several separate LMtests, one for each matrix. The results based on one matrix do not take into account what might happen in another matrix. This is, of course, unrealistic, since the parameter estimates would correlate if freed. But it gives you a view of one part of potential model modification without being affected by other parts.

Test Groups of Fixed Parameters

You can select the groups of fixed parameters to test with the check box shown in Figure 7.17. By default, it is not marked. If it is marked, you can select or unselect any of the particular matrix sections shown in the bottom part of the dialog box. As you can see, these matrix parts concern the covariance matrix of independent variables, the **P??** options. The **??** refer to part of a particular matrix. Since the only type of potential independent variables are **V, F, E,** and **D,** the various options are **PVV, PFV,** etc. as shown.

> *Note:* Correlated errors, which would appear in **PEE**, are not selected by the default option. So if you are interested in correlated errors, you must check that box.

Regression parameters always involve **Dependent** variables. The only possible dependent variables are **V** and **F** variables, so there are only two lines to each of the right sections. However, the predictor might be an independent variable, in which case it appears in the **G??** matrix, or another dependent variable, in which case it appears in the **B??** matrix. These two matrices are shown in the right part of the dialog box, under **Dependent ← Independent** (for **G??** matrix parts) and under **Dependent ← Dependent** (for **B??** matrix parts).

For example, factor loadings are always either in **GVF**, if the factors are independent variables, or **BVF**, if the factors are dependent variables. (Remember that the first variable listed in the pair is the dependent variable, and the second, the predictor. So **GVF** represent paths from **F**s to **V**s.)

For consistency with the Bentler-Weeks technical notation, the **P, G,** and **B** matrices involved are abbreviations of Greek names. That is, **P = Phi, G = Gamma,** and **B = Beta.**

Test Individual Fixed Parameters

The LM test has its best statistical rationale if you have an *a priori* hypothesis in mind. Then you should specify your test by picking the option to **Test Individual Fixed Parameters**. The dialog box shown in Figure 7.18 will appear. As you can see, you must specify the matrix.

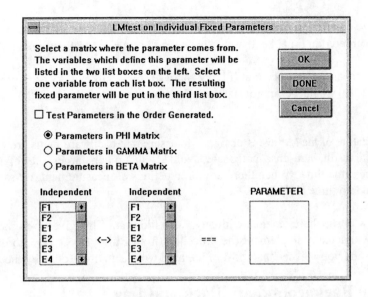

Figure 7.18 LMtest of Individual Fixed Parameters

By default, the **PHI** matrix is designated first. The possible independent variables in your model are given in the list boxes on the bottom left. When you select one variable from each list by clicking on its name, and then clicking **OK**, a parameter such as (E3,E1) is created in the **PARAMETER** list box shown on the bottom right.

For example, to create an *a priori* test on (E3,E1) and (E4,E2), click E3 in the first column and E1 in the second column and click **OK**; then repeat with E4 and E2. Then click **DONE** in this dialog box, and **OK** in the **Build Lmtest** dialog box. You get back to Figure 7.17. Do not click **OsK** yet, because we want to discuss **Build Block and Lag** below. However, when you do click **OK** in Figure 7.17, you will have an *a priori* test which looks as follows:

```
APRIORI=(E3,E1),(E4,E2);
```

Obviously, as shown in Figure 7.18, you can also select **Parameters in GAMMA Matrix** or **Parameters in BETA Matrix** by clicking on the appropriate radio buttons. By default, as shown above, you get an *a priori* test. In such a test, the parameters are actually evaluated in a forward stepwise fashion depending on their importance.

If you want to have the parameters enter the test in a particular sequence, you should click on the check box **Test Parameters in the Order Generated**. We really do not want to use an *a priori* test in this example, so edit the above lines out of your **work.eqs** file so that you are back to the default test.

Build Block and Lag

The LMtest can take up so much computer space that you may not be able to run it unless you are selective about parameters that you want to evaluate for inclusion in the model. The feature shown in the bottom right of Figure 7.17, **Build BLOCK and LAG**, permits you great control of the LMtest. Before explaining how you set up these features with **Build_EQS**, we would like to review their purpose.

Variables used in structural modeling often can be ordered implicitly or explicitly along a time dimension. For example, data may be gathered in three annual waves. In such a case, one can make

223

a strong *a priori* assumption that causal processes that might be specified among the variables should also be ordered in time, i.e. that no "backward in time" causal paths should be permitted.

If the waves of measurement occur at T1, T2, and T3, then only paths of the type T1 → T2, T1 → T3, and T2 → T3 would be appropriate. A backward path of the type T3 → T1 would not be appropriate.

The **BLOCK** feature of the LM test is designed to assure that backward paths are eliminated from the LM test. As a result, nonsense paths are avoided, and much larger sets of restrictions can be evaluated at the same time. When there are three periods of measurement, we say that the variables can be grouped into three blocks.

We discuss how to use these features with any ***.eqs** file first. This gives a bit more technical detail than necessary to actually implement the procedure from **Build_EQS**. How to do that is discussed subsequently—and you will see that most of the hard work actually is done by the program.

Technical Background on Block and Lag

To implement this feature, three commands must be used at the same time in the /LMTEST section of the program setup: **SET**, **BLOCK**, and **LAG**.

1. **SET**. This is the standard command of the LM test, illustrated above, that specifies which submatrices of parameter matrices are to be investigated by the LM test. In simple applications of the LM test, you can ignore the **SET** command. Then default matrices are chosen for the LM test. When used with the **BLOCK** feature, however, no default submatrices will be chosen, and those desired for analysis must be stated.

2. **BLOCK**. The **BLOCK** command, which permits one to group variables into blocks, partitions the matrices specified in **SET** into smaller submatrices for analysis and specifies the direction of possible paths. It also specifies possible covariance linkages among variables that are desired or intended to be eliminated.

    Only V and F types of variables can be listed; the program will search for E and D types of variables and group them appropriately based on their correspondence to V and F variables. **BLOCK** will group together into a single block all of the V and F variables that are listed in a statement, where the variables can be listed individually or in sequence via a TO convention.

    When listed separately, each variable must be separated from other variables by a comma. Each block must be identified by a pair of parentheses ( ). If there are to be several blocks of variables, each set must be surrounded by parentheses, and a comma must separate the blocks.

    Note: To choose contiguous variables, click on the first variable of the group; then, holding the <Shift> key, click on the last variable in the group. To choose noncontiguous variables, click on the first variable in the group; then, holding the <Ctrl> key, click on each of the other variables in the group.

    So, for example: BLOCK = (V1,V2,V3,F1), (V4,V5,V6,F2), (V7 TO V9, F3); creates three blocks of variables corresponding, for example, to three measurement times. V1-V3 and F1 are in the first block. V4-V6 and F2 are in the second block. V7-V9 and F3 are in the third block. The listing sequence of the blocks indicates the directional sequence in which paths are permitted to be evaluated. That is, only "forward" paths or covariances will be analyzed. (If you want to shift the direction of the paths, you must reverse the sequence listing of the blocks.) Still greater control is made possible by the **LAG** command.

3. **LAG.** The **LAG** specification defines the "time" lag desired for paths between variables in the LM test. Possible values are LAG = 0; up to LAG = b-1;, where b is the number of blocks created by the block statement.

LAG = 0; means that only variables within the same block will be selected; with 3 blocks, there would be 3 possible sets of within-block paths or covariances to evaluate. With LAG = 1; only paths or covariances across adjacent blocks would be evaluated. For example, LAG=1; might evaluate from T1 to T2 and from T2 to T3. If you want to study the cross-block effects from T1 to T3, you would write LAG = 2;.

In typical practice, one might consider only LAG = 0; in one analysis, LAG = 1; in another analysis, and so on. However, you can specify several lags simultaneously, for example, LAG = 1,2,4; When LAG is not specified, a default is implemented, which is ALL, i.e. 0,1, up to b-1.

Examples of the directional blocking feature are as follows:

```
/LMTEST
  BLOCK = (V1,V7,V9,F1), (V2,V3), (F2,V4,V5,V6), (F3,V10 TO V15);
  SET = BFF, BVV;
  LAG = 0;
```

In this example, there are four blocks, and only paths between adjacent blocks will be evaluated. Paths are to be of the type involving regression of dependent Vs on other dependent Vs, and dependent Fs on other dependent Fs.

```
/LMTEST
  BLOCK = (V1 TO V5), (V6 TO V10), (V11 TO V15);
  SET = PEE;
  LAG = 0;
```

In this example, correlated errors are evaluated, but only covariances within blocks are to be searched. If LAG = 1; had been used instead, only cross-time covariances with lag one would have been evaluated.

Block and Lag in Build_EQS

Fortunately, most of the difficult technical specification is done automatically for you in EQS for Windows, though the concepts are certainly important for you to know. First, in the basic **Build LMtest** dialog box shown in Figure 7.17, and discussed above, it was made clear how to select submatrices to study. These are selected initially, and essentially create the **SET** command as you have seen. It is not necessary to worry about it further. Only **BLOCK** and **LAG** remain to be specified.

When you click on the **Build BLOCK and LAG** button in the **Build LMtest** dialog box, you will see Figure 7.19 for this example. As you can see, it lists all of the **V** and **F** variables in the **Variable List** box on the bottom left.

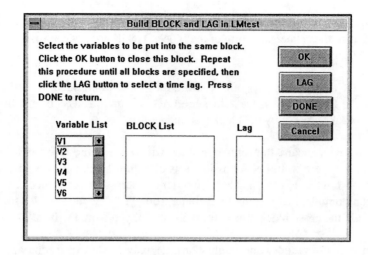

Figure 7.19 Build BLOCK and LAG Dialog Box

Holding down the <Ctrl> key, select **V1**, **V2**, **V3** and **F1** in turn, to define your first block. When you click **OK**, they are placed into the **BLOCK List**, as shown below. Then you select **V4**, **V5**, **V6** and **F2** for the second block and click **OK**. You can see both blocks in Figure 7.20.

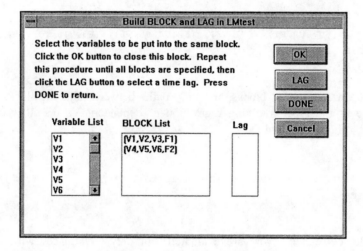

Figure 7.20 Build BLOCK and LAG Dialog Box with Blocks

When you are finished defining blocks, click on the **LAG** button. The **LAG** list displays **0**, **1**, and you can select the lag or lags that you want. When you are finished, click on **DONE**. This takes you out of this dialog box, and back to the **Build LMtest** dialog box. When you are satisfied, click **OK**.

In this example, click **CANCEL** instead, since blocking makes no sense. The variables are not time ordered. When you get back to the **Build LMtest** dialog box, click **OK** to get the LM test lines into **work.eqs**.

This completes our discussion of the LMtest.

Wald Test

The Wald Test is a test on the free parameters. It evaluates whether a free parameter could possibly be zero in the population. It is specified as shown in Figure 7.21.

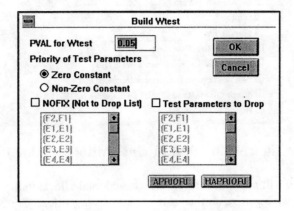

Figure 7.21 Build Wtest Dialog Box

By default, **PVAL for Wtest** is set to .05, but you can change this value in the edit box. You can specify whether parameters should be tested against a **Zero Constant** or some other **Non-Zero Constant**. **Zero Constant** is the default test. See **RETEST** below for tests on nonzero constants.

The list box **NOFIX (Not to Drop List)** on the left uses the double-label naming convention to show possible free parameters that you might be able to fix. Select those parameters which you would not want to drop even if their estimates were not significantly different from zero. The right list box, **Test Parameters to Drop**, permits you to specify particular parameters to test.

If you choose **Test Parameters to Drop**, you can click a button below to test the parameters either in an *apriori* or an *hapriori* way. The EQS manual explains that the former is a backward-stepping procedure with no particular order of stepping specified, while the latter specifies the procedure in a given, hierarchical way. When you click **OK**, the material is entered into the **work.eqs** file in the usual way. Press **Cancel** to eliminate these choices, since we do not plan to use them.

Print

The option **Print** from the **Build_EQS** procedure controls a variety of printing features. When this selection is chosen, the dialog box shown in Figure 7.22 becomes active. It permits you to control output in the ***.out** file as well as in a new ***.eqs** file that can be created.

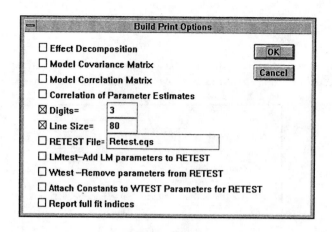

Figure 7.22 Build Print Options Dialog Box

Effect Decomposition will print the indirect effects and total effects in the model. These are defined in the EQS manual and elsewhere on the basis of path tracing rules. You will get both standardized and unstandardized effects, printed in an equation-like format. The **Model Covariance Matrix** and **Model Correlation Matrix** give the model-reproduced sigma and its standardized version. You also get the model covariances and correlations of measured and latent variables, whether they are dependent or independent variables. In the figure, these options are not chosen.

The **Correlations of Parameter Estimates** is the correlation matrix of the estimated parameters, which can be useful to study when there are linear dependencies among parameters. **Digits** and **Line Size** have some preselected defaults as shown. These control the accuracy of numbers in the output, as well as whether you want to print in standard computer paper (132 column) or microcomputer paper (80 column) format.

The next several options deal with a practical feature, called **Retest**, that has been incorporated in recent versions of the EQS program. You must specifically select **Retest** if you want it.

Retest

The **Retest** option saves a substantial amount of computer time, helping in program convergence of multiple job runs. Also, **Retest** makes it easier for you to do a sequence of model modifications. When specified, **Retest** takes the final parameter estimates from a completed EQS run and inserts them into a new file. You can submit that new file, with only minor modifications, for another EQS run. Specifically, **Retest** creates new /EQUATION, /VARIANCE, and /COVARIANCE sections that contain the optimal parameter estimates from the just-completed run. These sections are then used in a new run.

The option **LMtest - Add LM parameters to RETEST** takes parameters that are significant in the multivariate LM test and automatically adds them to the equations and variances and covariances as needed. You can recognize these newly added parameters in your model setup because they contrast with the original parameters. The parameters from the original run will have optimal estimates, while the parameters from the LM test results will only have * next to them.

Of course, you should only accept these new parameters if they make sense. You can use the option **Wtest - Remove parameters from RETEST** to flag parameters in the new file that were not significant in the previous run, based on the multivariate Wald test. To differentiate between significant and nonsignificant parameters, note that:

1.   All significant free parameters will have an * and the optimal estimate in front of the *.

2. Nonsignificant parameters will have the number **0** next to them.

An example might be V1 = 0F1 + .6*F2 + E1;. Without an * the **0** will have the effect of eliminating the parameter. If you decide to keep the parameter as a free parameter, you simply add an * and some estimated value. Wtest suggestions must always be taken with a grain of salt. For example, we would never remove variances as parameters even if they are not significant.

As you see in Figure 7.22, you implement **Retest** by checking the list box for **RETEST File** and giving a file name. A default name is provided, but it is always better to use a meaningful name, say, the next number in a sequence of models that you plan to run. So, if this is **?1.eqs**, a good next run might be called **?2.eqs**. If the current model file is saved as **manul7a1.eqs**, and appropriate name might be **manul7a2.eqs**. The effect, when finished, is to create the appropriate statements such as

```
/PRINT
digit=3;
linesize =80;
RETEST=`manul7a2.eqs';
lmtest=yes; wtest=yes;
```

based on the specifications shown in the figure. When you give the above specification, EQS puts the file that was used as the input file to the current run as the first set of material in the new file. In this example, the input file is **work.eqs**, or possibly **manul7a1.eqs**, which will then appear at the beginning section of **manul7a2.eqs**. EQS also creates new /EQUATIONS, /VARIANCES, and /COVARIANCES sections, based on final optimal parameter estimates, into the file **manul7a2.eqs**, following the current input file.

After you complete the modeling run, and have evaluated your ***.out** file, you can then bring up the new file **manul7a2.eqs**. You must edit it to delete parts of the file that are obsolete, and to update the model in the desired way.

For example, the /TITLE may need to be changed. The /SPECIFICATION section may be perfectly acceptable, or may need to be modified. The old /EQU, /VAR, and /COV sections, at the top of the file, can typically be completely removed. Other sections, such as /LMTEST also may need to be modified to be appropriate to the next run. The **Retest** file name will need updating again. As usual, the file to be submitted for an EQS run must end with /END.

You can select another option, **Attach Constants to WTEST Parameters for RETEST**, as shown in Figure 7.22. When chosen, it adds a line in the model file **WPARAMETER=YES;**. The new line controls a further set of statements in the new RETEST file. Specifically, it creates

```
/WTEST
    APRIORI=(E1,E1):4.38,(E2,E2):3.54,...,(V6,F1):0.00;
```

which specifies a Wtest for fixed parameters. The numbers are optimal values from the previous run. After selecting the parameters of interest, in the next run, the program will do a Wtest that compares final estimated values to the fixed values.

When the fixed values are the values from a prior model run, this procedure can evaluate changes in model estimates due to changes in the model specification. For example, the effects of correlated errors can be evaluated this way. Of course, any fixed nonzero values can be tested.

You can omit the numerical values 0.00. This means that just writing (V6,F1) would work in the above example. If you want to test zero constraints first, you must add **PRIORITY=ZERO;** in the /WTEST specification in the above example.

When testing a Wtest with a set of constraints, you also obtain a rank correlation of the constants and optimal estimates. This can evaluate the stability of estimates due to model changes.

Report Full Fit Indices

A final option shown in Figure 7.22 allows you to request EQS to compute and print a wider range of fit indices along with the standard options. There is a great deal of literature on the virtues and problems of various fit indices, so if your favorite index is not produced by default, you must request it. When you do, the work.eqs will include the line:

```
fit=all;
```

EQS for Windows now prints these additional indices which include: Independence Model Chi-square, Independence AIC, Model AIC, Independence CAIC, Model CAIC, Chi-square, Bentler-Bonett's Normed and Nonnormed Fit Indexes, Bentler's Comparative Fit Index, Bollen's IFI Fit Index, McDonald's MFI Fit Index, LISREL's GFI and AGFI Fit Indexes, Steiger's RMSEA, Root Mean Squared Residual (RMR), and Standardized RMR. You will find the formulas in Appendix V of the EQS manual.

All of this discussion jumped ahead quite a bit. We do not need **Retest** right now, so just press **Cancel** if you have been following along on your computer.

Technical

The option **Technical** selected from **Build_EQS** controls the convergence process. When you select this option, a dialog box as shown in Figure 7.23 appears.

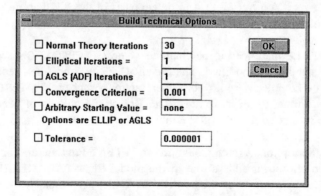

Figure 7.23 Build Technical Options Dialog Box

This option box sets up the /TECHNICAL input paragraph in the model file. It controls the maximum number of **Normal Theory Iterations**, which is defaulted to 30. If you are worried about convergence, you can increase this number.

In EQS, Elliptical and AGLS methods use a linearized method in which only one iteration is used unless you specify otherwise. You can specify your maximum number of iterations in the edit boxes associated with **Elliptical Iterations** and **AGLS (ADF) Iterations**. The convergence criterion, based on changes in parameter estimates from iteration to iteration, also has a default. You can modify the convergence criterion to be more or less stringent by checking **Convergence Criterion** and filling in the edit box.

Elliptical and AGLS methods use the optimal prior results from normal theory to form their start values. However, you can fill in the toggling options **ELLIP** or **AGLS** to use the arbitrary start values from your input file or from the program's defaults instead.

Finally, **Tolerance** is a technical term that controls when two or more parameters become linearly dependent. It is related to an R-square statistic that one could compute from the **Correlation Matrix of Parameter Estimates**.

You should see the EQS manual for details on these options. Here we can do no more than mention them.

Simulation

You can use the EQS program to perform simulations, including the bootstrap and jackknife, as described in the EQS manual. The specifications for such simulations are simplified when you click on the **Simulation** option of **Build_EQS** to bring up the dialog box shown in Figure 7.24.

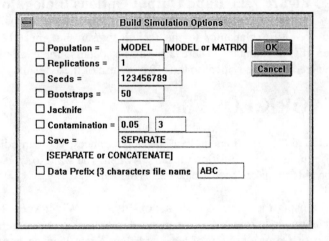

Figure 7.24 Build Simulation Options Dialog Box

Each of the check box options controls an aspect of the simulation procedure. The check boxes determine whether the population is constructed based on the model (equations and variances /covariances) or the covariance matrix. Also, you can specify the number of replications to be performed, a seed number for starting the process, the number of bootstrap samples, use of the jackknife, specifications for the contamination factor to develop elliptical samples, and procedures for saving the data files and output results generated. Each of these topics is quite technical, and you should consult the *EQS Structural Equations Program Manual*. Of course, filling out the dialog box and clicking **OK**, as usual, creates the appropriate text in the **work.eqs** file.

Output Control

In addition to the usual output log placed into the *.out** file being run, you can obtain other output from the analysis. The specifications from this output control dialog box all deal with technical topics that are described in detail in the EQS manual. When you select the **Build_EQS** menu **Output** option, the **Build Output Options** dialog box appears as shown in Figure 7.25.

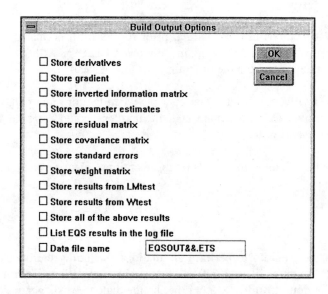

Figure 7.25 Build Output Options Dialog Box

The options listed are self-explanatory to the technical user, but must be used in accord with specifications given in the manual. There are various details, for example, on how the stored information is organized, that are critical to the effective use of these results from a modeling run.

Editing the WORK.EQS File

After you have specified the equations and variance/covariances, you can edit the **work.eqs** in any way you see fit. Use the mouse to position the cursor where you want to type, then click your mouse button. You will be able to make specific changes to the model.

You can edit the file using the types of basic actions that any Windows-based word processor will permit. The **Edit** command from the main menu can help you to accomplish a lot of standard actions, such as **Cut** or **Copy** a section of text, and then **Paste** it in an appropriate location. For example, you can highlight an entire section, then hit a key on the keyboard and the entire section will disappear. Or, you can **Copy** the material, and go to another word processor to paste it directly into your manuscript.

You can use the **Find/Replace** option from the **Edit** menu to quickly find any desired section of the file. You can then manually replace the section. Note that the **Replace** portion of this option will be operative in the next release of this software.

Although **Build_EQS** should make your standard models easy to set up, models with unusual features will require additional editing prior to running the job. You can tinker with several different ways to accomplish something. If you are not satisfied with your equations, for example, you can wipe them all out, and then start again with the Equations selection from **Build_EQS** to rebuild them in a form more suited to your goals.

Once you work with EQS, you will gain experience in which features you want to include in any modeling run. Some researchers, for example, always automatically include the default Lagrange Multiplier and Wald tests, while others always use the **Retest** option.

232

Running the Modeling Program

When the **work.eqs** file is completed, you are ready to run the modeling program. This is done by going again to the **Build_EQS** menu, and selecting **Run EQS/386**.

The **Save As** dialog box appears. Enter a new name for the **work.eqs** file, accept the **Text File** default **File format** and click **Save**. It is a good idea to use a name other than **work.eqs**, since you may perform several runs and you will want to keep the results separate.

In general, you should change the name to one that you can easily associate with this particular analysis. At the same time, you should keep the file designated as a *.eqs file, a text file format that holds EQS models.

In our example, the designation **manul7a.eqs** would associate this model file setup with the **manul7a.ess** data file, so we suggest that you enter that name now. Then click **Save**.

The program will run for a short while. When the EQS for Windows run is completed, you will see the **Open an EQS Output File** dialog box. See the **Examining and Printing the Output File** section below for details on opening the output file.

If you used the **Retest** option, you will have created a second file. That is the new *.eqs file which you may want to examine before submitting another run. We shall not discuss this file.

Occasionally a problem occurs, and the program will not run. One possible reason might be that your computer does not have sufficient memory available for the size of your job. The easiest way to increase available memory is to remove windows from memory. Go to **Window**, select a window, and close it to remove it from memory. The more windows you can remove from memory, especially those containing plots, the more memory will be available for an EQS run. If this does not solve the problem, it may be necessary to increase the amount of memory available to EQS.

Within **Build_EQS**, you can modify the working memory array by selecting **EQS Working Array**. This brings up a dialog box in which you can specify the amount of memory to be used. Of course, your specification must be consistent with your actual computer resources. See the discussion in Chapter 1 of this user's guide.

Examining and Printing the Output File

When the program has finished running, the EQS analysis is complete. You will want to bring the output file back to your screen so that you can examine it conveniently.

If you are using Windows 95, the DOS window will remain open. Click on the **Cross** button in the corner of the window shown in Figure 11.6 to close the DOS window and bring up the **Open an EQS Output File** dialog box.

If you are using Windows 3.1, the DOS window will close automatically. As shown in Figure 7.26, the **Open an EQS Output File** dialog box will appear.

The **Open an EQS Output File** dialog box displays *.out in the **File Name** edit box, and it has the file type correctly set. You must click on the **OK** button to bring the file name into the list. Then double click on the file name to open the output file.

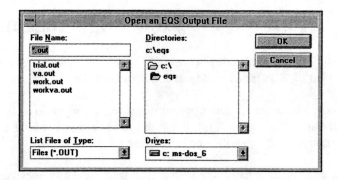

Figure 7.26 Open an EQS Output File Dialog Box

Note: You <u>must</u> click on **OK** in this dialog box to refresh the screen and bring your new output file into the list. Then double click on the file name to bring the file up in the usual way.

The name of the output file is always the input file name with **.out** replacing **.eqs**. Since we called the model file **manul7a.eqs**, the output file is called **manul7a.out**. We do not describe this output any further, because it is fully documented in the *EQS Structural Equations Program Manual*.

In general, you will want to scan the output for potential problems with your run, and to make decisions regarding further analyses. If the type seems too large or too small for viewing on your screen, you can go to **Fonts** in the main menu, and modify the size of the print. And, at some point, you may want to print the entire file or highlighted parts of the file. You can print via the **File** and **Print** commands, using standard Windows print procedures.

Moving EQS Output into Other Documents

One of the most valuable features of the Windows is the ability to use the **Clipboard** to take a program object from the file created by one program and place it into the file being used by another program. To illustrate this feature, we shall take a small section of the EQS output file and move it into this document, which is written with the Microsoft Word wordprocessor. In particular, you will take the standardized solution from **manul7a.out** and place it into a document.

You must make both EQS and MS Word active running programs at some point, either initially or sequentially. Suppose you run EQS first. Run the program and create various files, including the output file.

Go to the output file and highlight the part which you want to move. For example, select the equations from the standardized solution. Then choose **Edit** from the main menu, and **Copy**. This places the highlighted selection into the Windows clipboard.

Click on the gray square in the upper left corner of the EQS screen. Drag the cursor down to **Switch To....** You'll see the **Task List** of open applications. If MS Word is already running, click on **MS Word** in the list to move to Word. If Word is not running, it will not be in the list, so choose **Program Manager**. Within the **Program Manager**, bring up MS Word.

When you are in Word, open a document, and place the cursor in the desired position. While in Word, select **Edit** and then **Paste**, and the following EQS output appears:

```
V1    =V1  =    .646*F1    +  .764 E1
V2    =V2  =    .514*F1    +  .858 E2
V3    =V3  =    .885*F1    +  .465 E3
V4    =V4  =    .472*F2    +  .882 E4
V5    =V5  =    .874*F2    +  .485 E5
V6    =V6  =    .522*F2    +  .853 E6
```

These are the final standardized estimates of a confirmatory factor run with correlated factors, which can be compared to the factor analysis loadings from the orthogonally rotated exploratory solution shown in Figure 7.8.

Running Any *.eqs File

As you have now experienced, the main purpose of **Build_EQS** is to relieve you of the tedious details that often make developing a model harder than it needs to be. You found out that you need not worry about syntax or about forgetting some key parameter that is necessary for your model to run. Choices are menu-driven and once you are familiar with the default choices (the ones that are used most often), you should become a "whiz" at EQS, clicking away with abandon like a pro!

After you have constructed your basic model using the automated **Build_EQS** feature, in future runs you can modify and refine your model manually in your ***.eqs** text file. The best way to accomplish this is to edit the ***.eqs** file, save it, and then submit another run.

If you used **Retest**, then you would be editing the new file rather than the old file. In either case, you cannot invoke **Build_EQS** when editing an existing *.eqs file, unless you are completely abandoning the equation structure of the model and want essentially to start over. Thus, you must edit the existing file. After you have edited and updated the file, you can run it through the **Run EQS/386** option of **Build_EQS**. (And don't forget to update the model and output file names.)

To illustrate the model respecification procedure, let us make a simple modification to the **manul7a.eqs** file. Make this file the active window by using **Window** and clicking on the file. Then, when you see the file on the screen, find the section titled /COVARIANCES, and put an exclamation mark in front of the covariance, as follows:

```
/COVARIANCES
!F2,F1 = *;
```

The effect of the **!** is to tell the program to ignore the information behind it. As a result, the factors will now be uncorrelated, or orthogonal. You can resubmit this job by clicking on **Build_EQS** and then clicking on **Run EQS/386**. The **Save As** dialog box will appear, and you should now change the model file name to a logical follow-up to the current name, for example, **manul7b.eqs**.

When you make the name change, and click **OK**, the program will run. When it is finished, click **OK**, and the output will come back with a name for the output file, say **manul7b.out**. You will find in the output file that the model with uncorrelated factors still fits the data, though not quite as well as the initial model.

If you used the **Retest** option of EQS, you would not edit the original file. Rather, you would edit the newly created ***.eqs** file, eliminating the irrelevant material and assuring that the remaining material contains the model setup that you want. **Retest** is described above in the **Print** section.

Continuous and Categorical Data Models

This version of EQS for Windows incorporates a feature that permits the analysis of models that have categorical as well as continuous measured variables, based on theory developed by Drs. Sik-Yum Lee and Wai-Yin Poon, with some assistance by Bentler. The procedures to accomplish this will be described in this section.

Theory

It is assumed that any categorical variables that you plan to model are categorized versions of variables that are truly continuous, as well as multivariate normally distributed. This assumption is the same as that made by others in the literature, and it is a strong assumption that may not be appropriate in certain contexts. If it is not an assumption that you wish to make, you should not use this method. At present, there are no good diagnostics available for evaluating this assumption empirically.

When this assumption is true, then the correlations between the underlying variables can be estimated by coefficients known as polychoric and polyserial correlations. The correlation between the underlying variables yielding two categorical variables is known as the polychoric correlation. The correlation between the underlying variables that generate a categorical and a continuous variable is the polyserial correlation.

Structural modeling with such variables proceeds in two major stages.
1. These correlations are estimated without any concern for the structural model under consideration.
2. This correlation matrix is then considered to be a function of more basic parameters.

In this program, these parameters are the parameters of the Bentler-Weeks model. A generalized least squares procedure is used to estimate these model parameters, yielding the goodness of fit chi-square test and standard error estimates for the free parameters.

The literature contains several approaches to the estimation of polychoric and polyserial correlations. The statistics used in this program were developed by:
- Lee, S. -Y., Poon, W. -Y., & Bentler, P. M. (1994). Covariance and correlation structure analyses with continuous and polytomous variables. In T. W. Anderson, K. -T. Fang,, & I. Olkin (Eds.), *Multivariate Analysis and its Applications*: Vol. 24 (pp. 347-358). Hayward, CA: Institute of Mathematical Statistics.
- Lee, S. -Y., Poon, W. -Y., & Bentler, P. M. (in press). A two stage estimation of structural equation models with continuous and polytomous variables. *British Journal of Mathematical and Statistical Psychology*.

This work is based on prior work of Poon, W. -Y., & Lee, S. -Y. (1987). Maximum likelihood estimation of multivariate polyserial and polychoric correlation coefficients. *Psychometrika*, **52**, 409-430, and Lee, S. -Y., Poon, W. -Y., & Bentler, P. M. (1992). Structural equation models with continuous and polytomous variables. *Psychometrika*, **57**, 89-105. Technical details cannot be developed in this user's guide.

A modification to the Lee-Poon-Bentler approach is used in this program. In their approach, as with related approaches implemented in other programs, a correlation matrix is used as input.

When considering standard models with additive error or unique variances, such as factor analysis or standard latent variable models, the usual approach to setting up models is not appropriate for correlation matrices. The parameters of a correlation structure require nonlinear constraints so that the diagonals of the correlation matrix, all **1**, are reproduced exactly. This is difficult to do, so other researchers, as well as Lee-Poon-Bentler, consider the additive unique variances not as free parameters, but rather as functions of the remaining parameters in the model.

This method is convenient computationally, but has the difficulty that one cannot impose standard constraints, such as equality constraints, on the unique variances. Also, it is possible for these variances to be estimated as negative.

In EQS for Windows, we use the usual parameterization of standard models. As a result, the typical parameters are free parameters. We impose nonlinear constraints on the parameters so that the resulting matrix is in fact a correlation matrix.

The theory for these constraints was given, for example, in Bentler, P. M., & Lee, S. -Y. (1983). Covariance structures under polynomial constraints: Applications to correlation and alpha-type structural models. *Journal of Educational Statistics*, **8**, 207-222, 315-317, and Jamshidian, M., & Bentler, P. M. (1993). A modified Newton method for constrained estimation in covariance structure analysis. *Computational Statistics & Data Analysis*, **15**, 133-146.

Of course, the specific application is different from that considered in these previous discussions. You can evaluate whether the constraints have been imposed by checking the diagonal of the residual covariance matrix. If the constraints are not precisely imposed, the chi-square goodness of fit statistic will be too large by the sum of squares of the diagonal residual entries.

Implementation

We shall use the data file **poon.ess** that is distributed with the program. These data represent the scores of 200 subjects on eight variables, and will be modeled by a two factor confirmatory factor analysis model. **Open** this file now. Then, select the **Build_EQS** option from the main menu. Give the job an appropriate title. Then, when you get to specifications, you will see the options shown in Figure 7.27.

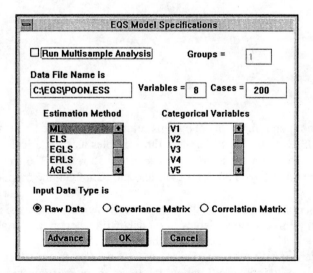

Figure 7.27 Model Specification for Categorical Variables

Whenever categorical data models are run, a standard method is first run. The **ML** option is the default, and is just fine. The main point to note is the section titled **Categorical Variables**. In this section, you must click on those variables that are categorical. Other than that, nothing else needs to be done.

Click on **V7** and **V8**, the categorical variables, and then click **OK** and proceed as usual. You should set up a two-factor model, with variables 1-4 being indicators of factor 1, and variables 5-8 being indicators of factor 2. Fix the factor variances, and let the factors correlate. When you are done, you will see the key part of the model file as follows:

```
/SPECIFICATIONS
!DATA=' c:\EQS\POON.ESS'; VARIABLEs=  8; CASES=  200;
 METHODS=ML;
 CATEGORY=V7,V8;
 MATRIX=RAW;
/LABELS
V1=V1; V2=V2; V3=V3; V4=V4; V5=V5;
V6=V6; V7=V7; V8=V8;
/EQUATIONS
V1 =  + *F1  + E1;
V2 =  + *F1  + E2;
V3 =  + *F1  + E3;
V4 =  + *F1  + E4;
V5 =  + *F2  + E5;
V6 =  + *F2  + E6;
V7 =  + *F2  + E7;
V8 =  + *F2  + E8;
/VARIANCES
F1 = 1;
F2 = 1;
E1 = *;
E2 = *;
E3 = *;
E4 = *;
E5 = *;
E6 = *;
E7 = *;
E8 = *;
/COVARIANCES
F2 , F1 = *;
```

Notice that there is nothing remarkable about this setup except for the line **CATEGORY = V7,V8;** in the /SPECIFICATIONS section. This identifies the variables as categorical variables. The program will do the rest. Go ahead and run EQS now by selecting **Run EQS/386** from the list of **Build_EQS** options. Use whatever names you want for the files, and then fetch the output and look at it.

> *Note:* There is one limitation to the current implementation. Consistent with the statistical theory, all measured variables in models with categorical variables must be dependent variables. However, we can trick the theory. If you want to use a measured variable as an independent variable, you can create a dummy factor to represent it. For example, if you want to include V7 in your model as an independent variable, create an equation like **V7=F7;** and use F7 in the model as if it were V7. Research will be needed to evaluate this procedure.

Output

By and large, the output from an EQS run with categorical variables follows the output from a run with AGLS. The normal theory method is run first, then the analysis based on categorical variables follows. There are, however some additional sections of output. These come immediately after the listing of the model file in the output.

```
YOUR MODEL HAS SPECIFIED CATEGORICAL VARIABLES
        TOTAL NUMBER OF VARIABLES ARE        8
        NUMBER OF CONTINUOUS VARIABLES ARE   6
        NUMBER OF DISCRETE   VARIABLES ARE   2


        INFORMATION ON DISCRETE VARIABLES
        V7  WITH    3 CATEGORIES
        V8  WITH    3 CATEGORIES
```

The program informs you that it has figured out how many categories your variables have. This is done whether or not you declared these variables as categorical in the **Data** and **Information** sections. The category information is used in the computations. Information on the polyserial correlations is presented first, for each of the variables in turn. The estimated thresholds are given first, followed by the covariance and correlation estimates. Standard error estimates also are provided.

```
RESULTS OF POLYSERIAL PARTITION USING V7 --  3 CATEGORIES
                        THRESHOLDS
                ESTIMATES        STD. ERR
                 -0.5113          0.0745
                  0.4319          0.0788
```

		ESTIMATES		
VARIABLE	COVARIANCE	STD. ERR	CORRELATION	STD. ERR
V 1	0.4161	0.0521	0.4151	0.0520
V 2	0.4451	0.0508	0.4440	0.0507
V 3	0.4967	0.0494	0.4955	0.0493
V 4	0.4290	0.0519	0.4279	0.0517
V 5	0.6192	0.0443	0.6177	0.0442
V 6	0.6369	0.0436	0.6353	0.0435

```
RESULTS OF POLYSERIAL PARTITION USING V 8 --  3 CATEGORIES
                        THRESHOLDS
                ESTIMATES        STD. ERR
                 -0.4567          0.0750
                  0.4988          0.0805
```

		ESTIMATES		
VARIABLE	COVARIANCE	STD. ERR	CORRELATION	STD. ERR
V 1	0.3818	0.0533	0.3808	0.0532
V 2	0.2660	0.0554	0.2653	0.0553
V 3	0.3563	0.0540	0.3554	0.0538
V 4	0.4397	0.0506	0.4386	0.0504
V 5	0.6228	0.0421	0.6213	0.0420
V 6	0.6737	0.0409	0.6720	0.0408

Information on polychoric correlations is presented next. Again, thresholds are computed and then the polychoric correlation estimates are given.

```
         RESULTS OF POLYCHORIC PARTITION
                                AVERAGE THRESHOLDS
                 V 7   -0.5044    0.4327
                 V 8   -0.4581    0.4855
    POLYCHORIC CORRELATION MATRIX BETWEEN DISCRETE VARIABLES
                    V  7        V  8
         V  7      1.000
         V  8      0.583       1.000
```

Following this output, the constructed correlation matrix to be analyzed is presented. Then, the usual normal theory statistics are given in the standard EQS format. While normal theory estimates may be useful, **the statistics in the normal theory output cannot be trusted**. That is, the chi-square goodness of fit values and z-statistics are in fact not distributed as chi-square and z, respectively.

In the subsequent section, the output for the polychoric/polyserial model are presented. This is titled

```
    GENERALIZED LEAST SQUARES SOLUTION (LEE, POON, AND BENTLER THEORY)
```

because the statistics implement the theory developed by these authors. The format for the output is exactly that of the AGLS method in EQS, which the manual describes in some detail. You will find that the model is statistically acceptable.

Multiple Group Structural Models

The **Build_EQS** procedure contains a feature which helps to set up multiple group models. In the specification box shown in Figure 7.10, there was a check box to **Run Multisample Analysis**. When you check this, you also must indicate the number of groups in the edit box called **Groups =** . When these choices are selected, the /SPECIFICATIONS that are created in the **work.eqs** file contain the statement **GROUPS=2;** (or whatever number you mentioned). Then you continue specifying your model as you did before.

When you have completed specifying the equation and variance-covariance information for the first group, you are immediately taken back to another round of model specifications. That is, you immediately confront a title dialog box, then the specifications dialog box, and the equations, and then variances-covariances.

The title, of course, should indicate that this is group 2. The specifications should indicate the correct data file or matrix for this group, and the correct number of subjects. The equations and variances and covariances are, by default, duplicates of the ones you provided for the first group. Thus, for all practical purposes, if you have a highly restricted model that is very similar across groups, it is automatically set up for you.

In the model file for the last group, when you set up **Constraints**, you will find that you are prompted automatically for information about the **Parameter List** and **Group List** from which you must specify your cross-group constraints.

The instructions are self-explanatory, and they follow the previous procedures. The result is that you can specify the cross-group constraints that are the heart of multiple group models. Figure 7.28

shows an example of the Constraints dialog box after selecting parameters (F1,F1). If you want this variance to be equal in all groups, select **ALL GROUPS** and click **OK**.

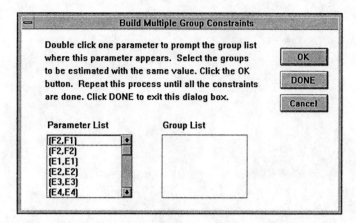

Figure 7.28 Build Multiple Group Constraints Dialog Box with Selection

Data File Specification for the Multiple Group Model

There is one customized feature that you must add to the multiple group setup. The /SPECIFICATIONS section in each group will point to the data file for each group. That is, you must not open the ***.ess** file in the Data Editor when you want to run the multiple group model.

You should edit the **DATA** lines in this section of each group so that they correctly point to the ***.dat** or ***.ess** files to be analyzed for each group.

To run EQS, call **EQS/386** as usual.

8. BUILD EQS BY DRAWING A DIAGRAM

It is virtually impossible to think about a complicated structural equation model, or a covariance structure model, without having a path diagram representation of the model. True, the diagram is in 1:1 correspondence to a set of equations and variance/covariance specifications, so the diagram is technically not needed. In reality, however, it is far easier to comprehend the diagram of the model than the algebraic specification of the model. Not only is a picture worth a thousand words, it is certainly worth dozens, if not hundreds, of equations!

We need diagrams of models in both the early stages of modeling, during model conceptualization, as well as in the final stages, when we are preparing to present our findings to the general scientific community via presentations or publications. In the early stages, a rough sketch drawn freehand may be quite adequate for personal use, but such an informal picture is inadequate for public presentation. In the past, this is where the researcher needed to turn to a graphic artist, or to a commercial drawing program, in order to produce an acceptable diagram. While artists are creative, they often overlook critical features of a model that are needed for an accurate portrayal of the results. And while drawing programs are very general and can create many interesting images, their very generality means that they are not specifically tailored to the task of creating the accurate path diagram that is so critical to structural modeling.

In Chapter 7, we showed how to build an EQS model by filling in tables that are subsequently used to create equations and variance/covariance specifications. In this chapter, you will learn how to build an EQS model by drawing a path diagram for the model, while in Chapter 9, you will learn how to customize your diagram.

The basic idea behind **Diagrammer** is that the **diagram you create is the model you run**. That is, the diagram is the model input. The program translates the diagram into the algebraic language used in the EQS model run. The diagram is also the model output, so that results are immediately available in publishable form.

You can retrieve the diagram at any time, modify it, and save and print the new diagram. Remember that making a modification of an existing diagram is a minor matter. If you want, you now can produce an accurate diagram for each model that you run—giving you a complete record of everything you do. Furthermore, whenever you work on a model that is similar to one that you have previously run, you can retrieve your previous diagram and adjust it to be relevant to your new data or model. There is no need to start from scratch, as is often routinely, but wastefully, done.

General Overview

A path diagram contains a set of variables and specifies the connections between the variables. Hence, when you draw a diagram, you must specify the variables in your model and show the connections between them.

You can draw a diagram for any model, whether this is a model that you plan to run with the EQS structural equations program or not. Because the diagram also serves as input to EQS, its initial labeling convention follows EQS. But you can modify this convention to show and print anything you want.

Variables

In EQS, every variable must be one of four types: V, F, E, or D. These are the variable types available by default in the **Diagrammer**. Typically, the most important ideas in a model are represented by the relations among V and F variables.

A V variable is a measured variable. You can use any V designations you like, such as V345. However, if you want to use the diagram as input to running EQS, you must use only those Vs that are actually in your data file. Variables in the data file are assumed to be ordered V1, V2, ..., up to Vx, where x is the largest integer representing the final variable in the file. Of course, you can select among these variables, e.g., using only V3, V8, and V23 for your diagram or the model.

> *Note:* The file you are using for various runs should contain only those variables which you plan to use in your models.

An F variable is a hypothetical common factor that accounts for the correlation between the variables it generates. Typically, you would number Fs sequentially such as F1, F2, ...,Fn . When used in a measurement model, the observed Vs are generated by underlying Fs. Such Fs are often called first-order factors. When used in a model with higher-order factors, several Fs will be generated by one or more Fs. When the latter Fs do not directly impact on any Vs, these factors are the higher-order factors. However, any type of connection is possible in general models.

> *Note:* It is wise to limit your models to those that are identified and can be estimated and tested.

There are also E and D variables. These are residual variables that arise automatically when Vs or Fs are dependent variables, that is, have one-way arrows aiming at them. A residual in a V variable is called an E variable. By default, the numerical part of the variable name is the same, so that E19 goes with V19 for example. A residual in an F variable is called a D variable, and the numerical part of the name is the same.

Arrows

Connections between variables are shown by one-way and two-way arrows.

1. A one-way arrow represents a directional influence in which one variable has an effect on another variable. A one-way arrow can be interpreted as a partial regression coefficient.

2. A two-way arrow represents the unanalyzed correlation or covariance between variables.

Dependent and Independent Variables

1. Every variable in your diagram that has at least one one-way arrow aiming at it is a dependent variable. Dependent variables are explained by other variables. Dependent variables cannot have covariances or two-way arrows as parameters. (If you want a dependent variable to covary with another variable, you must have its residual variable carry that covariance).

2. A variable that has no one-way arrow aiming at it is an independent variable. Independent variables have variances and, possibly, covariances as parameters. Only independent variables can covary with other variables, and those other variables must be

independent variables. Stated simply, only independent variables can be connected by two-way arrows. Residual variables (Es and Ds) must be independent variables in EQS. If you want to make a residual variable a dependent variable, just change its designation to an F variable.

Free and Fixed Parameters

1. Some parameters in a model are known ahead of time, without looking at the data. These are called fixed parameters. If a path or covariance is not shown in the diagram, the parameter that it represents is fixed at zero. If it is shown, its value will be nonzero, typically 1.0.

2. Other parameters are free parameters and need to be estimated with a modeling run.

In **Diagrammer**, you can specify whether a parameter is fixed or free, and what its value is. The values are called start values, although they may be final values because you do not intend to do another modeling run.

Three Basic Model Types

1. When you follow EQS naming conventions, if your model contains only Vs and Es, you have a standard path analysis, or simultaneous equation, model. Such a model may contain one-way and two-way arrows.

2. If your model contains only Vs, Es, and Fs, you have a factor analysis model. Such a model is also called a measurement model. In such a model, the Fs generate the Vs via one-way arrows.
   a If the Fs are not connected by two-way arrows, the factor analysis model is one of uncorrelated or orthogonal factors.
   b. Otherwise, it is an oblique factor model. Typically you will have a restricted oblique factor model, one that has a lot of missing paths, and/or some zero and nonzero factor correlations. Such a model is called a confirmatory factor analysis model.

3. If your model contains all four types of variables, you have a general linear structural equation model.

Drawing Procedure and Tools

A diagram is built up from its components, which are variables, and the connections between them. First you must specify two or more variables. Then, you can specify the arrow connections between these variables. Alternatively, you can specify a one-factor model which will create both the variables and the arrows needed for that structure. You can add additional variables, arrows, or factor structures, or remove variables, arrows, or factor structures, at any time.

This section provides details on various drawing options you can use to construct a path diagram model. Hopefully, you already practiced a bit on the examples in Chapter 2, **A Quick Start to EQS for Windows**. If you have not yet done so, you should go back to Chapter 2 for a little "hands-on" practice before getting into the details we show you in this chapter.

Object-Orientation

Before you get started, we want to give you a way to think about the diagram. You should think of **Diagrammer** as an "object-oriented" program. You will find that there is a drawing screen, or **Draw Diagram**, onto which you can place "objects".

An object is a variable, an arrow-connection between variables, a factor structure, or any superset of these. Objects will appear in the **Draw Diagram** after you designate the object that you desire, and then tell the program where you want that object to be.

After you place objects on the screen, you can manipulate these objects to achieve your goals. While you are manipulating the objects, they will maintain their identities and characteristics (unless you purposefully alter them).

For example, after you have placed an object into a particular position in the window, you can move it to another position. All of the characteristics of that object, such as its variable type, its name, its size, its connection to other objects, and so on, will be maintained.

Drawing Tools

You open **Diagrammer** by clicking on its icon, a 3-indicator, 1-factor structure, in the main menu.

Figure 8.1 The Diagrammer Icon

After opening **Diagrammer**, you will see the **Draw Diagram** window with menu bars as in Figure 8.2. The top of the window gives the title of your current diagram, the right has a vertical scroll bar.

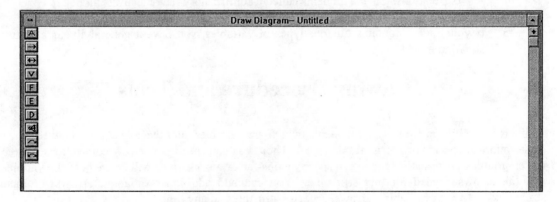

Figure 8.2 The Draw Diagram

Your drawing area is the blank center of the Draw Diagram. To draw in this area, you must make use of the tools on the left hand side.

The left side gives you the vertical **tool bar** with ten buttons representing the diagram drawing options. Each button has its own meaning and purpose, and refers to an action that will create an object. The first button, A, creates a text object, such as a title. The other nine buttons refer to three types of objects:

1. Variables of several types
2. Connections between variables, also of several types
3. A one-factor structure.

A path diagram contains a set of variables and specifies the connections between the variables. Hence, you must specify the variables in your model and show the connections between them. Generally, you must first specify two or more variables. Then, you can specify connections between those variables.

Alternatively, you can specify a one-factor model which will create both the variables and the connections between variables as necessary for that structure. At any time, of course, you can add additional variables, additional connections, or additional factor structures, or remove variables, connections, or factor structures.

To draw a diagram object, you must click once on the object icon in the tool bar. Then, move your mouse pointer to the diagram, and click the mouse button in the desired location. The object will appear there.

Each of the ten buttons has a specific function, as explained next. In all but the simplest models, you will find yourself making use of all of these buttons.

A. Text Button

Although you will probably use the text button, A, last, it is at the top of the tool bar. To add text to the diagram, click on A. Then move your mouse pointer to the place on the diagram where you want to add text. Click, and you can use your keyboard to enter text for a title or label on your diagram.

Your text will appear in the default font and size, which you can modify. You can also use the click-and-drag procedure to move the text to any location on the page.

B. One-way Arrow

A *causal* relationship is shown as a one-way arrow between two variables, with the direction of the arrow representing the direction of hypothesized causation. A one way arrow from an F to a V is used to represent a factor loading in a measurement model. More generally, a one-way arrow represents the coefficient, or weight, used in prediction of one variable from another variable. These one-way arrows, or coefficients, are sometimes called path coefficients.

In EQS, one-way arrows can aim only at V and F types of variables. Whenever you aim an arrow at a V or an F variable, the variable becomes a dependent variable that requires its own residual. These residuals are created automatically by **Diagrammer**, so you need not provide them.

Visually, a one-way arrow is a straight line that has arrowhead endpoints. If you move one or more of the variables that are connected by a one-way arrow, the variables will remain connected by a straight line.

C. Two-way Arrow

Two independent variables can be connected only by a two-way arrow, which represents a covariance or correlation between these variables. Since any type of variable—V, F, E, or D—can be an independent variable, you can connect any two of them. In general, you should connect only those variables that make sense to be connected.

Remember that you cannot correlate a dependent variable with any other variable, so you cannot connect a two-way arrow to a variable that also has a one-way arrow aiming at it. If you want to do something like that, use the residual variable associated with the dependent variable. The residual variable will, in general, be an independent variable, and can be correlated with any other independent variable. (But such a model can be tested only if it is identified!)

Visually, a two-way arrow is a straight line with an arrowhead at each end, connecting two variables. If you move one or more of the variables, they will remain connected by the straight line with arrowheads.

D. V-type Variable—A Measured Variable

Variables designated by the letter **V** are measured or observed variables. These are the variables in your data file, and, as such, are typically numbered sequentially V1, V2, ..., up to the number of variables in your file. Not all of these variables need to be in your diagram, nor in any model that you run.

A model with only V and E variables is a path analysis or simultaneous equation model. A model with no V variables cannot be tested against data.

E. F-type Variable—A Factor

A factor, or **F** variable, represents the common variance shared between the variables at which it aims. If an F variable aims at V variables only, it is a first-order common factor, a regular factor of factor analysis. It accounts for the correlations among the V variables.

Of course F variables may themselves be correlated, as shown by two-way arrow connections. When these two-way arrows are removed, and a new F variable is hypothesized to account for these correlations, the arrows go from the new F variable, the second-order factor, to the first-order factors. Generally the label *second-order* or *higher-order* factor implies that such an F has no one-way arrows aiming at Vs, but there is no special reason for such a restriction.

F. E-type Variable—An Error Variable

Whenever an arrow aims at a V variable, making it a dependent variable, you need a residual **E** variable to aim at that same V variable, so the **Diagrammer** adds an E variable. Thus E15 goes with V15. An E variable represents the variance in the V variable which is not explained by the predictors of the V variable.

E variables must be independent variables. Thus, they may correlate with other independent variables, but they cannot have one-way arrows aiming at them.

If you want to achieve the effect of making an E variable a dependent variable, just change its name from an E variable to an F variable. But don't forget to then add a residual to the F variable, namely, a new D variable.

> *Note:* In general, it is not necessary to create or draw E variables. They are created automatically.

You can, however, add and remove such variables as you like.

G. D-type Variable—A Disturbance Variable

Whenever an arrow aims at an F variable, making it a dependent variable, you must also add a residual **D** variable to aim at that same F variable. Thus D5 goes with F5. A D variable represents variance in the factor that is not explained by that factor's predictors. If the predictors cannot explain any variance in the factor, the D variable is synonymous with the factor.

D variables must be independent variables. Thus, they may have be connected to other variables by two-way arrows, and they cannot have one-way arrows aiming at them.

> *Note:* In general, it is not necessary to create or draw D variables. They are created automatically.

Nonetheless, you may find it necessary to add or remove such variables in special models.

H. Factor Structure

A factor structure is a completely drawn path diagram for a one-factor model with its indicators. It contains one F variable and as many V variables as you designate, as well as the associated errors in variables (Es).

I. Curved One-way Arrow

A curved one-way arrow connecting two variables is identical in meaning to a straight one-way arrow. Only the graphical representation differs. Visually, however, the connection between the two variables is smoothed and curved.

If you move one of the variables connected by a curved one-way arrow, the one-way connection stays and remains curved.

J. Curved Two-way Arrow

A curved two-way arrow connecting two variables is identical in meaning to an ordinary, straight two-way arrow connecting two variables. Visually, however, the connection is smoothed and curved.

If you move one of the variables connected by a curved two-way arrow, the connection stays and remains curved.

> *Note:* If you cannot see the arrow as you are drawing a curved arrow, you should slow down. That is, click on the starting object and stay on the object for a second or so. Then, holding down the mouse button, slowly move your mouse cursor across the screen and into the ending object. Let the mouse cursor remain on the ending object briefly before you release the mouse button.

Some Suggestions for Good Results

Before you draw many diagrams, you should try to study published path diagrams by your favorite authors. What makes a good diagram, i.e., one that communicates easily and accurately, and is also pleasing to the eye? There are a lot of possibilities, but among the important ideas are:

1. There is a logical organization to the picture, e.g., causal flow is in one direction.
2. There is balance and harmony in the diagram.
3. Variables are placed so that crossing lines are minimized.
4. Relative size and location of variables is meaningfully thought out.
5. Labeling of variables is clear and self-explanatory.
6. Not too much information is placed into one diagram.

Most of these points are obvious, but you should remember that what is obvious to you may not be at all obvious to your reader or audience. If some variables are shown larger than others, does that mean they are more important than others? If the causal flow appears to be in all directions, does that mean there is nothing systematic going on?

Since the diagram often will carry the critical information about your model, its clarity and meaningfulness implies success in your communication to your readers. If your diagram is hard to understand, your written explanations about your model, i.e., your theory, results, or discussion, are liable to be even more incomprehensible to your readers. Of course, even the best visual explanation of a complicated model may be too difficult for some readers, so you should always try to simplify your presentation.

Simplifying the Model

You can simplify the model by cutting the complete model into parts. Since it is not necessary to present a model in a single diagram, you can present meaningful parts separately. A standard approach is to use one diagram to show the measurement model, and another diagram to show the relations among latent variables. Also, you may find that some aspects of the model, such as correlated errors, may be best described in text. The **Diagrammer** permits you to create your actual model, which may be quite complex, but then also to visually present only selected aspects of that model.

Rules for Using the Diagrammer

Although EQS's **Diagrammer** is very flexible, and permits you to draw almost any kind of diagram, it is good practice to follow a set of rules every time you use the program. We will give our suggestions for these rules, but you may also develop your own. A standard set of rules will help you to organize your diagram to minimize potential mistakes, give you pleasingly consistent results, and help to assure that the **Diagrammer** works properly. In addition, when using the diagram as your actual model specification for an EQS run, these rules will help assure that you have set up the model correctly.

Here are our suggestions for good drawing practice:

1. Create a data file in which all variables will be used.

2. Use the variables in sequence from small to large (i.e., start with V1), and have the variables with the smallest numbers be indicators of factors with the smallest numbers (e.g., F1,...).

3. Use the factor button to simplify your task, creating structures for F1, F2, ..., in sequence. (This is described in detail later).

4. Do not draw E (error) and D (disturbance) variables. They will be generated automatically.

5. Lay out all factor structures and measured variables first, and align them properly, before connecting them.

6. Use the ordinary straight one-way arrow to draw a regression path.

7. Use the curved two-way arrow to connect two independent variables.

A complete diagram will require the use of many of the tools shown in the left part of Figure 8.2. Although we could start our exposition with elementary tools, let us start with a tool that will help us to build a large structure quickly.

Create a Factor Structure with the Factor Button

One of the most common parts of a covariance structure model is a factor with its indicators. While a model may contain many factors, each with its own indicators, the complete diagram is best built up one factor at a time starting with F1 up to Fx, where x is your largest factor number. The simplest way to do this is with our **F** (factor) button in the list of **Diagrammer** drawing tools.

It is important that you understand this approach. It will teach you diagramming elements that will be helpful in many situations. Later you will learn to achieve the same effect by building up from small parts.

Factor Loading Structure

A factor loading structure consists of one factor, its several measured variable indicators, and the errors in the variables. A typical example is the following three variable, one factor structure:

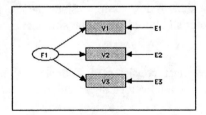

Figure 8.3 One Factor with Three Variable Indicators

Since F1 generates the Vs, the arrows go from F1 to the Vs. Each V also is influenced by its own residual error variable. Visually, this diagram created by **Diagrammer** uses the standard convention in the field. It puts latent variables into circles or ovals, and measured variables into squares or rectangles. Residual errors are not enclosed.

Diagrammer provides an easy way to create such a structure. Look at the **tool bar** in **Draw Diagram**, shown in Figure 8.2. On left side, there are ten picture buttons. The third from the bottom is the picture of the factor loading structure. You should click that button once to activate the factor loading object.

Next, move the mouse pointer to the spot in **Draw Diagram** where you want to place the structure (approximate position) and click the mouse pointer again. A **Factor Structure Specification** dialog box like Figure 8.4 will appear.

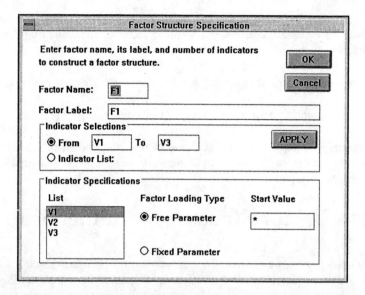

Figure 8.4 Factor Structure Specification Dialog Box

This dialog box provides everything you need to specify a factor loading structure. To complete the dialog box, you must enter the factor name (or use the default), fill in the factor label, specify the indicators of the factor, and possibly customize some aspects of the specifications. We will describe each of the dialog box elements in turn.

Factor Name

In the top part of the dialog box, a new factor number (i.e., F1) is given as the default. If this is indeed your F1, fine, there is nothing you need to do. However, if you want this particular factor to be F12, you must to change the default designation. Since the default factor number is augmented by 1 each time you invoke the factor structure button, the simplest approach is to generate the factors in sequence F1, F2, and so on.

> *Note*: The factor name must consist of F followed by a number. If you want a more descriptive name, use the Factor Label field to create a label.

Factor Label

Below the factor number, you enter a factor label. This is a mnemonic designation that will remind you and your readers about the interpretive meaning of the factor. If you do not have many factors and variables in your diagram, you can get away with quite a long label, but if you are planning to fit a lot of visual material into a small amount of space, you should consider using short labels. The factor label can include up to 32 characters. However, the program truncates labels to eight characters when transferring them to the model file.

A long label will require quite a lot of space, and your circle may be too small for it. Then it might be necessary to increase the size of your oval to contain the letters. You can also force a long label to appear on more than one line. To do that, enter a semi-colon (;) to specify the end of the first line, then continue entering the long label. You can create up to three lines.

When you have clicked OK in this dialog box and EQS has created the diagram, the diagram will display the factor name. The factor label will not automatically show in the completed diagram on the screen. While viewing the diagram, you can switch from the factor name to the factor label by choosing the **View** menu **Labels** option. Choose the **View** menu **Labels** option again to switch back to the factor name.

Specify Factor Indicators

There are two ways to specify the Vs that will serve as indicators of this factor, corresponding to choices given by the radio buttons for **From..To** and **Indicator List**. The first button permits you to select Vs from a sequential set of variables. The second button permits you to skip around and select variables arbitrarily.

Sequential Indicators

The **From..To** button provides a list of sequential indicators, as shown in Figure 8.4 as V1 to V3. You can substitute any beginning variable for V1, and any ending variable for V3.

Note that the default sequential indicators also appear in the **Indicator Specifications List** at the bottom of the dialog box. If you change the indicator list from its default setting by entering new beginning and ending Vs, you must also click the **APPLY** button. That action applies the changes you made to the current list of all variables already entered into the diagram, and hence the model.

The next time you invoke the factor structure, the program default will specify that the next variables in sequence will be used as indicators of the next factor in sequence. This default procedure simplifies your task if you proceed to generate the complete factor structure using variables, and factors, numbered from low to high.

Selected Indicators

If the Vs that should mark your factor cannot be specified by a list of sequential Vs, you must click on the second radio button in the dialog box, **Indicator List**. You would use selected indicators, for example, if you wanted V1, V6, V13, and V14 to be indicators of your factor.

After you click on the **Indicator List** radio button, the edit box appears. Click in the **Indicator List** edit box, then enter the names of the variables in that box, separating each variable designation with a comma (,). For example, you might type: **V1,V6,V13,V14**.

After you enter the indicators, click the **APPLY** button. This places your newly-entered indicators into the **List** box shown in the bottom left under **Indicator Specifications**. The list of variables in this box is the complete list of all variables in the model, as specified up to this time.

Parameter Types, Start Values, and Labels

In the bottom of the dialog box, there is a group box called **Indicator Specifications**. Some options in this box permit you to specify information about variables and parameters. In some models, you may find it necessary to choose one of these options.

Free and Fixed Factor Loadings

By default, the **Free Parameter Type** is checked. This means that each factor loading is considered to be a free parameter; all paths from a factor to its V indicators are assumed to be free to estimate.

To make one of the factor loadings fixed rather than free, you first highlight the appropriate indicator by clicking on its name in the **List** box. Then, select the parameter **Type** as **Fixed Parameter** by clicking on its radio button. To make a fixed parameter free, you would mark the variable in the list and choose **Free Parameter**.

Start Value

By default, EQS provides start values, so it is not necessary for you to enter a value. However, you may want particular values to appear in your diagram, or to be used in the program where **Diagrammer** is the model specification step. In this case, you should specify the start value of the indicator while the relevant V variable in the **List** is highlighted.

Variable Label

Without further designation, Vs are just Vs. If you prefer to have a more descriptive name for one of the Vs, **just double click on the indicator name** in the **List** box. A **Measured Variable Specification** dialog box like the one shown in Figure 8.5 will appear.

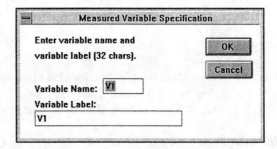

Figure 8.5 Measured Variable Specification Dialog Box

This dialog box allows you to enter a label of up to 32 characters to describe the chosen V variable. The variable label can include up to 32 characters. However, the program truncates labels to eight characters when transferring them to the model file.

A long label will require quite a lot of space, and your rectangle may be too small for it. You have two remedies:
    1. Increase the size of your rectangle to contain the letters

2. Force the label to appear on more than one line by entering a semi-colon (;) to specify the end of the first line, then continue entering the long label. You can create up to three lines.

After you have clicked **OK** in this dialog box and EQS has created the diagram, the diagram will display the variable name. The variable label will show on the screen if you switch from the variable name to the variable label by choosing the **View** menu **Labels** option.

OK or Cancel

When you have completed your choices in the **Factor Structure Specification** dialog box, or if you have made no choices but are happy with the defaults, press **OK**. EQS will draw the factor structure.

If you change your mind about your specifications, just press **Cancel**.

Create a Factor Structure Using Objects

Although most of the time we recommend using the above procedure to draw a factor with its indicators in one quick operation, you should still learn how to use the individual objects in the **tool bar**. It is likely that you will have occasion to use each of the tool bar objects. We shall now create the above factor structure element by element, using a series of steps.

As you can see from the diagram in Figure 8.3, to construct such a structure you must draw three rectangles to represent the three Vs, one circle or oval to represent the factor, and three one-way arrows to represent the three factor loadings. The three error variables and three error paths are drawn automatically. After the structure is drawn, you also can customize the structure by inserting variable labels, etc.

You will be placing each of these model components on the screen, one by one, in the location that you specify. If you are careful, the completed picture will be well organized and essentially finished with your last step. However, when putting the model components on the screen one by one, you may not be able to align these components very well. Don't worry. The program provides editing tools that help you to balance and beautify your diagram.

The sequence of steps needed to create the three variable factor loading structure is given next. We suggest that you work on this example on your computer.

Create a Factor and its Indicators

1. Click the **V** (variable) tool once and move the mouse pointer to the **Draw Diagram**. Click to create the Variable V1.

2. Repeat step 1 two times by placing the two new rectangles below the first rectangle. You have just created V2 and V3.

3. Click the **F** (factor) tool once and move the mouse pointer to the left of the vertically listed rectangles. Click to create factor F1.

4. Click the straight one-way arrow once. Click on the right border of F1's oval. Holding down the mouse button, drag the pointer to the closest point of the V1 rectangle, and release. The program draws a one way arrow that connects F1 and V1. In addition to the one way arrow, you should note that the color of V1 also changes, and that E1 has been

attached to V1. You can click on E1 and drag it to the right hand side of V1 to get it into a better position.

5. Repeat step 4 two additional times to create the connection between F1 and V2, and between F1 and V3, as well as the relevant error variates E2 and E3.

Customize the Factor Loading Structure

While the basic factor structure is now complete, it is generic. Typically, you will want to add special features to make the model really represent your particular application. Those features involve factor and variable labeling, and permit you to specify whether parameters are fixed or free, and their estimated values. In principle, these features are an integral part of any model. They may not be of interest to you now if simply drawing a diagram, or if the program defaults cover your situation. More generally, however, you should know the precise status of each parameter, since you may want to modify them, or you may want to create a particular display of your model for a scientific article.

In general, you can customize by locating the relevant object in the diagram, and double-clicking on that object. That action causes a dialog box to become active, in which you can make your specifications.

Customize the Factor

In your **Draw Diagram**, double click on the factor. As a result, you will get a **Variance Specification** dialog box as shown in Figure 8.6.

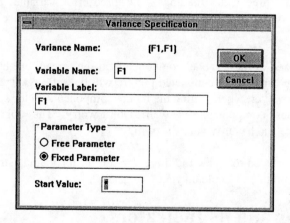

Figure 8.6 Variance Specification Dialog Box

Variance Name

This dialog box first gives the **Variance Name**, which is not an option you can modify directly, since it is tied to the **Variable Name**. If the F variable is an independent variable, then its variance is a parameter of the model. The name of this parameter is the doubly-listed name of the factor. That is, (F1,F1) is the **Variance Name** of F1, and it designates the diagonal entry of a matrix.

Variable Name

The default **Variable Name** is F1. However, you can change this default to any more appropriate F-numbered variable for your model, such as, F12.

Variable Label

Next, you can provide a more descriptive name for the factor by typing in the edit box a **Variable Label** with up to 32 characters. You can show this label on the screen, as discussed below. Only the first eight characters will be carried to the model file.

A long label will require quite a lot of space, and your oval may be too small for it. Then it might be necessary to increase the size of your oval to contain the letters. You can also force a long label to appear on more than one line. To do that, enter a semi-colon (;) to specify the end of the first line, then continue entering the long label. You can create up to three lines.

After you have clicked **OK** in this dialog box and EQS has created the diagram, the diagram will display the variable name. The variable label will not automatically show in the completed diagram on the screen. While viewing the diagram, you can switch from the variable name to the variable label by choosing the **View** menu **Labels** option. Choose the **View** menu **Labels** option again to switch back to the variable name.

Parameter Type

You can designate the **Parameter Type** as free or fixed by clicking on the appropriate radio button. Also, you can enter a desired **Start Value** or use the * character as the default starting value for a free parameter. The values you provide can be printed.

Dependent Factors

If, in the course of building the diagram, the factor becomes a dependent variable, it does not have a **Variance Name** since dependent variables do not have variances as parameters. In such a case, you can specify only the label of the factor. In fact, when double-clicking a dependent factor, you will be prompted by a **Factor Specification** dialog box instead of the **Variance Specifications** dialog box.

The **Factor Specification** dialog box is a subset of the **Variance Specifications** dialog box. As a subset, the **Factor Specification** dialog box does not show **Variance Name** and gives no options with regard to **Parameter Type** or **Start Value**. That is because the factor no longer has a variance as a parameter. The **Factor Specification** box is similar to the dialog box shown in Figure 8.7 for measured variables.

Customize the Measured Variables

Typically you will want to label the measured variables using more specific names. In the **Draw Diagram**, double click the particular V variable which interests you. You will obtain the **Measured Variable Specification** dialog box shown in Figure 8.7.

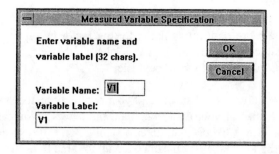

Figure 8.7 Measured Variable Specification Dialog Box

By default, the dialog box has V1 entered in the **Variable Name** field. You can change V1 to V5 or V22, whichever is the correct variable in your data file. You can also enter a character string in the text box **Variable Label** to give the variable a meaningful acronym. The string cannot exceed 32 characters, which will be truncated to eight characters in the model file.

A long label will require quite a lot of space, and your rectangle may be too small for it. Then it might be necessary to increase the size of your rectangle to contain the letters, or you can force the label to appear on more than one line, as discussed above.

After you have clicked **OK** in this dialog box and EQS has created the diagram, the diagram will display the variable name, but not the label unless you choose the **View** menu **Labels** option. Choose the **View** menu **Labels** option again to switch back to the variable name.

Dependent Variables

In a factor model, measured variables are dependent variables. Dependent variables do not have variances as parameters of the model. Thus, there is no need to specify their start values or whether they are fixed or free parameters.

Independent Variables

If this measured variable were an independent variable, you would see an extended version of the dialog box in Figure 8.7. The extended dialog box is the **Variance Specification** dialog box which permits you to specify information on variable variance, as well as name and label. As was shown in Figure 8.6, the **Variance Specification** dialog box also gives you options with regard to **Parameter Type** and **Start Value**, since an independent variable has a variance as a parameter. You can consult the discussion surrounding Figure 8.6 for details on these options.

Customize a Path or a Factor Loading

You can also customize a path or a factor loading by clicking on the path in the **Draw Diagram** to get a **Parameter Specification** dialog box. Precision is very important when clicking on the path. You should click on the line, or very close to it, near the midpoint of the two variables that are connected. Otherwise, the path object will not be picked or the wrong object could be picked. You will easily achieve precision with some practice.

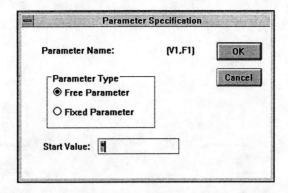

Figure 8.8 Parameter Specification Dialog Box

Figure 8.8 shows the **Parameter Specification** dialog box in which you specify information about the path. The **Parameter Name** is already printed in the dialog box. You will remember that in EQS the double-label convention gives the dependent variable first, and its predictor second. In the example, then, the parameter represents a path from F1 to V1, i.e., it is a factor loading.

You can modify the **Parameter Type** from free to fixed or vice-versa. You can also enter a number to be used as the **Start Value** if EQS is to be run, or if you want the value to be displayed. The default is an asterisk * which tells the program to select the most appropriate starting value.

Align the Variables

After you draw all of the objects, you may want to align the lines, ovals, and rectangles so that they look good on the screen, and hence will look good on paper when the diagram is printed. The diagram provides several ways to align objects, permitting you to create a customized and beautiful layout of your diagram. In this section we provide some basic information on this process, which is described more fully in Chapter 9.

> *Note:* To align several diagram objects, you must first highlight all the objects to be aligned by dragging a rubber rectangle to encircle them.

To encircle the objects of interest, click your mouse button in the top left location, hold down the mouse button and drag to the bottom right until the rubber rectangle encloses all the objects you want to align. After you select the objects, click on the **Layout** menu from the main menu, and select an alignment scheme. The various alignment schemes are discussed in detail in Chapter 9, **Diagram Customization**. Among all the alignment methods, you probably will use the tools **Align Vertical** and **Align Horizontal** most frequently.

The two sets of rectangles shown below illustrate the effect. On the left you see three variables that are not well-aligned. After we applied vertical alignment, they line up vertically in a straight line.

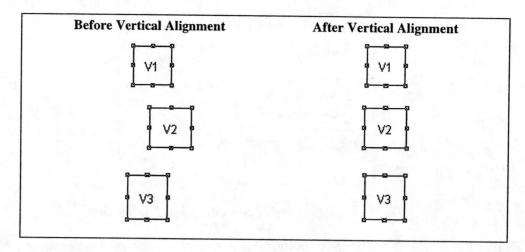

Strange effects can occur if you use the incorrect alignment. For example, if you use the **Align Horizontal** option on the example above, the objects will collapse onto each other. This happens because the program horizontally aligns objects by placing the objects equidistant from each other on a horizontal line.

If you have unanticipated results, you can always correct them. Simply make an object active and move it; make the next object active and move it, etc.

Create One Group Structure from Several Objects

In the above example, each V variable had been defined as a separate object. After you align all of these variables, they still remain as individual objects. If, for any reason, one of the Vs gets moved, the alignment will not be maintained, and you might have to align the objects again. To avoid this problem, **Diagrammer** allows you to group several objects into a single object.

> *Note:* To group a set of variables and linkages as an object, first encircle all the objects in a rubber rectangle. Then, pull down the Layout menu and select the Group menu item.

Thereafter, the highlighted individual object frames will disappear and be replaced by the group frame. After grouping, you can move or cut the entire structure as a single object. Thus, even while you are moving the objects, the interrelations among the objects that exist at the time of grouping is maintained. Whenever you are satisfied with a particular set of objects, it is a good idea to link them into one group object.

After you have made a set of objects into a single group, you can move this new object anywhere in the **Draw Diagram**, and its components will move as a unit. You can even edit or customize a group object. If you want to modify any component of a group object, e.g., the label of a factor, simply double click on the component. When the dialog box appears, make your changes and click **OK**.

Draw a Measured Variable

There are times when it is necessary to add a new V variable to your diagram. For example, you may want to add a new independent measured variable to your model. In such a situation, choose the V option from the **tool bar** on the left side of the **Draw Diagram**, and then click in the location of the draw window where this variable should be placed. Once there, you may need to modify the default variable name or add the relevant connections of this variable to other variables. For example, the variable may be another indicator of a factor.

Think about whether you can logically consider the added measured variable as a part of a particular structure, for example, as part of a one-factor model with its indicators. If so, it is a good idea to regroup the objects by including the new variable in that group.

Do *not* Draw Errors and Disturbances

As we have suggested in the drawing rules, you don't have to draw E and D variables. **Diagrammer** has been given internal rules to cover the typical uses of such variables and will generate these residual variables automatically. As an example, when you connect a V variable to an F variable by a one-way path such as F—>V, the V variable must become a dependent variable. Consequently, **Diagrammer** will generate an E variable automatically that will point to the V.

Likewise, when you are predicting an F variable by another F or a V variable, the F variable becomes a dependent variable and its residual D variable will be generated automatically. These internal rules permit **Diagrammer** to make your model accurate as well as complete.

> *Note*: There are times when generated E and D variables are not essential to your model. You must take responsibility for deleting them from the diagram.

Connect All Elements

After you have specified all of the diagram elements such as factor structures and independent manifest variables, you are ready to connect them. The principal rules for connecting variables are:
1. Use a one-way arrow as a regression predictor.
2. Use a two-way arrow as a correlation or covariance.

We shall use two examples to illustrate how arrows are drawn, one a straight arrow and the other a curved arrow. These two arrows require somewhat different strategies of connection.

Draw a Straight Arrow

In this example we want to create a two-factor structural equation model. This is done in sequence.

We use the F button on the Draw Diagram tool bar to create F1 with its indicators, and then repeat the process to create F2 with its indicators. At this point, the two factors F1 and F2 are not connected.

Confirmatory Factor Model

In a confirmatory factor model, you must connect the factors by a two-way arrow to represent their correlation.

Standard Regression Model

In a standard regression type of model, F2 is predicted from F1, so we must use a straight arrow to make the connection. This means that we create a simple regression where F1 is the predictor variable and F2 is the dependent variable.

Here are the steps to draw the arrow.

1. Click once on the straight one-way arrow in the **tool bar**.

2. Move the mouse pointer into the **Draw Diagram**. It becomes a crosshair (like a +). Place the crosshair just inside the right part of the circle representing F1, and click. *Please note that you must place the mouse pointer within the border that defines F1.*

3. Hold the mouse pointer down and drag the mouse arrow pointer to F2. Release the mouse pointer when the arrow pointer is located *just within the border of F2*.

4. After you release the mouse pointer, a straight line will be drawn that connects F1 and F2, with the arrowhead aiming at F2. The residual D2 will be attached to F2 automatically. If the alignment between D2 and F2 is not desirable, you can click on one of the objects and drag it into position or apply an alignment rule to correct it. Figure 8.9 is the result of this sequence of actions.

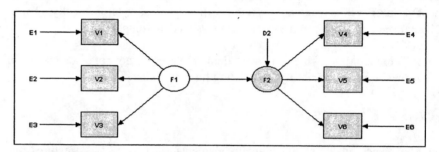

Figure 8.9 Two Factor Structural Equation Model

Draw a curved arrow

This time let us create a two-factor confirmatory factor model, in which the two factors are correlated. Create the two unconnected factors with their indicators, as in the previous example. We want to use a curved arrow to connect the two independent F variables F1 and F2.

1. In the **tool bar**, click once on the curved two-way arrow button.

2. Move the mouse pointer to the **Draw Diagram**. The mouse cursor will become a crosshair when it moves into the **Draw Diagram**. Put the mouse pointer slightly within the circle in the upper right corner of F1, and click and hold the mouse button. (A suggestion to left-handers: you can start drawing from the upper left corner of F2. The effect will be identical when drawing a two-way arrow.)

3. As you hold onto the mouse button, drag the mouse pointer. It will become an arrow. Draw a curved line, freehand, and end the curved line in the upper left corner of F2. Then, after confirming that the mouse pointer is within F2's circle, release the mouse button. Also, when you drag the mouse to form the curved line, try to make the line symmetric. Do not worry about the unevenness or jags in your curved line; **Diagrammer** will smooth the line in an optimal way.

4. After you release the mouse button, the curve that you drew will be redrawn with a smoothed curved two-way arrow. Figure 8.10 is an example of such a drawing.

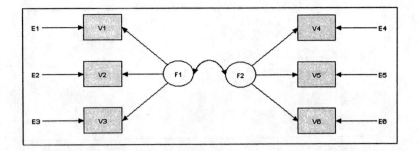

Figure 8.10 Two-Factor Confirmatory Factor Analysis Model

Edit a Curved Arrow

After you draw an arrow, you can edit the curve of that arrow, but you cannot move the endpoints of the arrow. To edit a curved arrow, click on the arrow. The arrow will be surrounded by a rectangle defined by eight small circles. Click on the middle circle on the top border of the rectangle and drag the border up. As you drag, the cursor will change to a hook as shown in Figure 8.11.

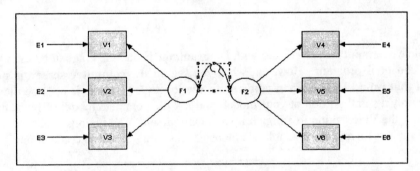

Figure 8.11 Dragging the Editing Cursor

Drag the cursor up to expand the curve of the arrow. Then click on the middle circle in the left border and drag it to the left. Finally, click on the middle circle in the right border and drag it to the right. These actions create a curve that is more rounded than the original. Of course, you can edit a curve to make it skewed or even, more curved or less curved.

Insert Labels

In the context of Figure 8.3, we showed how you can label each variable or factor in a model to achieve a more meaningful representation. If you apply labels, you can also display them.

Take your version of Figure 8.10, and add labels for the Vs and Fs by double-clicking on each and filling out the relevant information. If you have a question, review the discussion given above. We shall suppose that you use the designations var1, var2, ..., var6 and fac1 and fac2 to label your variables. In that case, choose the **View** menu **Labels** option to show the result as in Figure 8.12.

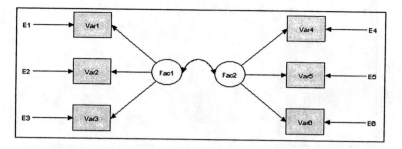

Figure 8.12 Factor Analysis Model with Labels

Display and Print Your Diagram

Display of your diagram is controlled by the **View** menu item within **Diagrammer**. Print is intimately tied to the view that you have chosen, and not to the complete diagram.

View

The complete diagram that you created with **Diagrammer** is the one that can be used to run the EQS structural equations program. However, **what you see on the computer screen is not necessarily the model that would be run when you submit the job to EQS**. This is because the screen display may show only a small portion of your model, and not the complete model. The screen's display is controlled by the **View** option in **Diagrammer**'s main menu. The options available under **View** are shown in Figure 8.13, and are available via mouse clicks using the usual conventions.

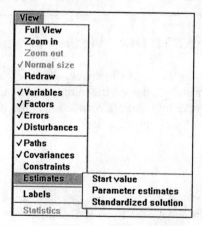

Figure 8.13 View Menu with Options Checked

The top part of the **View** menu provides options for displaying the diagram.

Full View

You can shrink the view by requesting a **Full View**.

Zoom In

If a diagram is very complex, you may want to **Zoom in** to some part of the diagram to visualize it more clearly or to make adjustments there. After you choose Zoom in, you will see an enlarged view of the upper left section of your diagram. Use the scroll bars to view the other sections of the diagram.

Zoom Out

Use **Zoom out** to go back to the normal size.

Normal Size

If you click on **Normal size** to check it, the size of the diagram you see on the screen is about the size that you will see when you print it. However, **Normal size** may not permit you to view the diagram in its entirety if you have a very large number of variables and factors. In small models, **Normal size** will give you a **Full view**.

The second part of the **View** menu controls the types of variables to be displayed on the screen. The variable types that are checked are displayed, while the unchecked ones are not displayed. If all four variable types are checked, you will see **V**s, **F**s, **E**s, and **D**s. In complex models, it may be desirable to not show the residual variables.

The third part of the **View** menu controls whether you want to show the **Paths** or **Covariance** connections between pairs of variables. In addition, you can choose to show **Constraints** and **Estimates**. If you choose Estimates, you will have the additional option to choose start values or estimates from the standardized solution.

Finally, if **Labels** is not checked, the diagram will consist only of Vs, Fs, Es, and Ds, depending on which you have specified. The mnemonic labels will not be shown. Checking **Labels** permits your names for the **V** and **F** variables to be shown on the diagram. Of course, if you did not provide any labels, these cannot be shown even if you check this selection.

Statistics

After you have completed an EQS run from a diagram, the **Statistics** option will be accessible while viewing that diagram. The **Statistics** option will display summary statistics from the EQS run. After you have displayed the statistics, they become attached to the diagram. When you save the diagram, the statistics are saved with it, and they are brought back up when you **Open** the file again.

You can access the **Statistics** option only in two specific instances:

1. when you have imported parameter estimates after an EQS run
2. when you have used the **File/Import Estimates** option to read in the parameter estimates from an external file.

When you click on the **Statistics** option, you get the **EQS Summary Statistics** window. If you then click on **Drop**, the statistics will be dropped or placed onto your diagram as a text object. At that point, you can move the text object into a desired position.

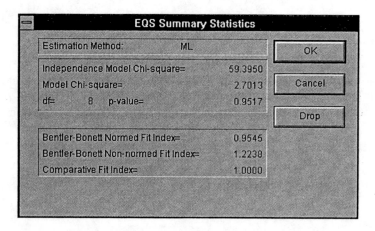

Figure 8.14 EQS Summary Statistics

Print

When you have completed drawing a diagram, you may want to see it on paper. You can print it using the standard **Print** command available in the **File** menu. You should remember, however, that **the print command will copy to paper only what is shown on the screen.** This means that you may get a printed copy of only part of the model, depending on your choices under **View**.

Of course, this effect may be precisely what you may want to achieve. Your model may contain some elements that you do not want to show to your reader in the given figure. Alternatively, you may want to print two different views of a model, emphasizing some part of it in one view, and some other part in the other view. Then a given view as printed would contain only those elements deemed important to your presentation.

As an example, the residuals to measured variables and residuals to factors are important to every model, but you may not want to show them because of the complexity of the figure. (However, we urge full disclosure! If your model diagram or diagrams do not fully represent the model that you ran, you owe it to your readers to discuss in text those features of the model that may not be shown diagramatically.)

In the current release, **Diagrammer** will print only a black, white, and gray-shaded diagram, even though the diagram file has retained color information. We expect the next version of EQS for Windows to print the diagram in the colors shown on the screen.

Run EQS from a Diagram

The diagram you created with **Diagrammer** is now ready for submitting as a structural equation modeling run. If the model you want to run is based on a diagram that you have just now completed, you should first save it and then proceed to run the model. You can also run a model based on a diagram that you created at some other time.

Save the Diagram

It is a good idea to save any diagram that you created. This option will save the diagram with all related parameter estimates and summary statistics if you have made a complete EQS run and the output file opened without an error message.

To save the diagram, select the **File** menu **Save As** option in the usual way. In principle, you can save the file with any name extension that you choose, but we suggest that you use the default ***.eds** convention. Thus, your file may be called mod1.eds, for example. Regardless of what name you use, drawings done under **Diagrammer** are saved as **Diagram Files**, which are *.eds files.

In practice, as you draw even part of a diagram, it is a good idea to **Save** it. Regular saving of work minimizes the chance of accidentally losing the results of a lot of effort and thought.

Retrieve a Diagram

You can open an existing **Diagram File** from either outside or inside **Diagrammer**. If the diagram contains parameter estimates and summary statistics, that information will be retrieved with the diagram file. If the parameter estimates and summary statistics are available, the **View** menu **Statistics** option will be enabled when the diagram appears on your screen.

To find your file, you must be sure to name the file with the **.eds** extension at creation. Then, by clicking on **File** and **Open** in the usual way, the file becomes active. You will see it, and you are ready to run.

Run EQS

Before we go into detail, we should note that any diagram produced by **Diagrammer** is its own entity; it represents a prototype model that is not necessarily tied to any particular data file. That is, the diagram may be a model for a set of variables that you do not have. For example, the diagram can represent a hypothetical theory for which no data exists. As a result, the diagram does not contain within it information about any raw data or covariance matrix that might be used to test the theory that is drawn. As a consequence, the diagram itself is insufficient information for a model run, because it is necessary to specify the data file to be used.

To set up your **EQS** run from the diagram, follow these steps:

1. Open the data file of interest.

2. In the Window menu, choose **Draw Diagram** to make the diagram active.

3. Click on **Build_EQS** in the main menu.

4. Click on **Title/Specifications**. This will bring up the dialog box **Title for EQS Model**, which permits you to give a description of your proposed modeling run. Type in your designation, and click **OK** when finished.

5. Next, you will automatically see the **EQS Model Specifications** dialog box. If you do not find the defaults acceptable, you should fill out all relevant edit boxes. Since you have opened the data file, this dialog box will show the name of the file and the number of variables and

subjects (cases) in that file. You can also specify the method of estimation and various other possibilities. Click **OK** when finished.

6. Immediately, you will see the model file that has been created in **work.eqs**. Your **Title** and **Specifications** have been adopted into the file, and you should be sure that these are what you want. You will also see the **Equations**, **Variances**, and **Covariances** (if any) that were created by the program from your diagram.

You have completed the heart of your model.

> *Note:* **Be sure to check whether these specifications represent the model that you intend to run. If not, change the diagram!**

Your diagram may contain features that should not really become part of the model. In particular, check whether the identification status of **F** variables has been taken care of correctly. Is the scale of each factor fixed by a loading, or by fixing a variance if the factor is an independent variable?

If the model is not correct, you have two options. You could simply edit the model file and run the job. The problem with this procedure is that the diagram and model file will no longer correspond! As a result, estimates from the model run cannot be transferred back to the diagram. Rather, you should go back to your model diagram and correct it. Then go to step 3, above.

Finally, you should complete the model specification by adding any other model features that are not yet included in your model, such as the LM test. You can add model features by typing the relevant information into the text file, or by invoking the **Build_EQS** menu item from the main menu again.

To run EQS, choose **Run EQS/386** from the **Build_EQS** menu, and follow the usual procedures.

9. DIAGRAM CUSTOMIZATION

We discussed the principles of drawing a diagram in Chapter 8, **Build EQS by Drawing a Diagram**. This chapter provides details on the options available for editing and laying out a diagram. You will find many useful options in the **Edit** and **Layout** menus from the **Diagrammer** menu bar.

Diagrammer

Each diagram element in the **Diagrammer** is an object. This includes the rectangle (for V variables), circle (for F variable), unenclosed residual (for E and D variables), one-way arrows, two-way arrows, and factor structure (a combination of objects).

> *Note:*   To manipulate an object, first you must select the object.

The edit and layout functions only apply to the selected objects. Therefore, you must be sure to select or highlight one or more objects before editing.

Select Objects

There are four ways to select objects.

Select a Single Object

To select a single object, simply click on the object. You must click **within** the rectangular form of the object. After you select it, the selected object will be framed by a marked rectangle.

Select a Group of Consecutive Objects

You can drag a rubber rectangle to encircle the target objects. You must enclose each entire object with the rectangle. Any partially-enclosed object will not be selected. Thus, if you enclose only one object which is part of a group of objects, neither the group nor the individual object will be selected.

Select a Group of Non-Consecutive Objects

You cannot drag a rubber rectangle to select non-consecutive objects because you would be selecting non-target objects as well. To select two objects separated by a third object, hold down the <Shift> key while you select each object.

Select All

You can select all diagram objects, all paths, or all variables using the **Edit** menu. See Figure 9.1.

Edit Menu in Diagrammer

The **Edit** menu includes following options:

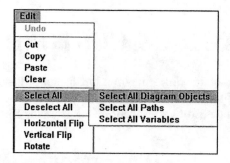

Figure 9.1 The Edit Menu

When you open the **Draw Diagram**, all menu items are grayed out except **Deselect All**. Since the **Draw Diagram** is empty, there is no need to activate edit options. This situation applies until you draw and select some objects.

When you select an object, all menu items other than **Paste** will be activated. The **Paste** option will be activated only after you perform a **Cut** or **Copy** action, filling the Clipboard.

Undo

The **Undo** option will undo your most recent **Layout** menu action in the **Draw Diagram**. **Undo** does not undo **Cut**, **Copy**, **Paste**, or **Clear**.

Cut

The **Cut** option copies the selected object(s) into the Clipboard and removes the selected object(s) from the **Draw Diagram**.

> **Procedure:**
> 1. Select one or more objects from the **Draw Diagram**.
> 2. Click on **Edit** in the main menu.
> 3. Select **Cut** from the menu.

Copy

Like the **Cut** option, the **Copy** option copies selected object(s) into the Clipboard. However, all of the copied objects remain in the **Draw Diagram**.

> **Procedure:**
> 1. Select one or more objects from the **Draw Diagram**.
> 2. Click on **Edit** in the main menu.
> 3. Select **Copy** from the menu.

Paste

The **Paste** option copies the contents of the Clipboard back into the **Draw Diagram**. To activate the **Paste** option, first copy or cut one or more objects.

270

Procedure:
1. Click on **Edit** in the main menu.
2. Select **Paste** from the menu.

After you have cut or copied an object once, you can paste it again and again. The act of pasting does not empty the Clipboard. You can paste an object in the Clipboard into any Windows word processor or back into the **Diagrammer**.

If you are pasting into the **Diagrammer**, be careful that you do not paste two or more identical objects onto the screen, because that may result in an unpredictable outcome. Thus, you should try to create a new object using the **Diagrammer** tools rather than pasting an existing object.

Note: The current **Paste** option works well only with one or more <u>unlinked</u> objects. Any linked objects will lose their logical link if you paste them.

Clear

The **Clear** option removes selected objects from the **Draw Diagram**. Unlike the **Cut** option, **Clear** does not copy the affected objects into the Clipboard.

Procedure:
1. Select one or more objects from the **Draw Diagram**.
2. Click on **Edit** in the main menu.
3. Select **Clear** from the menu.

Select All

The **Select All** option allows you to select all objects in the **Draw Diagram**. The option gives you three choices: **Select All Diagram Objects**, **Select All Paths**, or **Select All Variables**.

Select All Diagram Objects chooses all objects in the **Diagrammer** screen, whether they are individual objects or group objects. The other two choices can select only individual objects. **Select All Paths** will choose all of the diagram paths. **Select All Variables** will select all V, F, E, or D objects. This set of options provides a convenient way to select everything on the **Draw Diagram** without having to select each object individually.

You might use the **Select All** option to select all objects and clear the screen. Or, you can select all objects and make them into a single group (i.e. see the **Group** option discussion later in this chapter). Once you have made your diagram a single object, you can apply layout commands (see **Layout** options discussion later this chapter) to move the diagram to the center of the page before printing the diagram.

Procedure:
1. Click on **Edit** in the main menu.
2. Select **Select All** from the menu.
3. Choose **Select All Diagram Objects**, **Select All Paths**, or **Select All Variables**.

Deselect All

The **Deselect All** option is the opposite to the **Select All** option. It deselects all objects that you have selected. If no object was previously selected from the **Draw Diagram**, this option has no effect.

Procedure:
1. Click on **Edit** in the main menu.
2. Select **Deselect All** from the menu.

Horizontal Flip

The **Horizontal Flip** option allows you to create a mirror image of an object by flipping it horizontally. This is a convenient way to create such an effect without redrawing all of the objects.

Note: It is better to flip a group object than to flip the individual objects.

It does not make sense to apply **Horizontal Flip** to an individual object such as a variable, because the appearance will remain the same. **Horizontal Flip** may result in an unpredictable outcome when applied to a one-way arrow. Figure 9.2 shows objects before and after horizontal flipping.

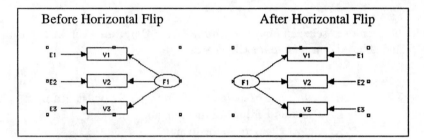

Figure 9.2 Example — Horizontal Flip

Procedure:
1. Select the object to be flipped in the **Draw Diagram**.
    (If more than one object, group the objects.)
2. Click on **Edit** in the main menu.
3. Select **Horizontal Flip** from the menu.

Vertical Flip

The **Vertical Flip** option is similar to the **Horizontal Flip** option. **Vertical Flip** flips an object vertically. Like the **Horizontal Flip** option, **Vertical Flip** is best used to flip a group object. Figure 9.3 shows the vertical flip effect.

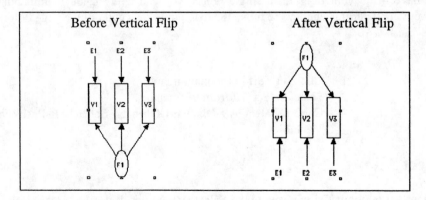

Figure 9.3 Example — Vertical Flip

Procedure:

1. Select the object to be flipped in the **Draw Diagram**.
2. Click on **Edit** in the main menu.
3. Select **Vertical Flip** from the menu.

Rotate

The **Rotate** option is another way to change the orientation of an object. Each time you choose the **Rotate** option, your object will turn 90 degrees clockwise. This option is best applied to a group object. Figure 9.4 is an example of the **Rotate** option effect.

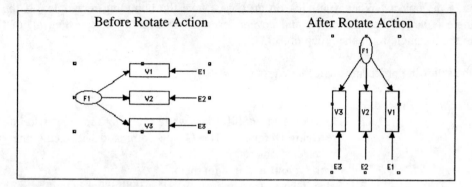

Figure 9.4 Example —Rotate

Procedure:

1. Select the object to be rotated in the **Draw Diagram**.
2. Click on **Edit** in the main menu.
3. Select **Rotate** from the menu.

Layout Menu

The commands in the **Layout** menu allow you to manipulate or change the orientation of a set of objects. Since you are going to work on a large number of objects, these simple and intuitive tools for organizing your objects will be very helpful. You can group several objects into one group object; break a group object into individual objects; align objects; center your diagram for a handsome printout; and even the distance between objects.

Here are the options in the **Layout** menu:

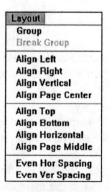

Figure 9.5 The Layout Menu

Group

The **Group** option is probably one of the most important editing options in the **Diagrammer.** It transforms several objects into one group object. After you group these objects, the relative position of each group member will remain constant. Thus, you can manipulate this group object without worrying about its members. For example, you can cut, paste, flip, and rotate a group object as if you were dealing with an individual drawing element.

You cannot visually distinguish a group object from an individual object in the draw window without selecting the object. When you click on an object, note the bounding rectangle. If the bounding rectangle is larger then the object and covers several neighboring objects, then all of the objects within the rectangle form one group object.

Use the following procedures to create a group

Procedure:
1. Hold down the <Shift> key while selecting the objects to be grouped in the **Draw Diagram**. The **Group** command will create one group from the selected objects.
2. Click **Layout** in the main menu.
3. Select **Group** from the menu. The individual bounding rectangles will disappear, replaced by a bounding rectangle that covers the entire group. Figure 9.6 shows an example of objects before and after grouping.

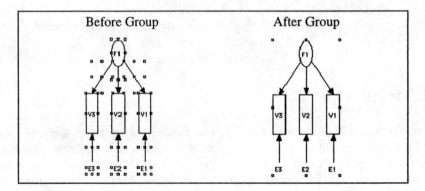

Figure 9.6 Example — Group

Break Group

The **Break Group** option has an effect opposite to that of the **Group** option. The **Break Group** option breaks a group object into individual drawing elements such as rectangles, one-way arrows, and factors. This option is essential when you want to modify the information on a drawing element which is a member of a group object.

Note: A group object will still respond to a double click from a mouse. To customize a group member, double click on the object to bring up the relevant dialog box.

Procedure:
1. Select a grouped object in the draw window.
2. Click **Layout** in the main menu.
3. Select **Break Group** in the menu.

274

Vertical Alignment

Creating a good-looking diagram takes creativity and precise mouse maneuvering. Although you can align all objects by eye, **Diagrammer** offers tools to help you do the alignment. The alignment commands only work when you have selected multiple objects. There will be no effect if you select a single object and then issue a layout command.

There are three ways to align your objects vertically. That is, you can align the selected objects to the left boundary, the right boundary, and the center of the bounding rectangle.

> *Note:*   Initially, the objects must be in an approximate vertical line

Align Left

This option will align the selected objects on the left-most boundary of the bounding rectangle.

> **Procedure:**
> 1. Select two or more objects.
> 2. Click **Layout** in the main menu.
> 3. Select **Align Left** in the menu.

Align Right

This option will align the selected objects on the right-most boundary of the bounding rectangle.

> **Procedure:**
> 1. Select two or more objects.
> 2. Click **Layout** in the main menu.
> 3. Select **Align Right** in the menu.

Align Vertical

This option will align the selected objects in the center of the bounding rectangle.

> **Procedure:**
> 1. Select two or more objects.
> 2. Click **Layout** in the main menu.
> 3. Select **Align Vertical** in the menu.

Figure 9.7 illustrates how these three vertical alignments work. The bounding rectangle is the thick black rectangle surrounding the three selected objects (V1, V2, and V3). When you activate **Align Left**, V1, V2, and V3 will align to the left hand side of the V3. Likewise, **Align Right** will align all of the objects to the right side of the V2. **Align Vertical** will align these three objects at the center, left of V3 and right of V2.

Not matter how you do the vertical alignment, the relative vertical distance between V1 and V2 or V2 and V3 will remain unchanged.

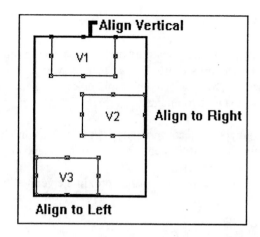

Figure 9.7 Vertical Alignment Options

Horizontal Alignment

Horizontal alignment aligns the selected objects on the horizontal. There are three choices of horizontal alignment: **Align Top, Align Bottom,** and **Align Horizontal**. On a series of horizontally laid out objects, the horizontal alignment commands will align them on the top, middle, and bottom boundary of the bounding rectangle.

Align Top

This option will align the selected objects on the top boundary of the bounding rectangle.

> **Procedure:**
> 1. Select two or more objects.
> 2. Click **Layout** in the main menu.
> 3. Select **Align Top** in the menu.

Align Bottom

This option will align the selected objects on the bottom boundary of the bounding rectangle.

> **Procedure:**
> 1. Select two or more objects.
> 2. Click **Layout** in the main menu.
> 3. Select **Align Bottom** in the menu.

Align Horizontal

This option will align the selected objects in the middle of the bounding rectangle.

> **Procedure:**
> 1. Select two or more objects.
> 2. Click **Layout** in the main menu.
> 3. Select **Align Horizontal** in the menu.

Figure 9.8 illustrates horizontal alignments. The bounding rectangle is the thick black rectangle surrounding the three selected objects (V1, V2, and V3). When you activate **Align Top**, V1, V2, and

V3 will align at the top of the V2. When you select **Align Bottom**, all of the objects will be aligned at the bottom of V3. **Align Horizontal** will align these three objects in the middle, between top of V2 and bottom of V3.

The relative horizontal distances between V1 and V2 or V2 and V3 will remain unchanged after you activate the horizontal alignment option.

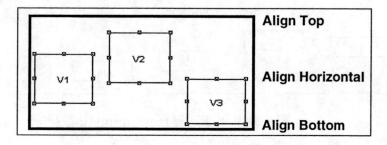

Figure 9.8 Horizontal Alignment Options

Automatic Spacing

In the last two sections, we showed how to align the drawing objects both vertically and horizontally. These alignments, however, do not change the relative distance between two objects. Evenly distributed objects will enhance the beauty of your diagram. It is difficult to draw by hand several objects with an even distance separating them. Thus, we have provided two additional tools to achieve this objective. They are **Even Horizontal Spacing** and **Even Vertical Spacing**.

Even Horizontal Spacing

The **Even Horizontal Spacing** option allows you to modify the distance between two objects without dragging the objects to new positions. It calculates the distance between the left and right edge of the bounding rectangle and evenly distributes the objects between the boundaries. Since there is only one space between two objects, if you select only two objects, there will be no change. Thus, you must select at least three objects to effectively apply the **Even Horizontal Spacing** option.

Figure 9.9 illustrates the effect before and after the Even Horizontal Spacing option. Notice that the relative vertical distances between objects remain unchanged.

> **Procedure:**
> 1. Select three or more objects.
> 2. Click **Layout** in the main menu.
> 3. Select **Even Hor Spacing**.

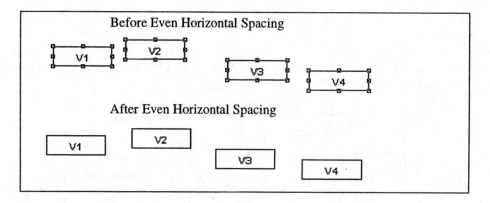

Figure 9.9 Even Horizontal Spacing

Even Vertical Spacing

The **Even Vertical Spacing** option will relocate the object between two vertical objects so that the distances between all selected objects are equal. The **Even Vertical Spacing** option requires three or more objects to be effective.

Figure 9.10 illustrates the effect before and after applying the **Even Vertical Spacing** option. Notice that the relative horizontal distances remain unchanged.

Procedure:
1. Select three or more objects.
2. Click **Layout** in the main menu.
3. Select **Even Ver Spacing**.

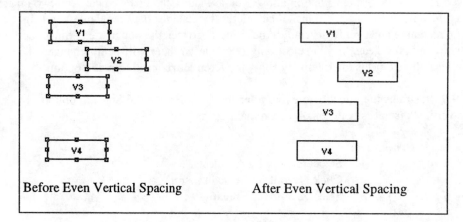

Figure 9.10 Even Vertical Spacing

10. HELP SYSTEM

The design of EQS for Windows is intended to make the functions and commands intuitive. The program makes data manipulations, statistical analysis, plotting, and generating an EQS model only a few clicks away. Because the program is easy to use, you may never find it necessary to look up an EQS for Windows interface topic. However, since there are so many topics involved in this program, we also provide an online help system to assist you.

If you do need more information, you can get online help via our hypertext-style interface. Although this initial release of the help system is not complete, you can access many topics. And, you will find it easy to use.

To access the online help system, pull down the Windows desktop by clicking on **Help** in the main menu, or using **Help Viewer** in the EQS for Windows program group. When you click on **Help**, you will see the **Help** option. Click on **Help** to access the Help dialog box shown in Figure 10.1.

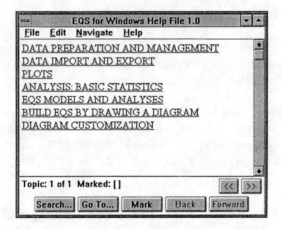

Figure 10.1 EQS for Windows Help File 1.0

Browsing Help Contents

Figure 10.1 shows the help file with its alphabetically arranged table of contents, listing a wide range of topics, from procedural matters to technical definitions in structural equation modeling. You click on a topic to select it.

Select a Topic

You can see the Help file list of topical headings in Figure 10.1. When you find the topic that interests you, click on it. A written discussion of the topic will appear.

Read Content Text

Figure 10.2 provides an example of the written text describing data preparation in EQS for Windows. In addition to reading the text, you can select a **Hot Topic**, **Search**, **Go To**, **Mark**, and go **Back** or **Forward**. Each of these options is described below.

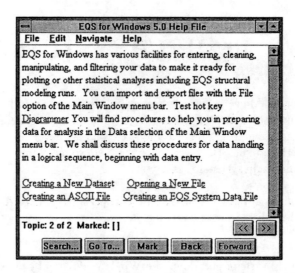

Figure 10.2 Illustrative Text in Help File

Access Hot Topic

The Help file text sometimes contains a key word or phrase that is highlighted in green. Some highlighted words and phrases are underlined in the text, as you can see in Figure 10.2. Such a highlighted word is called a **Hot Topic**.

If you click on the hot topic, you will be taken to a different window containing text that provides further information on that topic. When you have finished viewing the hot topic text, simply click once anywhere on the hot topic window. A hot topic may occur at several levels of text, but wherever it appears, you can click on a hot topic to choose it.

Search Options

If you click on the **Search** button at the bottom of the Help window, you will see the Search dialog box as shown in Figure 10.3 This dialog box displays two search options. You can search by **Topic** or by **Keyword**. Topic listings are broad categories of content related to EQS, alphabetically organized. Keywords currently refer to help topics only.

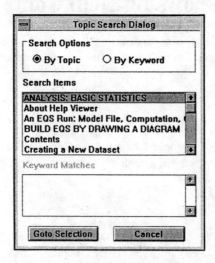

Figure 10.3 Search Options in Help File

You can scroll up and down the alphabetical list in the usual way. Make your selection by clicking on your choice. You can also click **Cancel** if you do not want to access any of the given choices.

To perform a search:
1. First choose your search option by clicking on the appropriate radio button.
2. Find your search item in the **Search Items** and click on it.
3. If you are using the **Keyword** option, you must also click to select your preferred **Keyword Match**.
4. Click on the **Go To Selection** button.

A discussion of your selected topic will appear in the **EQS for Windows 5.0 Help File** window.

Go To a Topic

If you click on the **Go To** button at the bottom of the Help window, you will get the **Go To** dialog box. Figure 10.4 shows a sample **Go To** dialog box with its **Index**, **Glossary**, **Contents**, and **Keyboard** options. Note that Index and Glossary are inactive in this first release of help. However, help does provide a **Bookmarks** list of the topics which you have marked.

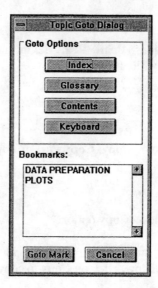

Figure 10.4 Go To Dialog Box in Help

Note that, before using the **Go To** option, you can use the **Mark** button in the Help window to mark any topics that interest you. Then, when you use the **Go To** option, the **Go To** Bookmarks list will display the names of all marked topics. You can double-click on them to go directly to those topics. This combination of options makes it easy for you to review all topics that interested you in your earlier preview of topics.

Mark Current Topic

If you click on the **Mark** button at the bottom of the Help window, you will mark the current Help screen. Then, whenever you use the **Go To** option, the **Go To** dialog box will list your bookmarks for fast access. This combination of options makes it easy for you to wander through many topics, marking particular topics for later use. You can also **Unmark** a topic to remove it from your list of bookmarks.

Back to Previous Topic

If you click on the **Back** button at the bottom of the Help window, you will go back to the previous Help screen, that is, to the Help topic immediately prior to the current topic. You can continue clicking on the Back button until you return to the list of topics in the Help file.

Forward to Next Topic

If you click on the **Forward** button at the bottom of the Help window, you will go to the Help screen that follows the current selection.

The Help Main Menu

While you are in Help, you have four menus that you can use. The **File, Edit, Navigate,** and **Help** menus provide flexibility in dealing with the Help topics.

File

The **File** menu includes three options: **Print, Print Setup,** and **Exit.** These options are the usual Windows options that you can use while in Help.

Edit

The **Edit** menu includes three options: **Copy, Copy Part of Topic,** and **Copy as Wrapped.**

Copy

The **Copy** option is the usual Windows **Copy** option.

To use this option, you must first find the text of interest in the **EQS for Windows Help File 1.0** window. When the text is in the window, click on **Copy** to copy all of the text to the Clipboard.

Copy Part of Topic

The **Copy Part of Topic** option allows you to select a section of the current topic for copying.

To use this option, you must first find the text of interest in the **EQS for Windows Help File 1.0** window. When the text is in the window, click on **Copy Part of Topic.**

A **Help Copy** window will appear, prompting you to select the desired text. After you have highlighted the text in the usual way, click on the **Edit** menu **Copy** option to copy the text to the Clipboard.

Copy as Wrapped

The **Copy as Wrapped** option is the toggle which gives you the choice of copying text in a flowing format or containing line breaks as defined by the current word wrap.

To copy text without any line breaks, click to choose **Copy as Wrapped**. That choice will place a check mark beside the option. Then choose either **Copy** or **Copy Part of Topic** to copy the text in a free-flowing continuous manner.

To copy flowing text with line breaks, confirm that **Copy as Wrapped** is not checked. Then, if you choose either **Copy** or **Copy Part of Topic** to copy, the text will appear as it did in the help file, with many lines.

Navigate

The **Navigate** menu provides another way to choose the seven options that are available as buttons on the **EQS for Windows Help File 1.0** window. The options are: Search, Go To, Mark, Back, Forward, <<, >>. These options duplicate functions previously described.

Help

The **Help** menu provides two options: **How to use Help** and **About Help**. In future releases of EQS for Windows, these options will provide more information on the Help file.

11. EQS FOR WINDOWS & WINDOWS 95

As we prepare this user's guide, Microsoft Corperation has announced that Windows 95 will be released in August, 1995. Windows 95 is the subsequent version of Windows 3.1. Windows 95 is a 32 bit operating system, while Windows 3.1 is a 16 bit operating environment.

In theory, the 32 bit operating system should make an application such as EQS for Windows run faster. However, EQS for Windows is not "native" to Windows 95. That is, the EQS for Windows user interface (e.g., data manager, basic statistics, and Diagrammer) is a 16 bit program. Thus, EQS for Windows will not take advantage of the internal architecture of Windows 95.

However, EQS for Windows 5.0 does run on Windows 95. We have succesfully tested EQS for Windows 5.0 on the April Release of Windows 95.

As a Windows 95 user, you can generally follow chapters 1 through 10 of this user's guide. However, there are three exceptions:
- Installation
- Starting EQS for Windows
- Completing an EQS Job

In all three of those situations, you should consult this chapter for details pertaining to using EQS with Windows 95.

Installation Procedure

The look and feel of Windows 95 is quite different from that of Windows 3.1. This section provides the initial steps for installing EQS for Windows 5.0 on Windows 95.

Windows 95 displays a background picture or wallpaper with icons on the screen. At the bottom of the screen, there is a status bar. It lists all of the active programs. The left-most icon of the status bar is a **Start** icon, as shown in the picture below. Click on the **Start** button to start the installation procedure.

Figure 11.1 Start Button

After clicking on the **Start** button, the menu shown in Figure 11.2 will appear. This menu appears whenever you start a program. To start installing EQS for Windows, click on **Run** in the menu.

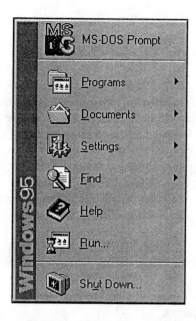

Figure 11.2 Windows 95 Menu

The **Run** dialog box will appear. If your EQS for Windows 5.0 install disk #1 is in A drive, enter **a:setup** in the **Open** edit box. See Figure 11.3 for an example of the Run dialog box at this point.

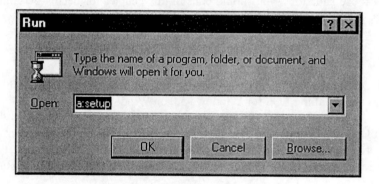

Figure 11.3 Run Dialog Box

Press the **OK** button to continue. For an outline of the next few steps, now go to the Installation Procedure section of this manual. Turn to page 4, and start at step 5 of the Installation Procedure section.

Running EQS for Windows under Windows 95

After you have installed EQS for Windows, you can run the program. To run EQS, click on the **Start** button on the left side of the status bar on the bottom of the screen. This is the same **Start** button that you saw in Figure 11.1

After the Start menu appears, click on the **Programs** menu item. The menu to the right of the **Programs** item will display all of the installed programs.

Find EQS for Windows and click on it. The EQS for Windows menu will appear to the right of the program menu. Click on **EQS for Windows.**

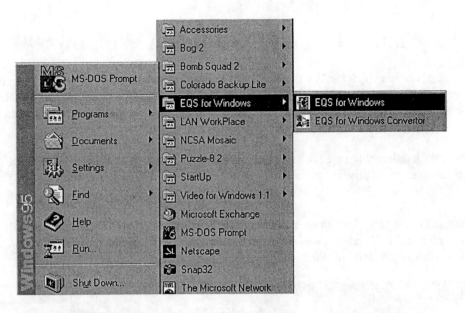

Figure 11.4 Programs Menu with EQS for Windows Option

The opening screen in EQS for Windows will appear. From this point, you can follow the instructions for using EQS for Windows.

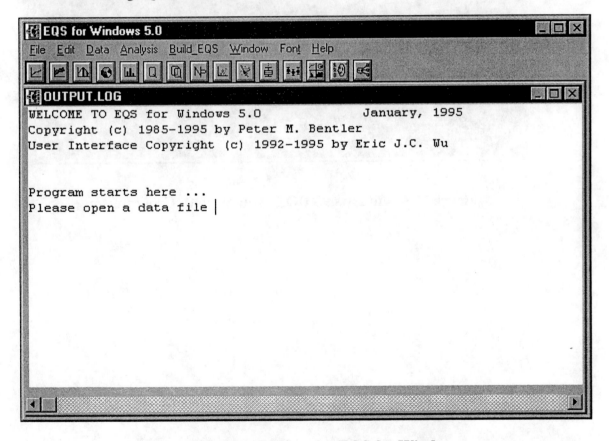

Figure 11.5 Initial Window for EQS for Windows

Completing an EQS Job in Windows 95

If you are a veteran EQS for Windows user, you know that, when an EQS job starts to run, the program will switch to DOS mode and begin running. When the job is complete, the DOS window will close automatically and the program will return to Windows. At that point, an Open file dialog box appears so that you can open the output file.

Windows 95 handles this process differently. When an EQS job is running, the DOS window is opened and you can see the progress of the program. When your EQS job is complete, you will see the "**... EQS is done ...**" message on the bottom of the screen.

In contrast to Windows 3.1, when you are running Windows 95 the DOS window will stay open until you click on the **Cross** button on the upper right corner of the window. That is, you must close the DOS window manually in Windows 95.

Figure 11.6 Windows 95 DOS Window with Cross Button

INDEX

EQS for Windows 5.7b Supplement
(07/20/98)

EQS **Diagrammer** has undergone significant changes in version 5.7. For those who have not used any drawing tool, **Diagrammer** may be an exciting yet new adventure. There are a few principles we would like to share with you.

1. Reduce the number of variables in your data set so that you can use all or most variables.
2. Label your variables with meaningful names (use Data/Information menu on your data editor).
3. Always open you data set onto the screen before you draw a diagram.
4. Deploy all measured variables on the drawing window if you are creating a path model and create all factor structures if you are creating a factor model.
5. Move and lay out all variables and factor structures to logical and readable positions. For example, make your reading flow from top to bottom and from left to right. Thus, the final diagram will not be confusing.
6. As a last step, connect all the regression coefficients or covariances.

For experienced **Diagrammer** users, who have used EQS for Windows 5.6 or earlier versions, the following are the changes on **Diagrammer** (in the following text , **EQS 5.7 includes EQS 5.7b**):

1. A new factor structure dialog box will appear if you have an ESS file open. This new dialog box lists all the measured variables so that you can select them as indicators to create a factor structure.
2. Most drawing functions will remain active after their use. For example, if you click on an one-way arrow tool, and move on to create a regression coefficient, the shape of your mouse cursor will remain the same so that you can draw another regression coefficient immediately. You can reset the mouse cursor shape to arrow point by clicking on your **right mouse button.**
3. When deploying measured variables on the drawing window, you have the option to deploy multiple variables. This option will be useful when you want to create a path model.
4. The default viewing label option is turned on, so that instead of seeing V1, V2,. .. etc., you will see the variable labels on your diagram. You can always reverse this if you want.
5. We changed the default drawing window to a full view, so that you can see and draw the entire piece of paper when it is printed. Of course you can go to a close-up view.
6. One-way and two-way curved arrows have changed so that they draw a smoother curved line. **By default, the curved line faces left. If you want to draw a curve facing right, press the SHIFT key before connecting two variables.**

Here is a brief further description of the changes. You might want to perform the actions described on a model of your own, to get some practice.

We also test EQS for Windows 5.7b on the newly released Windows 98. EQS has been behavior quite well. For those who are concerned about the compatibility of EQS on Windows 98, this test may ease your concern.

1. Create a Factor Model

The following section will illustrate the best way to create a factor model.

Step 1: Open an EQS Dataset

EQS works best with a customized EQS dataset (i.e. an *.ESS file). Before you create any model, you should either enter a new dataset using EQS' data entry function, import a raw data or covariance matrix from an ASCII file, or import a third party system file such as an SPSS system file.

After the dataset is imported, you should name each variable with a meaningful name so that these names can be used when creating a diagrammed model. Our illustration assumes that you have an EQS dataset present in the data editor.

Step 2: Create Diagram from Factor Structure

The best way to create a factor model is to create individual factor structures through the <u>Factor Structure</u> icon. This icon is located in the middle of the vertical icon tools in the **Diagrammer** window. Its shape is a little factor structure (factor with its indicators).

Click on the <u>Factor Structure</u> icon and you will see your cursor become a cross with a little factor structure shape in the lower right part of the cursor. Move the cursor to the client area (or display area) of your diagram window and click on the **left mouse button once** on the screen. A *Factor Structure Specification* dialog box will appear.

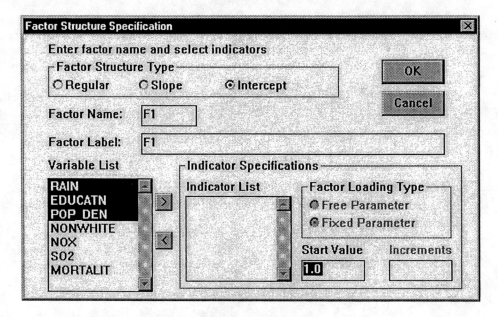

Figure 1: Factor Structure Specification Dialog Box

Please note that all the variables in your data set will be presented in the **Variable List** box (keeping this list short is one reason to limit your data set primarily to the variables that you plan to use in the model). To create a factor structure, you must move target variables from **Variable List** to **Indicator List.** You do this by first selecting all the relevant variables in the **Variable List**. If you need to select non-continuous variables from the list, **hold down the CTRL key** (known as the control key) **and use your mouse to click on the target variables.**

Once all the variables in a desired factor structure have been selected, push on the **>** button to move all the selected variables to the **Indicator List**. They move all at once. If you change your mind, you can modify the choice of variables by moving one or more variables back to the Variable List from the Indicator List by using the **<** arrow key. Obviously, you can move back or forth as you like. At some point you should have a result as shown in Figure 2.

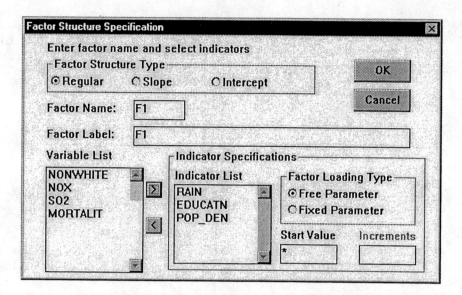

Figure 2: Factor Structure Specification with Indicators

This concludes variable selection. There are many other functions in this dialog box, some of which are new and others of which are old. These other functions will be discussed below. Let's click on the **OK** button to create the factor structure. A new factor structure will be created, as shown in Figure 3.

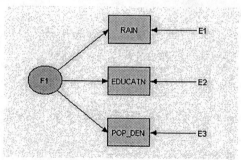

Figure 3: A Factor Structure

By default, EQS will make the variance of the factor as a free parameter. All the factor loadings will be set as free parameters except the first one, which is set as a fixed parameter. On the screen, a blue line means a fixed parameter, while a black line represents a free parameter.

Step 3: Connecting Factor Structures

We will create a two-factor Confirmatory Factor Analysis (CFA) model in this example. We first put two factor structures on the screen. We then need to connect them with a covariance. In **Diagrammer**, a covariance is presented as a two-way arrow.

To draw a two-way curved line, you have to **select** the icon with curved two-way arrowhead. Then move the cursor back to the drawing window. The cursor will become a small cross with a little two-way arrow line under it. **You must select the first variable where the curved two-way arrow line is going to be drawn. Then, hold down the left mouse button, and move the cursor until the cursor is well into the target (2nd) variable, and then release the left mouse button.** A two-way curved arrow line facing left will be drawn on the screen. **Notice that after the curved line has been drawn, the shape of the cursor still remains the same.** This mean that you can draw another two-way curved arrow line immediately.

To turn off the continuous cursor, you must click on the right mouse button.

You can also draw a curved line that faces your right hand side. To do this, hold down the **SHIFT** key while drawing the curved line. For example, hold down the SHIFT key and click on the E1 variable; keep pressing the left mouse button and move the cursor down until the cursor is well inside the E4 variable. EQS will draw a curved line facing your right, as you can see in Figure 4.

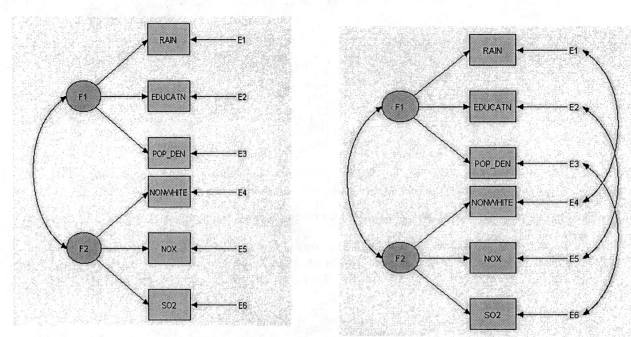

Figure 4: Two-factor CFA Model

Step 4: Run an EQS Model

You have created an EQS model and can now run it. Please consult the *EQS for Windows User's Guide* for details.

Step 5: Present your Model

After your EQS model has run, you have to inspect your model fit. EQS provides an easy way for you to do this, while also creating a good presentation of your model for later printing. From your **Diagrammer View** menu, you can pull down the menu and select **Diagram Title**. A **Diagram Titles** dialog will appear. By default, EQS provides a generic title which briefly describes your model and its fit. You can enter your own title in this single line edit box. Although appearing as a single line, the printing on the diagram will cover multiple lines breaking at each ";". **The semicolon means line-separation.**

The bottom rectangle in Figure 5 shows the title line. You will note that it has some strange abbreviations that start with a back slash (\) character. The back slash starts a control key. Meaningful numbers from your model output will replace these control keys after the model is run. **Please note that the control key values will be available only after your EQS model has been run.** In the example, the chi-square statistic, its degrees of freedom, and the associated probability value will be put into the diagram after the model has been run. A listing of possible information to present, i.e., control keys and what they represent, can be obtained by pressing the **Key Words**. This list is given at the back of this document.

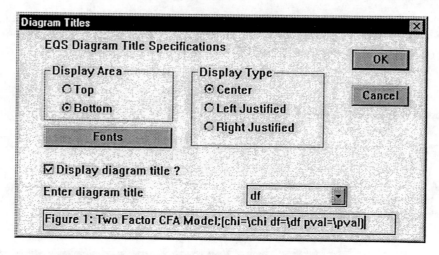

Figure 5: Diagram Titles

As you can see in Figure 5, displaying the title is an option. It is also subject to display choices that you can make. Note also that **the diagram title is visible only in the Full View mode**. It will print only if the **Display diagram title** option is chosen.

Step 6: Printing a Diagram

You are encouraged to examine your model before printing it on paper. Since the diagram window you are working with may be off-centered relative to a piece of paper, you should be sure to get a full view of your diagram. To get a full view, go to the **View** menu of the diagram window, pull down the menu and select **Full View**. If your diagram is not centered, you may want to:

    a.   Go to **Edit** menu and **Select All Diagram Objects**
    b.   Go to **Layout** menu and **Group** all the diagram objects
    c.   Go to **Layout** menu and do an **Align Page Center** and **Align Page Middle.**

By doing these steps you will get a good printed copy of your diagram. A reduced size example is shown next.

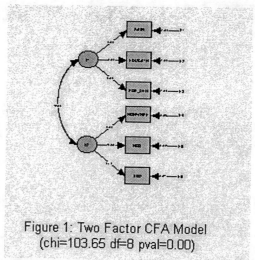

Figure 1: Two Factor CFA Model
(chi=103.65 df=8 pval=0.00)

Figure 6: Full View of a Two Factor Confirmatory Factor Analytic Model

305

2. Create a Path Model

A path model uses only measured variables. It sometimes is also called a simultaneous equations model. EQS **Diagrammer** lets you deploy all the measured variables on the drawing screen in a convenient way. Thus, you can arrange them in the desired location and build the model.

Step 1: Open an EQS Dataset

Before creating a path model, you must open a data set. Make it the active window on EQS' data editor.

Step 2: Deploy Measured Variables

After your data editor is on the screen, click on the **Diagrammer** icon from the horizontal tool bar. Wait until the diagram has opened, then click on the vertical tool bar icon that represents a V variable. You will be asked if you want to deploy more than one variable in the draw window.

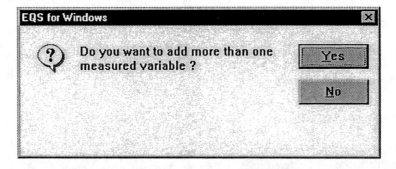

Figure 7: Multiple Variable Query Box

If you answer *No* to this question, you will be able to place variables sequentially without selection. Move your mouse cursor to the drawing window. Your mouse cursor will turn to a cross with a small rectangle attached to its lower right. Then, you are ready to deploy a measured variable: with every click on the diagram window, one measured variable will be put on the screen. You can see that these variables are deployed according to their sequence in the data. Click on the *YES* button if you want to select variables to place into the draw window. A second dialog box will appear:

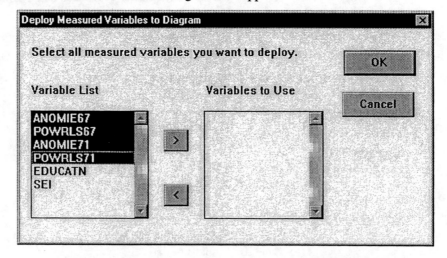

Figure 8: Multiple Measured Variables Deployment Dialog Box

You must select the variables you want to use in the model, then click on the > button. The variables you have just selected will move to the list box **Variables to Use**. You must verify whether these variables are the ones that you want to use in the model. If they are correctly chosen, click on the OK button to deploy the variables onto the draw window. If not, select variables and use the > and < arrow keys to move the variables into their correct position. Then click OK.

In Figure 9 we give an example that shows four variables were selected for a path model. After clicking the OK button, these variables will be deployed onto the draw window.

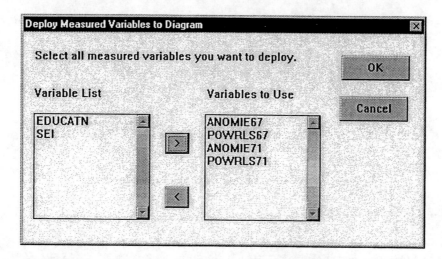

Figure 9: Variables to Use in a Path Model

Step 3: Layout Variables

It is important that your diagram be laid out in a meaningful fashion. The causal flow should go in a certain direction, for example, you could put the ultimate dependent variables on the right hand side of the draw window, the independent variables on the left, and mediating variables in between. The purpose of a good layout is to let your reader easily understand the causal flow implied by your diagram in a natural way. Individual or groups of variables can be selected, and then moved to a good location on the page.

After variables have been placed and spaced meaningfully on the draw window, you can also align them carefully, especially if you are ready to prepare a publication quality drawing. The **Layout** menu provides a number of options for you to align variables vertically (**Align Vertical**) as well as horizontally (**Align Horizontal**). It can space them so that the variables have an even space between them. When using the layout tool, you must select target variables. Only selected variables are affected by the layout tool.

Step 4: Connect Variables

After all variables are nicely laid out, you can connect these variables. In a path model, there are two kinds of connections. These are regression coefficients and covariances. Regression coefficients are created with the one-way straight arrow tool, and covariances with the two-way curved tool.

To connect variables with a regression coefficient, you first click on the one-way straight arrow tool. The mouse cursor will become a little cross with an one-way arrow on its lower-right corner. Then use a left mouse click on the originating variable, hold down the mouse button, and move the mouse cursor until the cursor is well inside the target variable. Let go. A straight one-way arrow line will be drawn between origin and target variables, with the arrowhead pointing to the target variable. An error variance will also automatically attach to the target variable.

To correlate two independent variables, use the two-way curved arrow tool, applying the same operational principle. That is, click on the originating variable, hold down the mouse button, move the mouse pointer, and release the mouse button when it is well inside the target variable. Remember that **the default curve line always faces left, unless you hold down the SHIFT key when drawing the two-way arrow.**

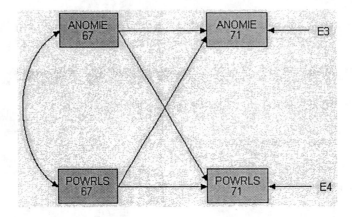

Figure 10: A Four Variable Path Model

Step 5: Run the Path Model

When a model is completely drawn and carefully laid out, your are ready to run this model. You must go to the BUILD_EQS menu and click on the **Title** menu, fill in the title of your model in the dialog box, choose additional options from the list if desired, finally click on **Run/EQS 386**. You will see a DOS screen (typically, blue) open and display the status of your model until the model run has been completed. Depending on your system setup, you may have to close the DOS window after the EQS model run is finished. You will have to open the output file so that model statistics can be imported to your diagram file.

Step 6: Display Diagram Title and Model Statistics

As noted above, you can display EQS model statistics using the **Diagram Titles** option. After your EQS model has run, click on **View** menu and select **Program Title**. You will be given a dialog box in which you can specify some display text along with some keywords. These keywords all start with a control character "\" or a back-slash character. If a character string following "\" matches a set of pre-defined keys, the keyword will be replaced by equivalent output statistics from the EQS run.

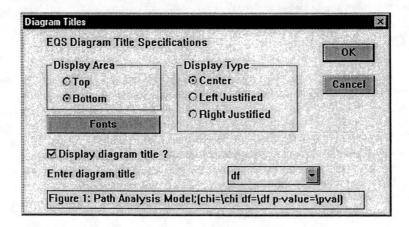

Figure 11. Example of Diagram Titles

Please note that the semicolon ";" character is the line separator in the edit box. Based on this dialog box, the string "Path Analysis Model" will be displayed in the first line of the title, and the model statistics will be displayed on the second line. Figure 12 illustrates a diagram with title information.

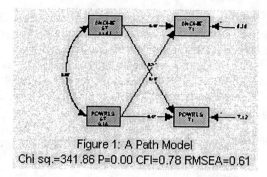

Figure 1: A Path Model
Chi sq.=341.86 P=0.00 CFI=0.78 RMSEA=0.61

Figure 12. Model with Title and Results

Step 7: Display your Diagram

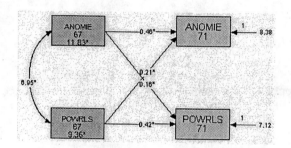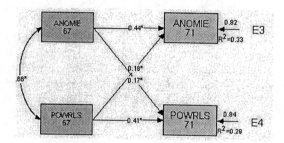

Diagram with parameter estimates   **Diagram with standardized solution**

EQS 5.7 for Windows also made some changes in its display of starting values, parameter estimates, and the standardized solution with the **View** and **Estimates** choices. The **Start value** option no longer gives starting values; the diagram that is obtained with this choice is the starting model without any estimates, and with "*" denoting free parameters. The other options are shown in the two diagrams illustrated above. The left hand side is the diagram with **Parameter estimates** displayed. Please note that there are numbers in place with all independent variables. These numbers are the variances of the variables. For example, the variance of ANOMIE67 is 11.83 and the variance of POWRLS67 is 9.36.

The diagram in the right hand side displays the **Standardized solution** of the model. There is no number in the place with the independent variables because their variances are 1.0 when standardized. However, there is $R^2 = 0.33$ on the right hand side of the equation. This newly introduced information is the squared multiple correlation coefficient of the equation. The ANOMIE71 diagram R^2 corresponds to the following equation:

ANOMIE71 = 0.44*ANOMIE67 + 0.18*POWRLS67 + 0.82 E3   with R^2=0.33

We hope that the new display will convey more complete information on important aspects of your model.

3. Create a Latent Growth Curve Model

The Latent Growth Curve Model has become very popular in recent years. It is a model that measures growth or progress on some well-understood measurement variables. The data for this type of model represent repeated measures of the same variable over time. Typically, there are several repeated measures, but not as many as there would be in a time series design. The time lags between measurement can be equal interval or unequal interval. Furthermore, the repeated measures may represent repeated observations on a measured variable or repeated measures on a latent variable which has its own indicators via an appropriate factor structure.

We shall use a hypothetical model with three time points to build a latent growth curve model.

Step 1: Open an EQS Dataset

It is a standard practice to open an EQS *.ESS data file before building any model. We shall use a dataset called GROWTH.ESS with three variables. These variables are measuring the same event at three different time points. The time intervals between measurements are equal. The variables are named TIME1, TIME2, and TIME3.

Step 2: Deploy the Latent Growth Curve Model

To create a Latent Growth Curve model we need to start with a factor structure as the basic building block. Click on the **Diagrammer** icon at the horizontal tool bar and then click on the factor structure icon on the vertical tool bar of the draw window. You will see a **Factor Structure Specification** dialog box appear.

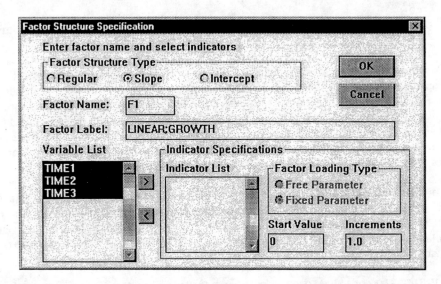

Figure 13: Factor Structure Specification Dialog for Latent Growth Curve Model

The top part of the box makes it apparent that there are three possible types of factors. In addition to the default **Regular** factors – the usual kind – there are **Slope** and **Intercept** factors. Regular factors have the typical pattern of free factor loadings. In contrast, slope and intercept factors have a very specific pattern of fixed parameters. By default, there are no free loading parameters. We recommend that you change the **Factor Structure Type** to a **Slope** factor. By default, the factor label called "LINEAR GROWTH" appears; you can change this name as you like. The semi-colon in the edit box assures that this label will be displayed on two separate lines. In the bottom left **Variable List** are three variables representing three time points of measurement. You must click on the "moving" button ">" to move the variables from the **Variable List** into the **Indicator List**. Click the OK button when done, and you are ready to move on to the remaining specifications for a growth curve model.

Step 3: Add an Intercept Factor and a Constant Variable

You need to add a factor that represents the starting point or **Intercept** of the growth process. After you have specified the **Slope** factor, the program automatically asks you about whether you also will want to specify an **Intercept** factor, and a **Constant** variable. The intercept factor gives information about the starting point of the growth process. The constant is needed in the standard model where you are modeling both means and covariances, i.e., a moment structure. If you are modeling only the covariances, the constant is not needed. The dialog box is shown in Figure 14.

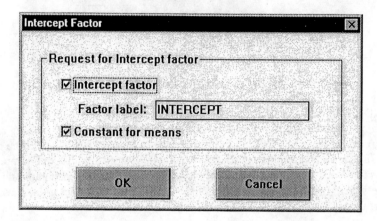

Figure 14: Check Boxes for Intercept Factor and Constant

The default is to include both the intercept factor and the constant, so you can click OK if that is what you want. However, suppose that you do <u>not</u> want these additional features. Then, uncheck both of these boxes, and click OK. The result is shown in Figure 15.

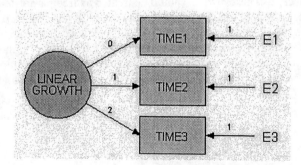

Figure 15: Factor Structure for Linear Growth Factor

As you will note, this factor structure has created a basic building block for an equal time interval linear growth factor. What makes this factor unique is that all the paths from the factor to the variables are fixed at known values as shown in blue; these values will not be changed during iterations. The factor loadings are all fixed, and the fixed values are 0, 1, and 2. If you do not have equal time intervals between measurements, you will have to calculate what the appropriate fixed coefficients should be, and replace the default values we provide. Please notice that, technically, the path from LINEAR GROWTH to TIME1 is not really there – a zero path has no effect. It would be possible, and indeed less confusing, to simply to remove it from the diagram. However, due to standard presentations in the field, this is one case where we leave a zero, i.e., nonexistent, path in the diagram.

311

In the typical latent growth curve model, however, you will also add the intercept factor and, most likely, a constant variable, and so the check boxes of Figure 14 would stay at their checked default values and you would simply click OK. In that case, you immediately would get the final result shown in Figure 16, which includes the two latent **Slope** and **Intercept** factors, as well as the **Constant** which is needed to transform the model from a covariance structure to a mean and covariance structure model.

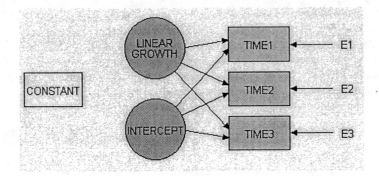

Figure 16: Linear Growth and Intercept Factors with Constant

Notice that the INTERCEPT and CONSTANT factor labels have been used by default. If you want to change these names, do so in the usual way by double-clicking on them and making appropriate changes in the dialog box that appears. From the blue line shown in Figure 16, it also will be apparent that the paths from the **Intercept** factor to its measured variable indicators are all fixed parameters. In fact, each of these paths is fixed at 1.0, as you could verify by double-clicking on each path and seeing the default value of the coefficient in the dialog box that appears. The **Intercept** factor deals with the starting point of the growth process.

The **CONSTANT** variable is the standard V999 constant in EQS' usual setup, but here it is called "CONSTANT" due to conventions in the field. V999 is what transforms a covariance structure into a mean structure model. As you can see from Figure 16, by default there are no connections from the CONSTANT to the factors or the variables. These should be added by you. In the standard growth model, you should add a one-way straight arrow from the **Constant** variable to each of the two factors **Linear Growth** and **Intercept**. These arrows should be treated as free parameters, since they represent the average linear growth coefficient and average intercept, respectively, which usually are unknown and need to be estimated. The relevant residuals D1 and D2 will be added automatically. These residuals represent individual differences in linear growth, and individual differences in intercept, respectively. In general, these residuals should be correlated, and you should create that correlation by adding the two-way arrow between D1 and D2 after they appear. As a result, you should obtain something like Figure 17.

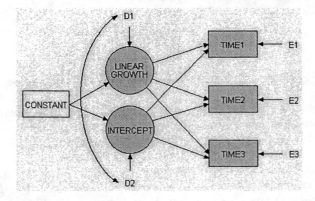

Figure 17: Complete Two-factor Latent Growth Curve Model

The model we created is sometimes called a two factor **Initial Status Latent Growth Model** with equal time lags. When the time between successive measurements of your variable is not given in equal time intervals, the fixed values of the coefficients have to be adjusted. Please also note that we only discussed linear growth in this example. A general growth curve model can include exponential growth, cubic growth, or even quadratic growth factors in your model.

There are also other types of Latent Growth Curve Models such as the **Time Averaged Latent Growth Curve Model** and the **Spline Latent Growth Curve Model**. These two types of models involve more complex computations of start values. These will not be covered here. If you are interested in the Latent Growth Curve model, you are encouraged to find other literature and publications for further study.

We did not emphasize here an alternative sequence you could have used to create the growth curve model of Figure 17. In our presentation we presumed that you would start with a **Slope** factor, as shown selected in Figure 13. However, it would have been perfectly all right to start with the **Intercept** factor by making the appropriate selection (see Figure 13). In that case, a dialog box similar to Figure 14 would appear, asking you whether you also intended to create a **Slope** factor and a **Constant**. Depending on your choice, you would get only the **Intercept** factor, or also a **Slope** factor, or also the **Constant**.

4. Keywords Available for Diagram Title

We have previously mentioned in several places (i.e. Step 5 of Create a Factor Model and Step 6 of Create a Path Model) that you can specify some keywords in your diagram title so that it will achieve a more dynamic output. These keywords provide for automatic inclusion of key parts of a model run as specified by you. The keywords you can use are as follows:

Keyword	Description
\df	Degrees of freedom
\null	Independence model chi-square value
\chi	Model chi-square
\pval	Normal theory p value
\nfi	Bentler-Bonett fit index
\nnfi	Bentler-Bonett non-normed fit index
\cfi	Comparative fit index
\afit	AGLS fit index
\aafit	AGLS adjusted fit index
\gfi	LISREL's standard fit index
\agfi	LISREL's adjusted fit index
\rmr	Root mean-square residual
\srmr	Standardized root mean-square residual
\rmsea	Root mean square error of approximation
\rmlo	Lower bound of RMSEA confidence interval
\rmhi	Upper bound of RMSEA confidence interval
\iter	Number of iterations to convergence
\rchi	Robust (Satorra-Bentler) chi-square value
\rpval	Robust p-value based on robust chi-square
\rcfi	CFI based on robust chi-square
\yb	Yuan-Bentler AGLS corrected chi-square
\ypval	Pval for Yuan-Bentler chi-square
\ycfi	Yuan-Bentler corrected comparative fit index
\np	Number of free parameters
\nc	Number of cases in your data file
\fname	File name that houses this model

5. Summary of Changes in EQS for Windows 5.7

Most of the changes in EQS for Windows 5.7 are in Diagrammer. Most of these changes have been mentioned above. We want to re-iterate these changes, and note some added points.

A. Full view is the default Diagrammer window

Previous version of EQS used an actual diagram size as the default Diagrammer startup window. The advantage of this is that the drawing objects are clearly visible. There is one draw back on this approach: it is hard to draw a diagram that will fill the complete page. We decided to take some users' suggestions to make the full view as the default startup window, and make the drawing tool available. Diagram titles with dynamic results show in this view only.

The Diagrammer startup window has been formatted to the size of a standard 8.5" x 11" sheet of paper. You have to fit all your drawing objects within the boundary of the drawing area.

B. A multiple drawing feature creates the same type of object repeatedly

As you may have noticed, prior to EQS 5.7, you had to click on the vertical tool bar whenever you wanted to create a new drawing object. Not only that, you needed to click on the tool bar even if you wanted to create the same object. We now eliminate some redundant clicks by introducing the multiple drawing feature. Now you can create the same drawing object repeatedly without ever having to go back to click on the vertical tool bar.

To use the multiple drawing feature, you only need to repeatedly draw the same object. The drawing cursor will stay in the same shape with the same function until you (1) click on the vertical tool bar to reset it, or (2) **click on the right mouse button to reset the shape of the cursor.**

C. Curved lines are smoother

A free hand drawing technique was used to draw a curved line in Diagrammer. This is no longer necessary. The previous curved line implementation allowed you to customize the fullness or flatness of the one-way or two-way curved lines, but this may not be a good idea after all. We accepted some users' suggestions to smooth the curved line in the program.

To draw a one-way or two-way curved line, you only need to activate the curved line tool, click on the original object, hold down the mouse button and drag across the diagram window, and release the mouse button when the mouse pointer is well inside the destination object. A one-way or two-way curved line will be drawn with the curve **facing left** if both objects are relatively vertical to each other, or **facing down** if both objects are relatively horizontal to each other. **If you need to draw a curved line facing in the opposite direction, you must hold down the SHIFT hey and do the same drawing.**

D. Child objects move automatically and meaningfully

A child object is defined as the drawing object that must coexist with another drawing object, such as an E variable that is attached to a V variable, and a D variable that is attached to an F variable. An E is V's child object, and a D is F's child object. In general, if you move a parent object, you probably want to have its child object nearby for clearer presentation.

In EQS 5.7, whenever you move a V variable, its E variable will be moved accordingly and its relative position will remain unchanged. Likewise, if you move an F variable, its associated D variable will be moved accordingly.

E. Selected objects move more logically

In EQS 5.6 and earlier versions, you had to group some drawing objects so that you could move them across diagram window simultaneously, maintaining the same relative position. You don't need to group them anymore. When several objects are selected, if you drag any of the objects to its new location in the window, the other selected objects also will be moved to the new location, and maintaining the same relative position as the dragged object. This implementation allows you to move several objects at once without the need to group them.

F. A new diagram title section dynamically presents model results

Most key model information, test statistics, and fit indices are saved in the diagram file if you use Diagrammer to create and run a model. This information can be dynamically displayed on the **Full View** diagram window, and printed, if you enter their keywords in the Diagram Title section of the View menu. A default diagram title will be given upon the completion of your model run. With a minor modification, you can create an informative diagram for your model presentation.

G. Drawing object information is displayed in the title bar

When you click on any drawing object, its information -- such as, what the variable is and its label, or a fixed or free parameter and the parameter labels -- will be displayed in the title bar of the drawing window. This is especially useful in the full view, which is now used as the default startup window for Diagrammer, where variable labels and parameter information may be too small to be visible otherwise.

H. Variances of independent variables with parameter estimates are displayed

Previous version of Diagrammer did not to display the variances of independent variables. This information is now added to the Diagrammer. If the independent variable is a V or an F variable, the parameter variance will be appended to the variable label. If the independent variables are E or D variables, the variances will be displayed in their place.

I. Growth curve models are convenient to create

Slope and intercept factors are now created automatically, and the constant needed to specify the mean structure is generated as well. Only minor modifications need to be made to finalize the setup for standard linear growth models.

J. An R–square is displayed for each equation

In presenting the results of an analysis, one often wants to present the R^2 to summarize the predictability of the dependent variable in an equation. EQS 5.7 for Windows now computes this information and prints it in the standardized solution of the EQS output file. This information also is given in Diagrammer when presenting the standardized solution.

K. A single variable and its connections can be viewed with Control-Click

In a complex diagram, a lot of drawing objects may be seen within a small area. Too many such objects may be confusing. A vastly simplified view is now available. You can invoke a single variable display option by **holding down the Control key and clicking on a variable**. As a result, you will see only those paths coming from and going to the targeted variable. The other connections will be turned off. As a result, you will get a clear view of the relationships involving that targeted variable. You can then add or delete paths from this variable to other variables, and the reverse, without the interference of other connections.

L. Resampling procedures can be applied to ESS files

EQS now supports resampling procedures (i.e., bootstrap or jackknife) using ESS files. In previous versions, you could only use ASCII data files when running resampling procedures.

M. Symbolic names are supported in model files

EQS now supports the use of symbolic names in a limited way. You can use the real variable names in /EQUATION, /VARIANCE, and /COVARIANCE sections. The symbolic name should be defined in the /LABEL section, where each variable label should be 8 or fewer characters in length without any embedded blank characters. Please note that EQS will allow you to use any combination of uppercase or lowercase characters, but these characters will be converted into uppercase automatically and so printed in the output.

EQS will read the symbolic names and perform a regular analysis. There are no changes in EQS' printout, however, so the output will correspond to that previously available. The following model file provides an example of the use of names in model specification.

```
/TITLE
 An example of using symbolic variable names in a path analysis model
/SPECIFICATIONS
 DATA='MANUL4.ESS';
 VARIABLES=6; CASES=632;
 METHODS=ML;
 MATRIX=COVARIANCE;
/LABELS
V1=ANOMIE67; V2=POWRLS67; V3=ANOMIE71; V4=POWRLS71; V5=V5;
V6=V6;
/EQUATIONS
ANOMIE71 =   *anomie67 + *powrls67 + E3;
POWRLS71 =   *anomie67 + *powrls67 + E4;
/VARIANCES
anomie67 = *;
powrls67 = *;
E3 = *;
E4 = *;
/COVARIANCES
anomie67 , powrls67 = *;
/END
```

N. EQS now reads SPSS® 8.0 *.SAV files

SPSS Inc. has just upgraded its popular statistical software to version 8.0 and thus its system file (i.e. *.SAV files) also has been upgraded. EQS 5.6 for Windows cannot import *.SAV files produced by SPSS 8. We have hence upgraded the SPSS *.SAV file importing facility so that EQS can import SPSS 8 *.SAV files. We thank SPSS' release of its file importing DLL for public use.

O. Summary statistics from simulation results are printed out

EQS now prints basic summary statistics to describe results of any simulation study concerned with test statistics, fit indexes, parameter estimates, standard errors, and robust standard errors. These summary statistics are divided in three parts. First of all, summary results for all replications are reported. Next, summary results on all successful runs are given. Finally, the results of all failed runs, i.e., runs with condition codes or that did not converge, are printed.

There are 6 pieces of statistical information provided for each parameter in the simulation. These statistics are mean, standard deviation, skewness, kurtosis, the boundary marking the lower 5th

percentile of the simulated scores, and the boundary marking the upper 5th percentile of the simulated scores.

These summary statistics are listed at the bottom of the EQS output. An example of such summary statistics is given as follows:

```
SUMMARY STATISTICS OF REPLICATIONS FOR METHOD=ML

SUCCESS (CONVERGENCE WITH NO CONDITION CODE) OCCURRED IN
   10 REPLICATIONS OUT OF   10 (100.00 PERCENT)

NUMBERED STATISTICS ARE
    1. NULL MODEL CHI-SQUARE
    2. MODEL CHI-SQUARE
    3. PROBABILITY LEVEL
    4. BENTLER-BONETT     NORMED FIT INDEX
    5. BENTLER-BONETT NON-NORMED FIT INDEX
    6. COMPARATIVE FIT INDEX
    7. LISREL GFI
    8. LISREL AGFI
    9. ROOT MEAN-SQUARE RESIDUAL
   10. STANDARDIZED ROOT MEAN-SQUARE RESIDUAL
   11. ROOT MEAN-SQUARE ERROR OF APPROXIMATION (RMSEA)
   12. CONFIDENCE INTERVAL FOR RMSEA (LOWER BOUND)
   13. CONFIDENCE INTERVAL FOR RMSEA (UPPER BOUND)


    STATISTIC         1         2         3         4         5
    MEAN         476.8342    8.8780    0.5496    0.9814    1.0026
    STANDARD DEV. 38.2943    3.3627    0.2674    0.0068    0.0073
    SKEWNESS (G1) -0.1867   -0.2147    0.2424    0.3935    0.4249
    KURTOSIS (G2) -1.4742   -0.6922   -1.1389   -0.9946   -0.5244
    LOWER   5%    425.9869    4.3598    0.2435    0.9736    0.9944
    UPPER   5%    521.0556   12.8500    0.9080    0.9910    1.0128

    STATISTIC         6         7         8         9        10
    MEAN           0.9984    0.9804    0.9706    0.2493    0.0355
    STANDARD DEV.  0.0027    0.0112    0.0169    0.1416    0.0104
    SKEWNESS (G1) -1.6949   -0.4795   -0.4794    0.8454   -0.2606
    KURTOSIS (G2)  1.9514   -1.2257   -1.2261   -0.6098   -0.6642
    LOWER   5%     0.9944    0.9639    0.9458    0.1165    0.0208
    UPPER   5%     1.0000    0.9908    0.9861    0.4821    0.0493

    STATISTIC        11        12        13
    MEAN           0.0171   -9.9000    9.9911
    STANDARD DEV.  0.0239   31.3065   31.2746
    SKEWNESS (G1)  0.8962   -2.6667    2.6667
    KURTOSIS (G2) -0.5241    5.1111    5.1111
    LOWER   5%     0.0000  -49.5000    0.0646
    UPPER   5%     0.0517    0.0000   49.5680


PARAMETER ESTIMATES

    PARAMETER       E1,E1     E2,E2     E3,E3     E4,E4     E5,E5
    MEAN           0.9691    0.9178    1.0145    0.9410    0.8962
    STANDARD DEV.  0.2166    0.1388    0.2715    0.1863    0.3901
    SKEWNESS (G1)  0.2234   -0.4844   -0.0037   -0.8057   -0.1322
    KURTOSIS (G2) -1.0037   -0.2317   -1.2919   -0.1010   -1.3596
    LOWER   5%     0.6835    0.7065    0.6551    0.6632    0.3830
    UPPER   5%     1.2906    1.0995    1.3722    1.1516    1.3845

    PARAMETER       D1,D1     D2,D1     D2,D2    F1,V999   F2,V999
    MEAN           0.9558    0.0323    1.0445    0.0083    0.9909
    STANDARD DEV.  0.2734    0.1010    0.1533    0.1341    0.0946
    SKEWNESS (G1) -0.4774    0.0671   -0.6367    0.1506    0.0141
    KURTOSIS (G2) -0.1450   -1.3622   -0.1993   -0.9866   -0.8315
    LOWER   5%     0.5150   -0.0972    0.8245   -0.1658    0.8703
    UPPER   5%     1.2961    0.1596    1.2178    0.1994    1.1195


PARAMETER STANDARD ERRORS

    PARAMETER       E1,E1     E2,E2     E3,E3     E4,E4     E5,E5
    MEAN           0.2269    0.1650    0.1727    0.2123    0.3335
    STANDARD DEV.  0.0262    0.0203    0.0376    0.0165    0.0471
    SKEWNESS (G1)  0.4581   -0.3686   -0.0306   -1.5213    0.2140
    KURTOSIS (G2) -0.9738   -0.4827   -1.3660    1.8720   -1.1172
    LOWER   5%     0.1956    0.1331    0.1233    0.1872    0.2714
    UPPER   5%     0.2671    0.1915    0.2215    0.2273    0.3970

    PARAMETER       D1,D1     D2,D1     D2,D2    F1,V999   F2,V999
    MEAN           0.2309    0.1357    0.1619    0.1233    0.1067
    STANDARD DEV.  0.0320    0.0151    0.0210    0.0101    0.0072
    SKEWNESS (G1) -0.6465   -0.0534   -0.6030   -1.0657   -0.7267
    KURTOSIS (G2)  0.9893   -0.5219   -0.3753    1.0844   -0.2081
    LOWER   5%     0.1858    0.1131    0.1320    0.1077    0.0963
    UPPER   5%     0.2698    0.1575    0.1851    0.1344    0.1144
```

P.   Bugs that have been fixed in EQS 5.7

(1) Fail to access a data file specified in EQS model

EQS can read a data file name up to 60 characters in length (including the path name). There were situations in which the program complained that a file could not be found, even if the length of the data file was within 60 characters. The problem was caused by a bug that has been corrected.

(2) Correct a fixed covariance in Diagrammer

BUILD_EQS failed to build a covariance in an EQS model if this covariance was a fixed parameter. This problem has been corrected.